First published 1956
This impression 2011

ISBN 978 0 7110 3655 0

Published by Ian Allan Publishing

an imprint of Ian Allan Publishing Ltd, Hersham, Surrey, KT12 4RG
Printed in England by Ian Allan Printing Ltd, Hersham, Surrey, KT12 4RG

Code: 1107/B2

Distributed in the United States of America and Canada by BookMasters
Distribution Services

Visit the Ian Allan Publishing website at www.ianallanpublishing.com

Front cover: Southern Region 'U1' class 2-6-0 No 31898 leaves Southampton with
the Brighton–Salisbury service in September 1957. *B. J. Swain / Colour-Rail
(BRS414)*

Rear cover: Scottish Region-allocated Class J37 No 64584 is seen at Kittybrewster.
C. W. Woodhead

THE abc OF
BRITISH RAILWAYS
LOCOMOTIVES

PART I—Nos. 1-9999
and
B.R. STANDARD AND EX-W.D. LOCOMOTIVES AND DIESEL RAILCARS

WINTER
1956/7
EDITION

LONDON :

Ian Allan Ltd

NOTES ON THE USE OF THIS BOOK

1. This booklet lists British Railways locomotives numbered between 1 and 9999 and Diesel Railcars in service at August 11th, 1956. This range of numbers covers all Western Region (ex-G.W.R.) engines, with the exception of diesel and gas turbine locomotives, which are dealt with in the ABC OF BRITISH RAILWAYS LOCOMOTIVES Part 2—Nos. 10000-39999.

2. For convenience, the full list of British Railways standard classes and Class "WD" locomotives in service is now included in this part of the ABC OF BRITISH RAILWAYS LOCOMOTIVES.

3. This book is divided into three parts :—
   (a) A list of ex-G.W. classes, with dimensions and sub-divisions, and summary of locomotives in the class.
   (b) A numerical list of ex-G.W. locomotives showing the class of each, and the name, if any.
   (c) A list of B.R. standard and Class "WD" locomotives.

4. The following notes are a guide to the system of reference marks and other details given in the lists of dimensions shown for each class in the list of classes.
   (a) In the lists of dimensions "Su" indicates a superheated class, and "SS" indicates that some locomotives of the class are superheated.
   (b) Locomotives are fitted with two inside cylinders, slide valves and Stephenson link motion, except where otherwise shown, e.g. (O) indicates outside cylinders and "P.V." piston valves.
   (c) The date on which a design of locomotive first appeared or was modified is indicated by "Introduced."
   (d) The code given in smaller bold type at the head of each class, e.g., "4MT" denotes its British Railways power classification.

5. All locomotives are of G.W.R. origin, except where otherwise shown.

6. The following is a list of abbreviations used to indicate the pre-grouping owners of certain Western Region locomotives :

AD	Alexandra (Newport and South Wales) Docks & Railway.	RR	Rhymney Railway.
		SHT	Swansea Harbour Trust.
BPGV	Burry Port & Gwendraeth Valley Railway.	TV	Taff Vale Railway.
		V of R	Cambrian Railways (Vale of Rheidol).
Car.R.	Cardiff Railway.		
P & M	Powlesland & Mason (Contractor).	W & L	Cambrian Railways (Welshpool and Llanfair).

BRITISH RAILWAYS LOCOMOTIVE
SHEDS AND SHED CODES

THIS LIST INCLUDES ONLY THOSE DEPOTS WHICH HAVE ENGINES
ALLOCATED TO THEM. IT DOES NOT INCLUDE OVERNIGHT
STABLING OR SIGNING-ON POINTS.

ALL B.R. LOCOMOTIVES CARRY THE CODE OF THEIR HOME DEPOT
ON A SMALL PLATE AFFIXED TO THE SMOKEBOX DOOR.

LONDON MIDLAND REGION

1A	**Willesden**
1B	Camden
1C	Watford
1D	Devons Road (Bow)
1E	Bletchley
	Leighton Buzzard
2A	**Rugby**
	Seaton
2B	Nuneaton
2C	Warwick
2D	Coventry
2E	Northampton
2F	Market Harborough
3A	**Bescot**
3B	Bushbury
3C	Walsall
3D	Aston
3E	Monument Lane
5A	**Crewe North**
	Whitchurch
5B	Crewe South
5C	Stafford
5D	Stoke
5E	Alsager
5F	Uttoxeter
6A	**Chester**
6B	Mold Junction
6C	Birkenhead
6D	Chester (Northgate)
6E	Wrexham
6F	Bidston
6G	Llandudno Junction
6H	Bangor
6J	Holyhead
6K	Rhyl
8A	**Edge Hill**
8B	Warrington
	Warrington (Arpley)
8C	Speke Junction
8D	Widnes
8E	Brunswick (Liverpool)

9A	**Longsight**
9B	Stockport (Edgeley)
9C	Macclesfield
9D	Buxton
9E	Trafford Park
9F	Heaton Mersey
9G	Northwich
10A	**Springs Branch (Wigan)**
10B	Preston
10C	Patricroft
10D	Sutton Oak
11A	**Carnforth**
11B	Barrow
	Coniston
11C	Oxenholme
11D	Tebay
11E	Lancaster
12A	**Carlisle (Upperby)**
12B	Penrith
12C	Workington
14A	**Cricklewood**
14B	Kentish Town
14C	St. Albans
15A	**Wellingborough**
15B	Kettering
15C	Leicester
15D	Bedford
16A	**Nottingham**
16B	Kirkby
16C	Mansfield
17A	**Derby**
17B	Burton
	Horninglow
	Overseal
17C	Coalville
17D	Rowsley
	Cromford
	Middleton
	Sheep Pasture

3

18A	**Toton**		24A	**Accrington**
18B	Westhouses		24B	Rose Grove
18C	Hasland		24C	Lostock Hall
18D	Staveley		24D	Lower Darwen
	Sheepbridge		24E	Blackpool
				Blackpool North
19A	**Sheffield**		24F	Fleetwood
19B	Millhouses			
19C	Canklow			
			*25A	**Wakefield**
			*25B	Huddersfield
*20A	**Leeds (Holbeck)**		*25C	Goole
	Keighley		*25D	Mirfield
*20B	Stourton		*25E	Sowerby Bridge
*20C	Royston		*25F	Low Moor
*20D	Normanton		*25G	Farnley Junction
*20E	Manningham			
*	Ilkley			
20F	Skipton		26A	**Newton Heath**
20G	Hellifield		26B	Agecroft
			26C	Bolton
			26D	Bury
21A	**Saltley**		26E	Lees
21B	Bournville			
21C	Bromsgrove			
			27A	**Bank Hall**
			27B	Aintree
22A	**Bristol**		27C	Southport
22B	Gloucester		27D	Wigan (L. & Y.)
	Dursley		27E	Walton
	Tewkesbury			

EASTERN REGION

30A	**Stratford**		32A	**Norwich**
	Brentwood			Cromer Beach
	Chelmsford			Swaffham
	Enfield Town			Wymondham
	Epping		32B	Ipswich
	Ilford			Aldeburgh
	Wood St. (Walthamstow)			Felixstowe Beach
30B	Hertford East			Stowmarket
	Buntingford		32C	Lowestoft
	Ware		32D	Yarmouth (South Town)
30C	Bishops Stortford		32E	Yarmouth (Vauxhall)
30D	Southend (Victoria)		32F	Yarmouth Beach
	Southminster		32G	Melton Constable
30E	Colchester			Norwich City
	Braintree			
	Clacton		33A	**Plaistow**
	Maldon			Upminster
	Walton-on-Naze		33B	Tilbury
30F	Parkeston		33C	Shoeburyness
31A	**Cambridge**		34A	**Kings Cross**
	Ely		34B	Hornsey
	Huntingdon East		34C	Hatfield
	Saffron Walden		34D	Hitchin
31B	March		34E	Neasden
	Wisbech			Aylesbury
31C	Kings Lynn			Chesham
	Hunstanton			
31D	South Lynn		35A	**New England**
31E	Bury St. Edmunds			Spalding
	Sudbury (Suffolk)			Stamford
			35B	Grantham
			35C	Peterborough (Spital)

See N.E. Region Codes 53, 55 and 56

4

36A	**Doncaster**
36B	Mexborough
	Wath
36C	Frodingham
36D	Barnsley
36E	Retford
	Newark
38A	**Colwick**
38B	Annesley
38C	Leicester (G.C.)
38D	Staveley
38E	Woodford Halse

39A	**Gorton**
	Dinting
	Hayfield
40A	**Lincoln**
	Lincoln (St. Marks)
40B	Immingham
	Grimsby
	New Holland
40C	Louth
40D	Tuxford
40E	Langwith Junction
40F	Boston
41A	**Sheffield (Darnall)**

NORTH EASTERN REGION

50A	**York**
50B	Leeds (Neville Hill)
50C	Selby
50D	Starbeck
50E	Scarborough
50F	Malton
	Pickering
50G	Whitby
51A	**Darlington**
	Middleton-in-Teesdale
51B	Newport (Yorks)
51C	West Hartlepool
51D	Middlesbrough
51E	Stockton
51F	West Auckland
51G	Haverton Hill
51H	Kirkby Stephen
51J	Northallerton
51K	Saltburn
52A	**Gateshead**
	Bowes Bridge
52B	Heaton
52C	Blaydon
	Alston
	Hexham
52D	Tweedmouth
	Alnmouth
52E	Percy Main
52F	North Blyth
	South Blyth

53A	**Hull (Dairycoates)**
53B	Hull (Botanic Gardens)
53C	Hull (Springhead)
	Alexandra Dock
53D	Bridlington
†53E	*Goole (25C)*
54A	**Sunderland**
	Durham
54B	Tyne Dock
54C	Borough Gardens
54D	Consett
†55A	**Leeds (Holbeck) (20A)**
	Keighley
†55B	*Stourton (20B)*
†55C	*Farnley Junction (25G)*
†55D	*Royston (20C)*
†55E	*Normanton (20D)*
†55F	*Manningham (20E)*
	Ilkley
†55G	*Huddersfield (25B)*
†56A	**Wakefield (25A)**
56B	Ardsley
56C	Copley Hill
†56D	*Mirfield (25D)*
†56E	*Sowerby Bridge (25E)*
†56F	*Low Moor (25F)*
56G	Bradford

SCOTTISH REGION

60A	**Inverness**
	Dingwall
	Kyle of Lochalsh
60B	Aviemore
	Boat of Garten
60C	Helmsdale
	Dornoch
	Tain
60D	Wick
	Thurso
60E	Forres
61A	**Kittybrewster**
	Ballater
	Fraserburgh
	Inverurie
	Peterhead

61B	Aberdeen (Ferryhill)
61C	Keith
	Banff
	Elgin
62A	**Thornton**
	Anstruther
	Burntisland
	Ladybank
	Methil
62B	Dundee (Tay Bridge)
	Arbroath
	Dundee West
	Montrose
	St. Andrews
62C	Dunfermline
	Alloa

† Altered Shed Codes in course of adoption, former code in brackets.

63A	**Perth South**	65D	Dawsholm
	Aberfeldy		Dumbarton
	Crieff	65E	Kipps
63B	Stirling South	65F	Grangemouth
	Killin	65G	Yoker
	Stirling (Shore Road)	65H	Helensburgh
63C	Forfar	65I	Balloch
63D	Oban	65J	Fort William
	Ballachulish		Mallaig
64A	**St. Margarets**	66A	**Polmadie (Glasgow)**
	(Edinburgh)	66B	Motherwell
	Dunbar	66C	Hamilton
	Galashiels	66D	Greenock (Ladyburn)
	Longniddry		Greenock (Princes Pier)
	North Berwick	67A	**Corkerhill (Glasgow)**
64B	Haymarket	67B	Hurlford
64C	Dalry Road		Beith
64D	Carstairs		Muirkirk
64E	Polmont	67C	Ayr
64F	Bathgate	67D	Ardrossan
64G	Hawick		
	Riccarton	68A	**Carlisle (Kingmoor)**
	St. Boswells	68B	Dumfries
		68C	Stranraer
65A	**Eastfield (Glasgow)**		Newton Stewart
	Arrochar	68D	Beattock
65B	St. Rollox	68E	Carlisle Canal
65C	Parkhead		

SOUTHERN REGION

70A	**Nine Elms**	72B	Salisbury
70B	Feltham	72C	Yeovil
70C	Guildford	72D	Plymouth
70D	Basingstoke		Callington
70E	Reading	72E	Barnstaple Junction
70F	Fratton		Ilfracombe
70G	Newport (I.O.W.)		Torrington
70H	Ryde (I.O.W.)	72F	Wadebridge
71A	**Eastleigh**	73A	**Stewarts Lane**
	Andover Junction	73B	Bricklayers Arms
	Lymington	73C	Hither Green
	Winchester	73D	Gillingham (Kent)
71B	Bournemouth	73E	Faversham
	Branksome	74A	**Ashford (Kent)**
71G	Bath (S. & D.)	74B	Ramsgate
	Radstock	74C	Dover
71H	Templecombe		Folkestone
71I	Southampton Docks	74D	Tonbridge
71J	Highbridge	74E	St. Leonards
		75A	**Brighton**
72A	**Exmouth Junction**		Newhaven
	Bude	75B	Redhill
	Exmouth	75C	Norwood Junction
	Lyme Regis	75D	Horsham
	Okehampton	75E	Three Bridges
	Seaton	75F	Tunbridge Wells West

WESTERN REGION

81A	**Old Oak Common**	81D	Reading
81B	Slough		Henley-on-Thames
	Watlington	81E	Didcot
81C	Southall	81F	Oxford
			Fairford

82A	**Bristol (Bath Road)**
	Bath
	Wells
	Weston-super-Mare
	Yatton
82B	St. Philip's Marsh
82C	Swindon
	Chippenham
82D	Westbury
	Frome
82E	Yeovil
82F	Weymouth
	Bridport
83A	**Newton Abbot**
	Ashburton
	Kingsbridge
83B	Taunton
	Bridgwater
	Minehead
83C	Exeter
	Tiverton Junction
83D	Laira (Plymouth)
	Launceston
83E	St. Blazey
	Bodmin
	Moorswater
83F	Truro
83G	Penzance
	Helston
	St. Ives
84A	**Wolverhampton**
	(Stafford Road)
84B	Oxley
84C	Banbury
84D	Leamington Spa
84E	Tyseley
	Stratford-on-Avon
84F	Stourbridge Junction
84G	Shrewsbury
	Builth Road
	Clee Hill
	Craven Arms
	Knighton
84H	Wellington (Salop)
84J	Croes Newydd
	Bala
	Penmaenpool
	Trawsfynydd
84K	Chester
85A	**Worcester**
	Evesham
	Kingham
85B	Gloucester
	Brimscombe
	Cheltenham
	Cirencester
	Lydney
	Tetbury

85C	Hereford
	Ledbury
	Leominster
	Ross
85D	Kidderminster
86A	**Newport**
	(Ebbw Junction)
86B	Newport (Pill)
86C	Cardiff (Canton)
86D	Llantrisant
86E	Severn Tunnel Junction
86F	Tondu
86G	Pontypool Road
	Abergavenny
86H	Aberbeeg
86J	Aberdare
86K	Tredegar
87A	**Neath**
	Glyn Neath
	Neath (N. & B.)
87B	Duffryn Yard
87C	Danygraig
87D	Swansea East Dock
87E	Landore
87F	Llanelly
	Burry Port
	Pantyfynnon
87G	Carmarthen
87H	Neyland
	Cardigan
	Milford Haven
	Pembroke Dock
	Whitland
87J	Goodwick
87K	Swansea (Victoria)
	Gurnos
	Llandovery
	Upper Bank
88A	**Cardiff (Cathays)**
	Radyr
88B	Cardiff East Dock
88C	Barry
88D	Merthyr
	Cae Harris
	Dowlais Central
	Rhymney
88E	Abercynon
88F	Treherbert
	Ferndale
89A	**Oswestry**
	Llanidloes
	Moat Lane
	Welshpool (W. & L.)
89B	Brecon
	Builth Wells
89C	Machynlleth
	Aberayron
	Aberystwyth
	Aberystwyth (V. of R.)
	Portmadoc
	Pwllheli

SUMMARY OF WESTERN REGION
STEAM LOCOMOTIVE CLASSES

WITH HISTORICAL NOTES AND DIMENSIONS

4-6-0   6MT   1000 Class
"County"

Introduced 1945: Hawksworth design.
*Fitted with double chimney.
Weight: Loco.   76 tons 17 cwt.
        Tender 49 tons 0 cwt.
Pressure: 280 lb. Su.
Cyls.: (O) 18¼" × 30".
Driving Wheels: 6' 3".
T.E.: 32,580 lb.
P.V.

1001–8/10–26/8/9
*1000/9/27   Total 30

4-6-0   5P   4000 Class
"Star"

Introduced 1907: Churchward design.
Developed from No. 4000 (originally
No. 40, introduced 1906 as a 4-4-2),
earlier locomotives subsequently
fitted with new boilers and super-
heaters, remainder built as such.
Weight: Loco.   75 tons 12 cwt.
        Tender 46 tons 14 cwt.
Pressure: 225 lb. Su.
Cyls.: (4) 15" × 26".
Driving Wheels: 6' 8½".
T.E.: 27,800 lb.
Inside Walschaerts gear and rocking
shafts. P.V.

4056/61/2   Total 3

4-6-0   7P   4073 Class
"Castle"

*Introduced 1923: Collett design, de-
  veloped from "Star" (4000/37,
  5083–92 converted from "Star").
†Introduced 1946: existing locos.
  modified with 3-row superheater.
‡Introduced 1947: existing locos.
  modified with 4-row superheater.
¶Introduced 1956: fitted with double
  blastpipe and chimney.

Weight: Loco.   79 tons 17 cwt.
        Tender 46 tons 14 cwt.
Pressure: 225 lb. Su.
Cyls.: (4) 16" × 26".
Driving Wheels: 6' 8½".
T.E.: 31,625 lb.
Inside Walschaerts gear and rocking
shafts. P.V.

*4000/37/73–86/8–96/8/9, 5000–
  25/7–32/4/5/7–42/4–8/51 – 6/8–
  60/2/6–70/3/6/8/80/3–92

†5065/72/4/5/7/9/81/2/93/6–9,
  7000–3/5–20/1/3/5–8/31–3/5–7

‡4087/97, 5026/33/6/43/9/50/7/61/
  3/4/71/94/5, 7004/19/22/4/9/
  30/4

†¶7018

                              Total 167

4-6-0   5MT   4900 Class
"Hall"

*Introduced 1924: Collett rebuild with
  6' 0" driving wheels of "Saint"
  (built 1907).
†Introduced 1928: Modified design for
  new construction, with higher-
  pitched boiler, modified footplating
  and detail differences.
Weight: Loco. { 72 tons 10 cwt.*
               { 75 tons 0 cwt.†
        Tender 46 tons 14 cwt.
Pressure: 225 lb. Su.
Cyls. (O) 18½" × 30".
Driving Wheels: 6' 0".
T.E.: 27,275 lb.
P.V.

*4900

†4901–10/2–99, 5900–99, 6900–58

                              Total 258

4-6-0 8P 6000 Class "King"

*Introduced 1927: Collett design.
†Introduced 1947. Fitted with 4-row superheater.
‡Introduced 1955. Fitted with double chimney.
Weight: Loco. 89 tons 0 cwt.
Tender 46 tons 14 cwt.
Pressure: 250 lb. Su.
Cyls.: (4) $16\frac{1}{4}$" × 28".
Driving Wheels: 6' 6".
T.E.: 40,285 lb.
Inside Walschaerts gear and rocking shafts. P.V.

*6014/26
†6000/4/7/8/12/6/8–21/3–5/7–9
†‡6001–3/5/6/9–11/3/5/7/22

Total 30

4-6-0 5MT 6800 Class "Grange"

Introduced 1936: Collett design, variation of "Hall" with smaller wheels, incorporating certain parts of withdrawn 4300 2-6-0 locos.
Weight: Loco. 74 tons 0 cwt.
Tender 40 tons 0 cwt.
Pressure: 225 lb. Su.
Cyls.: (O) $18\frac{1}{2}$" × 30".
Driving Wheels: 5' 8".
T.E.: 28,875 lb.
P.V.

6800–79

Total 80

4-6-0 5MT 6959 Class "Modified Hall"

Introduced 1944: Hawksworth development of "Hall," with larger superheater, "one-piece" main frames and plate framed bogie.
Weight: Loco. 75 tons 16 cwt.
Tender 46 tons 14 cwt.
Pressure: 225 lb. Su.
Cyls.: (O) $18\frac{1}{2}$" × 30"
Driving Wheels: 6' 0".
T.E.: 27,275 lb.
P.V.

6959–99, 7900–29

Total 71

4-6-0 5MT 7800 Class "Manor"

Introduced 1938: Collett design for secondary lines, incorporating certain parts of withdrawn 4300 2-6-0 locos.
Weight: Loco. 68 tons 18 cwt.
Tender 40 tons 0 cwt.
Pressure: 225 lb. Su.
Cyls.: (O) 18" × 30".
Driving Wheels: 5' 8".
T.E.: 27,340 lb.
P.V.

7800–29

Total 30

4-4-0 2P 9000 Class

Introduced 1936: Collett rebuild, incorporating "Duke" type boiler and "Bulldog" frames for light lines.
Weight: Loco. 49 tons 0 cwt.
Tender { 40 tons 0 cwt.
36 tons 15 cwt.
Pressure: 180 lb. SS.
Cyls.: 18" × 26".
Driving Wheels: 5' 8".
T.E.: 18,955 lb.

9004/5/8–18/20–8

Total 22

2-8-0 8F 2800 Class

*Introduced 1903: Churchward design, earlier locos. subsequently fitted with new boiler and superheater.
†Introduced 1938: Collett locos., with side window cab and detail alterations.
Weight: Loco. { 75 tons 10 cwt.*
76 tons 5 cwt.†
Tender 40 tons 0 cwt.
Pressure: 225 lb. Su.
Cyls.: (O) $18\frac{1}{2}$" × 30".
Driving Wheels: 4' $7\frac{1}{2}$".
T.E.: 35,380 lb.
P.V.

*2800–2883
†2884–99, 3800–66

Total 167

9

2-8-0   7F   R.O.D. Class

Introduced 1911: Robinson G. C. design
(L.N.E.R. O4), built from 1917 for
Railway Operating Division, R.E.,
taken into G.W. stock from 1919 and
subsequently fitted with G.W boiler
mountings and details
Weight: Loco.   73 tons 11 cwt.
         Tender 47 tons 6 cwt.
Pressure: 185 lb. Su.
Cyls.:(O) 21″ × 26″.
Driving Wheels: 4′ 8″.
T.E.: 32,200 lb.
P.V.

3011/5–8/24/36/41/3/4

Total 10

2-8-0   7F   4700 Class

Introduced 1919: Churchward mixed
traffic design (4700 built with smaller
boiler and later rebuilt).
Weight: Loco.   82 tons 0 cwt
         Tender 46 tons 14 cwt.
Pressure: 225 lb. Su.
Cyls.: (O) 19″ × 30″.
Driving Wheels: 5′ 8″.
T.E.: 30,460 lb.
P.V.

4700–8

Total 9

2-6-0   4MT   4300 Class

*Introduced 1911: Churchward design.
†Introduced 1925: Locos. with detail
   alterations affecting weight.
‡Introduced 1932: Locos. with side
   window cab and detail alterations
Weight: Loco. $\begin{cases} \text{62 tons 0 cwt.*} \\ \text{64 tons 0 cwt.†} \\ \text{65 tons 6 cwt.‡} \end{cases}$
         Tender   40 tons 0 cwt.
Pressure: 200 lb. Su.
Cyls.: (O) 18½″ × 30″.
Driving Wheels: 5′ 8″
T.E.: 25,670 lb.
P.V.

*4326/58/75/7, 5306/7/10–5/7–9/
21–6/8/30–9/41/4/5/7/50/1/
3/5–8/60–2/7–72/5–82/4–6/8/
90–4/6–9, 6300–14/6–20/2–82/
4–99, 7305–21
†7300–4   ‡9300–19

Total 212

0-6-0   3MT   2251 Class

Introduced 1930: Collett design.
Weight:
   Loco.   43 tons 8 cwt.
   Tender $\begin{cases} \text{36 tons 15 cwt.} \\ \text{47 tons 6 cwt. (ex-R.O.D.} \end{cases}$
              tender from 3000 Class
              2-8-0).
Pressure: 200 lb. Su.
Cyls.: 17½″ × 24″.
Driving Wheels: 5′ 2″.
T.E.: 20,155 lb.

2200–99, 3200–19   **Total 120**

0-6-0   2MT   2301 Class

Introduced 1883: Dean design, later
fitted with superheater.
Weight: Loco.   36 tons 16 cwt.
         Tender 34 tons 5 cwt.
Pressure: 180 lb. Su.
Cyls.: 17½″ × 24″.
Driving Wheels: 5′ 2″.
T.E.: 18,140 lb.

2538

Total 1

2-8-2T   8F   7200 Class

Introduced 1934: Collett rebuild with
extended bunker and trailing wheels
of Churchward 4200 class 2-8-0T.
Weight: 92 tons 2 cwt.
Pressure: 200 lb. Su.
Cyls.: (O) 19″ × 30″.
Driving Wheels: 4′ 7½″.
T.E.: 33,170 lb.
P.V.

7200–53

Total 54

2-8-0T $\left\{ \begin{matrix} 7F* \\ 8F† \end{matrix} \right\}$ 4200 Class

*Introduced 1910: Churchward design.
†5205 class. Introduced 1923: with enlarged cyls. and detail alterations.
Weight: $\begin{cases} 81 \text{ tons } 12 \text{ cwt.*} \\ 82 \text{ tons } 2 \text{ cwt.†} \end{cases}$
Pressure: 200 lb. Su.
Cyls.: $\begin{cases} (O) \ 18\frac{1}{2}'' \times 30''.* \\ (O) \ 19'' \times 30''.† \end{cases}$
Driving Wheels: 4' 7½".
T.E. $\begin{cases} 31,450 \text{ lb.*} \\ 33,170 \text{ lb.†} \end{cases}$
P.V.

*4200/1/3/6–8/11–5/7/8/21–33/5–8/41–3/6–8/50–99, 5200–4
†5205–64   **Total 151**

2-6-2T 4MT 3100 Class

Introduced 1938: Collett rebuild with higher pressure and smaller wheels of Churchward 3150 class (introduced 1906).
Weight: 81 tons 9 cwt.
Pressure: 225 lb. Su.
Cyls.: (O) 18½" × 30".
Driving Wheels: 5' 3".
T.E.: 31,170 lb.
P.V.

3100–4   **Total 5**

2-6-2T 4MT 3150 Class

Introduced 1906: Churchward design, developed from his original 3100 class of 1903, but with larger boiler, subsequently fitted with superheater.
Weight: 81 tons 12 cwt.
Pressure: 200 lb. Su.
Cyls.: (O) 18½" × 30".
Driving Wheels: 5' 8".
T.E.: 25,670 lb.
P.V.

3150/63/70–2/4/6/7/80/3/6/7/90
                                      Total 13

2-6-2T 4MT 4500 Class

*Introduced 1906: Churchward design for light branches, developed from 4400 class with larger wheels, earlier locos. subsequently fitted with super-heater.
†4575 class. Introduced 1927: with detail alterations and increased weight.
‡Introduced 1953. Push-and-pull fitted.
Weight: $\begin{cases} 57 \text{ tons } 0 \text{ cwt.*} \\ 61 \text{ tons } 0 \text{ cwt.†} \end{cases}$
Pressure: 200 lb. Su.
Cyls.: (O) 17" × 24".
Driving Wheels: 4' 7½".
T.E.: 21,250 lb.
P.V.

*4505/7/8/19/24/6/36/8/40/5–74
†4575–9/80/2–5/7/8/90-9, 5500–10/2–23/5–8/30–3/6–44/6–54/6–8/61–7/9–71/3
‡4578/81/9, 5511/24/9/34/5/45/55/9/60/8/72/4   **Total 138**

2-6-2T 4MT 5100 & 6100 Classes

*5100 class. Introduced 1928: Collett rebuild with detail alterations and increased weight of Churchward 3100 class (introduced 1903 and sub-sequently fitted with superheater).
†5101 class. Introduced 1929. Modified design for new construction.
‡6100 class. Introduced 1931: Locos. for London suburban area with increased boiler pressure.
Weight: $\begin{cases} 75 \text{ tons } 10 \text{ cwt.*} \\ 78 \text{ tons } 9 \text{ cwt.†‡} \end{cases}$
Pressure: $\begin{cases} 200 \text{ lb. Su.*†} \\ 225 \text{ lb. Su.‡} \end{cases}$
Cyls.: (O) 18" × 30".
Driving Wheels: 5' 8".
T.E. $\begin{cases} 24,300 \text{ lb.*†} \\ 27,340 \text{ lb.‡} \end{cases}$
P.V.

*5148
†4100–79, 5101–10/50–8/60–99
‡6100–69   **Total 210**

2-6-2T 4MT 8100 Class

Introduced 1938: Collett rebuild with higher pressure and smaller wheels of Churchward locos. in 5100 class.
Weight: 76 tons 11 cwt.
Pressure: 225 lb. Su.
Cyls.: (O) 18″ × 30″.
Driving Wheels: 5′ 6″.
T.E.: 28,165 lb.
P.V.

8100-9   Total 10

2-6-2T unclass. V of R

*Introduced 1902: Davies and Metcalfe design for V. of R. 1′ 11½″ gauge.
†Introduced 1923: G.W. development of V. of R. design.
Weight: 25 tons 0 cwt.
Gauge: 1′ 11½″
Pressure: 165 lb.
Cyls. (O) $\begin{cases} 11″ \times 17″.* \\ 11½″ \times 17″.† \end{cases}$
Driving Wheels: 2′ 6″.
T.E. $\begin{cases} 9,615 \text{ lb.*} \\ 10,510 \text{ lb.†} \end{cases}$

*9
†7/8   Total 3

0-6-2T 5MT 5600 Class

*Introduced 1924: Collett design for service in Welsh valleys.
†Introduced 1927: Locos. with detail alterations.
Weight: $\begin{cases} 68 \text{ tons 12 cwt.*} \\ 69 \text{ tons 7 cwt.†} \end{cases}$
Pressure: 200 lb. Su.
Cyls.: 18″ × 26″.
Driving Wheels: 4′ 7½″.
T.E.: 25,800 lb.
P.V.

*5600-99
†6600-99   Total 200

0-6-2T 4F Rhymney Rly.

Introduced 1921: Hurry Riches Rhymney "R1" class, development of "R." (Introduced 1907.)
Weight: 66 tons 0 cwt.
Pressure: 175 lb.
Cyls.: 18½″ × 26″.
Driving Wheels: 4′ 6″.
T.E. 24,520 lb.

35-8, 42/3
                                    Total 6

0-6-2T 4P TV

Introduced 1924: G.W. rebuild with superheated taper boiler of Cameron T.V. "A" class (introduced 1914).
Weight: 65 tons 14 cwt.
Pressure: 200 lb. Su.
Cyls.: 17½″ × 26″.*
Driving Wheels: 5′ 3″.
T.E. 21,480 lb.†
304/5/47/9/61/4/5/8/70/3/6/8/80/
1/3/5/7/8/90/1/3/7-9
                                    Total 24

0-6-0PT 2F 850 Class

Introduced 1910: Dean saddletanks, subsequently rebuilt with pannier tanks.
Weight: 36 tons 3 cwt.
Pressure: 165 lb.
Cyls.: 16″ × 24″.
Driving Wheels: 4′ 1½″.
T.E.: 17,410 lb.

2008/1/2
                                    Total 2

0-6-0ST   0F   1361 Class

Introduced 1910: Churchward design for dock shunting.
Weight: 35 tons 4 cwt.
Pressure: 150 lb.
Cyls.: (O) 16" × 20".
Driving Wheels: 3' 8".
T.E.: 14,835 lb.

1361–5   Total 5

0-6-0PT   1F   1366 Class

Introduced 1934: Collett development of 1361 class, with pannier tanks.
Weight: 35 tons 15 cwt.
Pressure: 165 lb.
Cyls.: (O) 16" × 20".
Driving Wheels: 3' 8".

1366–71   Total 6

0-6-0PT   4F   1500 Class

Introduced 1949: Hawksworth short-wheelbase heavy shunting design
Weight: 58 tons 4 cwt.
Pressure: 200 lb.
Cyls.: (O) 17½" × 24".
Driving Wheels: 4' 7½".
T.E.: 22,515 lb.
Walschaerts gear.   P.V.

1500–9   Total 10

0-6-0PT   2F   1600 Class

Introduced 1949: Hawksworth light branch line and shunting design.
Weight: 41 tons 12 cwt.
Pressure: 165 lb.
Cyls.: 16½" × 24".
Driving Wheels: 4' 1½".
T.E.: 18,515 lb.

1600–69   Total 70

0-6-0PT   2F   2021 Class

2021 class. Introduced 1897: Dean saddletank, subsequently rebuilt with pannier tanks. Nos. 2101 onwards built with domeless boiler and Belpaire firebox, interchanged later throughout the class.
Weight: 39 tons 15 cwt.
Pressure: 165 lb.
Cyls.: 16½" × 24".
Driving Wheels: 4' 1½".
T.E.: 18,515 lb.

2027/40/69, 2134/60

                                          Total 5

0-6-0PT   1P   5400 Class

Introduced 1931: Collett design for light passenger work, push-and-pull fitted.
Weight: 46 tons 12 cwt.
Pressure: 165 lb.
Cyls.: 16½" × 24".
Driving Wheels: 5' 2".
T.E.: 14,780 lb.

5400–24

                                          Total 25

0-6-0PT   3F   5700 Class

*Introduced 1929: Collett design for shunting and light goods work developed from 2021 class.
†Introduced 1930: Locos. with steam brake and no A.T.C. fittings, for shunting only.
§Introduced 1933: Locos. with detail alterations, modified cab (except 8700) and increased weight.
‡Introduced 1933: Locos. with condensing gear for working over L T. Metropolitan line.
¶ Introduced 1948: Steam brake locos. with increased weight.
Weight: { 47 tons 10 cwt.*†
          50 tons 15 cwt.‡
          49 tons 0 cwt.§ ¶
Pressure: 200 lb.
Cyls.: 17½" × 24".
Driving Wheels: 4' 7½"
T.E.: 22,515 lb.

*5701–61/3–99, 7700–99, 8701–49
†6700–49
§3600–3799, 4600–99, 8700/50–99
9600–82, 9711–99
‡9700–10
¶6750–79

Total 861

0-6-0PT   2P*   2F†
6400 & 7400 Classes

*6400 class. Introduced 1932: Collett design for light passenger work, variation of 5400 class with smaller wheels, push-and-pull fitted.

†7400 class. Introduced 1936 : Non-push-and-pull fitted locos.

Weight: {45 tons 12 cwt.*
        {45 tons 9 cwt.†
Pressure: 180 lb.
Cyls.: 16½″ × 24″.
Driving Wheels: 4′ 7½″.
T.E.: 18,010 lb.

*6400–39
†7400–49

Total : 6400 Class 40
7400 Class 50

0-6-0PT   4F   9400 Class

*Introduced 1947: Hawksworth taper boiler design for heavy shunting.
†Introduced 1949: Locos. with non-superheated boiler.
Weight: 55 tons 7 cwt.
Pressure: 200 lb. SS.
Cyls.: 17½″ × 24″.
Driving Wheels: 4′ 7½″.
T.E.: 22,515 lb.

*9400–9
†3400–9, 8400–99, 9410–99

N.B.—Locomotives of this class are still being delivered.

0-6-0T   1F   BPGV

Introduced 1910 : Hudswell Clarke design for B.P.G.V., rebuilt by G.W.R.

Weight: 37 tons 15 cwt.
Pressure: 165 lb.
Cyls.: (O) 15″ × 22″.
Driving Wheels: 3′ 9″.
T.E.: 15,430 lb.

2198   **Total 1**

0-6-0T   Unclass.   W & L

Introduced 1902: Beyer Peacock design for 2′ 6″ gauge W. & L. Section, Cambrian Railways.
Weight: 19 tons 18 cwt.
Gauge: 2′ 6″.
Pressure: 150 lb.
Cyls.: (O) 11½″ × 16″.
Driving Wheels: 2′ 9″.
T.E.: 8,175 lb.

822/3   **Total 2**

0-4-2T   1P
1400 & 5800 Classes

*1400 class introduced 1932: Collett design for light branch work (originally designated 4800 class). Push-and-pull fitted.

†5800 class introduced 1933: Non push-and-pull fitted locos.
Weight: 41 tons 6 cwt.
Pressure: 165 lb.
Cyls.: 16″ × 24″.
Driving Wheels: 5′ 2″.
T.E.: 13,900 lb.

*1400–3/5–12/4–24/6–59/61–74
†5800–19

Total 91

0-4-0T   3F   1101 Class

Introduced 1926: Avonside Engine Co. design to G.W. requirements for dock shunting.
Weight: 38 tons 4 cwt.
Pressure: 170 lb.
Cyls.: (O) 16″ × 24″.
Driving Wheels: 3′ 9½″.
T.E.: 19,510 lb.
Walschaerts gear.

1101–6   **Total 6**

0-4-0ST OF Cardiff Rly.

Introduced 1893: Kitson design for Cardiff Railway.

Weight: 25 tons 10 cwt.

Pressure: 160 lb.

Cyls.: (O) 14″ × 21″.

Driving Wheels: 3′ 2½″.

T.E.: 14,540 lb.

Hawthorn Kitson valve gear.

1338	Total 1

0-4-0ST OF P & M

Introduced 1907: Peckett design for P. & M.

Weight: 33 tons 10 cwt.

Pressure: 150 lb.

Cyls.: (O) 15″ × 21″.

Driving Wheels: 3′ 7″.

T.E.: 14,010 lb.

1151/2	Total 2

0-4-0ST OF SHT

Introduced 1905: Barclay design for S.H.T.

Weight: 28 tons 0 cwt.

Pressure: 160 lb.

Cyls.: (O) 14″ × 22″.

Driving Wheels: 3′ 5″.

T.E.: 14,305 lb.

1140	Total 1

Introduced 1906: Peckett design for S.H.T. (similar to 1151/2).

Weight: 33 tons 10 cwt.

Pressure: 150 lb.

Cyls.: (O) 15″ × 21″.

Driving Wheels: 3′ 7″.

T.E.: 14,010 lb.

1143/5	Total 2

Introduced 1909: Hawthorn Leslie design for S.H.T.

Weight: 26 tons 17 cwt.

Pressure: 150 lb.

Cyls.: (O) 14″ × 22″.

Driving Wheels: 3′ 6″.

T.E.: 13,090 lb

1144	Total 1

Introduced 1911: Hudswell Clarke design for S.H.T

Weight: 28 tons 15 cwt.

Pressure: 160 lb.

Cyls.: (O) 15″ × 22″.

Driving Wheels: 3′ 4″.

T.E.: 16,830 lb.

1142	Total 1

LOCOMOTIVE SUPERINTENDENTS AND CHIEF
MECHANICAL ENGINEERS OF THE G.W.R. & W.R.

Sir Daniel Gooch	1837—1864
Joseph Armstrong	{ 1854—1864* 1864—1877
George Armstrong ... *(Bro. of J. Armstrong)*	{ 1864— 1877—1892*
William Dean	{ —1877* 1877—1902
G. J. Churchward	1902—1921
Charles B. Collett	1922—1941
F. W. Hawksworth	1941—1949

* In charge of standard gauge locomotives at Stafford Road Works, Wolverhampton, with wide powers in design and construction. The exact dates of Geo. Armstrong's and Dean's terms of service there cannot be definitely ascertained from existing records.

STREAMLINED DIESEL RAIL-CARS

Car No.	Date	Engines	Total b.h.p.	Seats	Car No.	Date	Engines	Total b.h.p.	Seats
1	1934	1	121	69	18§	1937	2	242	70
3/4*	1934	2	242	44	19-21/3-32	1940	2	210	48
5-7	1935	2	242	70	34‡	1941	2	210	—
8	1936	2	242	70	35	1941	2	210	48
11/12†	1936	2	242	63	22, 38‖	1942	4	420	104
13-16	1936	2	242	70					
17‡	1936	2	242	—					

* Buffet and lavatory facilities.

† Lavatory facilities.

‡ Parcels cars.

§ Experimentally geared to haul trailer car, became prototype of subsequent designs.

‖ Twin-coach units with buffet and lavatory facilities. Adjoining statistics apply per 2-car unit. These units can work as 3-car sets by the addition of an ordinary corridor coach.

1	6	12	16	20	24	27	30	35
3	7	13	17	21	25	28	31	36
4	8	14	18	22	26	29	32	38
5	11	15	19	23				

Right: Ex-Cardiff Rly. 0-4-0ST No. 1338 [P. H. Wells

Below: Ex-Welshpool & Llanfair 0-6-0T No. 822 [R. E. Vincent

Right: Ex-Vale of Rheidol 2-6-2T No. 8 Llywelyn [R. E. Vincent

1101 Class 0-4-0T No. 1102   [*K. R. Pirt*

Ex-S.H.T. 0-4-0ST No. 1143 (*Left*) and 1142   [*K. L. Cook*

Ex-P.M. 0-4-0ST No. 1152   [*A. R. Carpenter*

Right: 1361 Class
0-6-0PT No. 1369
[A. R. Carpenter

Centre: 1500 Class
0-6-0PT No. 1503
[G. Wheeler

Bottom: 9400 Class
0-6-0PT No. 9440
[R. J. Buckley

Left: 5600 Class 0-6-2T
No. 6633
[*Brian E. Morrison*

Below: Ex-R.R. RI Class
0-6-2T No. 43
[*P. H. Groom*

Left: Ex-TV A Class
0-6-2T No. 373 (with
rounded side tanks)
[*D. Penney*

Right: Ex-TV A Class
0-6-2T No. 388
[K. R. Pirt

Below: 1400 Class
0-4-2T No. 1432
[F. W. Day

Right: 5800 Class
0-4-2T No. 5811
[G. Wheeler

850 Class 0-6-0PT No. 2012   [Brian E. Morrison

5700 Class 0-6-0PT No. 6717   [R. E. Vincent

5700 Class 0-6-0PT No. 9705 (fitted with condensing apparatus)
                                                     [Brian E. Morrison

1600 Class 0-6-0PT No. 1669   [G. Wheeler

5400 Class 0-6-0PT No. 5404   [C. G. Pearson

6400 Class 0-6-0PT No 6437   [A. R. Carpenter

6000 Class 4-6-0 No. 6017 *King Edward IV* [A. E. Brown

4073 Class 4-6-0 No. 7018 *Drysllwyn Castle* (with double chimney) [G. Wheeler

4073 Class 4-6-0 No. 4088 *Dartmouth Castle* [R. E. Vincent

NUMERICAL LIST OF WESTERN REGION STEAM LOCOMOTIVES

Locomotives are of G.W. origin except where indicated by other initials

2-6-2T   **V of R**

7 Owain Glyndŵr
8 Llywelyn
9 Prince of Wales

0-6-2T   **RR**

35	38
36	42
37	43

0-6-2T   **TV**

304	365	380	390
305	368	381	391
347	370	383	393
349	373	385	397
361	376	387	398
364	378	388	399

0-6-0T   **W & L**

822   823

4-6-0   **1000 Class**
" County "

1000 County of Middlesex
1001 County of Bucks
1002 County of Berks

1003 County of Wilts
1004 County of Somerset
1005 County of Devon
1006 County of Cornwall
1007 County of Brecknock
1008 County of Cardigan
1009 County of Carmarthen
1010 County of Caernarvon
1011 County of Chester
1012 County of Denbigh
1013 County of Dorset
1014 County of Glamorgan
1015 County of Gloucester
1016 County of Hants
1017 County of Hereford
1018 County of Leicester
1019 County of Merioneth
1020 County of Monmouth
1021 County of Montgomery
1022 County of Northampton
1023 County of Oxford
1024 County of Pembroke
1025 County of Radnor
1026 County of Salop
1027 County of Stafford
1028 County of Warwick
1029 County of Worcester

0-4-0T   **1101 Class**

1101	1103	1105
1102	1104	1106

0-4-0ST   **SHT**

1140	1143	1145
1142	1144	

1151—2198

0-4-0ST PM

1151   1152

0-4-0ST Car. R.

1338

0-6-0ST 1361 Class

| 1361 | 1363 | 1365 |
| 1362 | 1364 | |

0-6-0PT 1366 Class

| 1366 | 1368 | 1370 |
| 1367 | 1369 | 1371 |

0-4-2T 1400 Class

1400	1420	1439	1457
1401	1421	1440	1458
1402	1422	1441	1459
1403	1423	1442	1461
1405	1424	1443	1462
1406	1426	1444	1463
1407	1427	1445	1464
1408	1428	1446	1465
1409	1429	1447	1466
1410	1430	1448	1467
1411	1431	1449	1468
1412	1432	1450	1469
1414	1433	1451	1470
1415	1434	1452	1471
1416	1435	1453	1472
1417	1436	1454	1473
1418	1437	1455	1474
1419	1438	1456	

0-6-0PT 1500 Class

1500	1503	1506	1509
1501	1504	1507	
1502	1505	1508	

0-6-0PT 1600 Class

1600	1618	1636	1654
1601	1619	1637	1655
1602	1620	1638	1656
1603	1621	1639	1657
1604	1622	1640	1658
1605	1623	1641	1659
1606	1624	1642	1660
1607	1625	1643	1661
1608	1626	1644	1662
1609	1627	1645	1663
1610	1628	1646	1664
1611	1629	1647	1665
1612	1630	1648	1666
1613	1631	1649	1667
1614	1632	1650	1668
1615	1633	1651	1669
1616	1634	1652	
1617	1635	1653	

0-6-0PT 850 Class

2008   2012

0-6-0PT 2021 Class

| 2027 | 2069 | 2134 | 2160 |
| 2040 | | | |

0-6-0T BPGV Rly.

2198

26

0-6-0   2251 Class

2200	2225	2250	2275
2201	2226	2251	2276
2202	2227	2252	2277
2203	2228	2253	2278
2204	2229	2254	2279
2205	2230	2255	2280
2206	2231	2256	2281
2207	2232	2257	2282
2208	2233	2258	2283
2209	2234	2259	2284
2210	2235	2260	2285
2211	2236	2261	2286
2212	2237	2262	2287
2213	2238	2263	2288
2214	2239	2264	2289
2215	2240	2265	2290
2216	2241	2266	2291
2217	2242	2267	2292
2218	2243	2268	2293
2219	2244	2269	2294
2220	2245	2270	2295
2221	2246	2271	2296
2222	2247	2272	2297
2223	2248	2273	2298
2224	2249	2274	2299

2828	2846	2864	2882
2829	2847	2865	2883
2830	2848	2866	2884
2831	2849	2867	2885
2832	2850	2868	2886
2833	2851	2869	2887
2834	2852	2870	2888
2835	2853	2871	2889
2836	2854	2872	2890
2837	2855	2873	2891
2838	2856	2874	2892
2839	2857	2875	2893
2840	2858	2876	2894
2841	2859	2877	2895
2842	2860	2878	2896
2843	2861	2879	2897
2844	2862	2880	2898
2845	2863	2881	2899

2-8-0   R.O.D. Class

3011	3017	3028	3043
3015	3018	3036	3044
3016	3024	3041	

0-6-0   2301 Class

2538

2-8-0   2800 Class

2800	2807	2814	2821
2801	2808	2815	2822
2802	2809	2816	2823
2803	2810	2817	2824
2804	2811	2818	2825
2805	2812	2819	2826
2806	2813	2820	2827

2-6-2T — 3100 Class

3100	3102	3103	3104
3101			

2-6-2T — 3150 Class

3150	3172	3180	3190
3163	3174	3183	
3170	3176	3186	
3171	3177	3187	

0-6-0 — 2251 Class

3200	3205	3210	3215
3201	3206	3211	3216
3202	3207	3212	3217
3203	3208	3213	3218
3204	3209	3214	3219

0-6-0PT — 9400 Class

3400	3403	3406	3408
3401	3404	3407	3409
3402	3405		

0-6-0PT — 5700 Class

3600	3617	3634	3651
3601	3618	3635	3652
3602	3619	3636	3653
3603	3620	3637	3654
3604	3621	3638	3655
3605	3622	3639	3656
3606	3623	3640	3657
3607	3624	3641	3658
3608	3625	3642	3659
3609	3626	3643	3660
3610	3627	3644	3661
3611	3628	3645	3662
3612	3629	3646	3663
3613	3630	3647	3664
3614	3631	3648	3665
3615	3632	3649	3666
3616	3633	3650	3667

3668	3701	3734	3767
3669	3702	3735	3768
3670	3703	3736	3769
3671	3704	3737	3770
3672	3705	3738	3771
3673	3706	3739	3772
3674	3707	3740	3773
3675	3708	3741	3774
3676	3709	3742	3775
3677	3710	3743	3776
3678	3711	3744	3777
3679	3712	3745	3778
3680	3713	3746	3779
3681	3714	3747	3780
3682	3715	3748	3781
3683	3716	3749	3782
3684	3717	3750	3783
3685	3718	3751	3784
3686	3719	3752	3785
3687	3720	3753	3786
3688	3721	3754	3787
3689	3722	3755	3788
3690	3723	3756	3789
3691	3724	3757	3790
3692	3725	3758	3791
3693	3726	3759	3792
3694	3727	3760	3793
3695	3728	3761	3794
3696	3729	3762	3795
3697	3730	3763	3796
3698	3731	3764	3797
3699	3732	3765	3798
3700	3733	3766	3799

2-8-0 — 2800 Class

3800	3811	3822	3833
3801	3812	3823	3834
3802	3813	3824	3835
3803	3814	3825	3836
3804	3815	3826	3837
3805	3816	3827	3838
3806	3817	3828	3839
3807	3818	3829	3840
3808	3819	3830	3841
3809	3820	3831	3842
3810	3821	3832	3843

3844	3850	3856	3862
3845	3851	3857	3863
3846	3852	3858	3864
3847	3853	3859	3865
3848	3854	3860	3866
3849	3855	3861	

4-6-0   4073 Class
" Castle "

4000 North Star
4037 The South Wales Borderers

4-6-0   4000 Class
" Star "

4056 Princess Margaret
4061 Glastonbury Abbey
4062 Malmesbury Abbey

4-6-0   4073 Class
" Castle "

4073 Caerphilly Castle
4074 Caldicot Castle
4075 Cardiff Castle
4076 Carmarthen Castle
4077 Chepstow Castle
4078 Pembroke Castle
4079 Pendennis Castle
4080 Powderham Castle
4081 Warwick Castle
4082 Windsor Castle
4083 Abbotsbury Castle
4084 Aberystwyth Castle
4085 Berkeley Castle
4086 Builth Castle
4087 Cardigan Castle
4088 Dartmouth Castle
4089 Donnington Castle
4090 Dorchester Castle
4091 Dudley Castle
4092 Dunraven Castle
4093 Dunster Castle
4094 Dynevor Castle
4095 Harlech Castle

4096 Highclere Castle
4097 Kenilworth Castle
4098 Kidwelly Castle
4099 Kilgerran Castle

2-6-2T   5100 Class

4100	4120	4140	4160
4101	4121	4141	4161
4102	4122	4142	4162
4103	4123	4143	4163
4104	4124	4144	4164
4105	4125	4145	4165
4106	4126	4146	4166
4107	4127	4147	4167
4108	4128	4148	4168
4109	4129	4149	4169
4110	4130	4150	4170
4111	4131	4151	4171
4112	4132	4152	4172
4113	4133	4153	4173
4114	4134	4154	4174
4115	4135	4155	4175
4116	4136	4156	4176
4117	4137	4157	4177
4118	4138	4158	4178
4119	4139	4159	4179

2-8-0T   4200 Class

4200	4226	4250	4268
4201	4227	4251	4269
4203	4228	4252	4270
4206	4229	4253	4271
4207	4230	4254	4272
4208	4231	4255	4273
4211	4232	4256	4274
4212	4233	4257	4275
4213	4235	4258	4276
4214	4236	4259	4277
4215	4237	4260	4278
4217	4238	4261	4279
4218	4241	4262	4280
4221	4242	4263	4281
4222	4243	4264	4282
4223	4246	4265	4283
4224	4247	4266	4284
4225	4248	4267	4285

4286-4921

4286	4290	4294	4298
4287	4291	4295	4299
4288	4292	4296	
4289	4293	4297	

2-6-0   4300 Class

4326	4358	4375	4377

2-6-2T   4500 Class

4505	4552	4568	4584
4507	4553	4569	4585
4508	4554	4570	4587
4519	4555	4571	4588
4524	4556	4572	4589
4526	4557	4573	4590
4536	4558	4574	4591
4538	4559	4575	4592
4540	4560	4576	4593
4545	4561	4577	4594
4546	4562	4578	4595
4547	4563	4579	4596
4548	4564	4580	4597
4549	4565	4581	4598
4550	4566	4582	4599
4551	4567	4583	

0-6-0PT   5700 Class

4600	4610	4620	4630
4601	4611	4621	4631
4602	4612	4622	4632
4603	4613	4623	4633
4604	4614	4624	4634
4605	4615	4625	4635
4606	4616	4626	4636
4607	4617	4627	4637
4608	4618	4628	4638
4609	4619	4629	4639

4640	4655	4670	4685
4641	4656	4671	4686
4642	4657	4672	4687
4643	4658	4673	4688
4644	4659	4674	4689
4645	4660	4675	4690
4646	4661	4676	4691
4647	4662	4677	4692
4648	4663	4678	4693
4649	4664	4679	4694
4650	4665	4680	4695
4651	4666	4681	4696
4652	4667	4682	4697
4653	4668	4683	4698
4654	4669	4684	4699

2-8-0   4700 Class

4700	4703	4705	4707
4701	4704	4706	4708
4702			

4-6-0 " Hall " 4900 Class

4900 Saint Martin
4901 Adderley Hall
4902 Aldenham Hall
4903 Astley Hall
4904 Binnegar Hall
4905 Barton Hall
4906 Bradfield Hall
4907 Broughton Hall
4908 Broome Hall
4909 Blakesley Hall
4910 Blaisdon Hall
4912 Berrington Hall
4913 Baglan Hall
4914 Cranmore Hall
4915 Condover Hall
4916 Crumlin Hall
4917 Crosswood Hall
4918 Dartington Hall
4919 Donnington Hall
4920 Dumbleton Hall
4921 Eaton Hall

4922 Enville Hall
4923 Evenley Hall
4924 Eydon Hall
4925 Eynsham Hall
4926 Fairleigh Hall
4927 Farnborough Hall
4928 Gatacre Hall
4929 Goytrey Hall
4930 Hagley Hall
4931 Hanbury Hall
4932 Hatherton Hall
4933 Himley Hall
4934 Hindlip Hall
4935 Ketley Hall
4936 Kinlet Hall
4937 Lanelay Hall
4938 Liddington Hall
4939 Littleton Hall
4940 Ludford Hall
4941 Llangedwyn Hall
4942 Maindy Hall
4943 Marrington Hall
4944 Middleton Hall
4945 Milligan Hall
4946 Moseley Hall
4947 Nanhoran Hall
4948 Northwick Hall
4949 Packwood Hall
4950 Patshull Hall
4951 Pendeford Hall
4952 Peplow Hall
4953 Pitchford Hall
4954 Plaish Hall
4955 Plaspower Hall
4956 Plowden Hall
4957 Postlip Hall
4958 Priory Hall
4959 Purley Hall
4960 Pyle Hall
4961 Pyrland Hall
4962 Ragley Hall
4963 Rignall Hall
4964 Rodwell Hall
4965 Rood Ashton Hall
4966 Shakenhurst Hall
4967 Shirenewton Hall
4968 Shotton Hall
4969 Shrugborough Hall

4970 Sketty Hall
4971 Stanway Hall
4972 Saint Brides Hall
4973 Sweeney Hall
4974 Talgarth Hall
4975 Umberslade Hall
4976 Warfield Hall
4977 Watcombe Hall
4978 Westwood Hall
4979 Wootton Hall
4980 Wrottesley Hall
4981 Abberley Hall
4982 Acton Hall
4983 Albert Hall
4984 Albrighton Hall
4985 Allesley Hall
4986 Aston Hall
4987 Brockley Hall
4988 Bulwell Hall
4989 Cherwell Hall
4990 Clifton Hall
4991 Cobham Hall
4992 Crosby Hall
4993 Dalton Hall
4994 Downton Hall
4995 Easton Hall
4996 Eden Hall
4997 Elton Hall
4998 Eyton Hall
4999 Gopsal Hall

4-6-0 "Castle" 4073 Class

5000 Launceston Castle
5001 Llandovery Castle
5002 Ludlow Castle
5003 Lulworth Castle
5004 Llanstephan Castle
5005 Manorbier Castle
5006 Tregenna Castle
5007 Rougemont Castle
5008 Raglan Castle
5009 Shrewsbury Castle
5010 Restormel Castle
5011 Tintagel Castle
5012 Berry Pomeroy Castle

5013 Abergavenny Castle
5014 Goodrich Castle
5015 Kingswear Castle
5016 Montgomery Castle
5017 The Gloucestershire
       Regiment 28th, 61st
5018 St. Mawes Castle
5019 Treago Castle
5020 Trematon Castle
5021 Whittington Castle
5022 Wigmore Castle
5023 Brecon Castle
5024 Carew Castle
5025 Chirk Castle
5026 Criccieth Castle
5027 Farleigh Castle
5028 Llantilio Castle
5029 Nunney Castle
5030 Shirburn Castle
5031 Totnes Castle
5032 Usk Castle
5033 Broughton Castle
5034 Corfe Castle
5035 Coity Castle
5036 Lyonshall Castle
5037 Monmouth Castle
5038 Morlais Castle
5039 Rhuddlan Castle
5040 Stokesay Castle
5041 Tiverton Castle
5042 Winchester Castle
5043 Earl of Mount Edgcumbe
5044 Earl of Dunraven
5045 Earl of Dudley
5046 Earl Cawdor
5047 Earl of Dartmouth
5048 Earl of Devon
5049 Earl of Plymouth
5050 Earl of St. Germans
5051 Earl Bathurst
5052 Earl of Radnor
5053 Earl Cairns
5054 Earl of Ducie
5055 Earl of Eldon
5056 Earl of Powis
5057 Earl Waldegrave
5058 Earl of Clancarty
5059 Earl St. Aldwyn
5060 Earl of Berkeley
5061 Earl of Birkenhead
5062 Earl of Shaftesbury
5063 Earl Baldwin
5064 Bishop's Castle
5065 Newport Castle
5066 Sir Felix Pole
5067 St. Fagans Castle
5068 Beverston Castle
5069 Isambard Kingdom Brunel
5070 Sir Daniel Gooch
5071 Spitfire
5072 Hurricane
5073 Blenheim
5074 Hampden
5075 Wellington
5076 Gladiator
5077 Fairey Battle
5078 Beaufort
5079 Lysander
5080 Defiant
5081 Lockheed Hudson
5082 Swordfish
5083 Bath Abbey
5084 Reading Abbey
5085 Evesham Abbey
5086 Viscount Horne
5087 Tintern Abbey
5088 Llanthony Abbey
5089 Westminster Abbey
5090 Neath Abbey
5091 Cleeve Abbey
5092 Tresco Abbey
5093 Upton Castle
5094 Tretower Castle
5095 Barbury Castle
5096 Bridgwater Castle
5097 Sarum Castle
5098 Clifford Castle
5099 Compton Castle

2-6-2T		**5100 Class**	
5101	5103	5105	5107
5102	5104	5106	5108

5109	5162	5176	5190	5367	5376	5384	5393
5110	5163	5177	5191	5368	5377	5385	5394
5148	5164	5178	5192	5369	5378	5386	5396
5150	5165	5179	5193	5370	5379	5388	5397
5151	5166	5180	5194	5371	5380	5390	5398
5152	5167	5181	5195	5372	5381	5391	5399
5153	5168	5182	5196	5375	5382	5392	
5154	5169	5183	5197				
5155	5170	5184	5198				
5156	5171	5185	5199				
5157	5172	5186					
5158	5173	5187					
5160	5174	5188					
5161	5175	5189					

0-6-0PT   5400 Class

5400	5407	5414	5421
5401	5408	5415	5422
5402	5409	5416	5423
5403	5410	5417	5424
5404	5411	5418	
5405	5412	5419	
5406	5413	5420	

2-8-0T   4200 Class

5200	5217	5234	5251
5201	5218	5235	5252
5202	5219	5236	5253
5203	5220	5237	5254
5204	5221	5238	5255
5205	5222	5239	5256
5206	5223	5240	5257
5207	5224	5241	5258
5208	5225	5242	5259
5209	5226	5243	5260
5210	5227	5244	5261
5211	5228	5245	5262
5212	5229	5246	5263
5213	5230	5247	5264
5214	5231	5248	
5215	5232	5249	
5216	5233	5250	

2-6-2T   4500 Class

5500	5519	5538	5557
5501	5520	5539	5558
5502	5521	5540	5559
5503	5522	5541	5560
5504	5523	5542	5561
5505	5524	5543	5562
5506	5525	5544	5563
5507	5526	5545	5564
5508	5527	5546	5565
5509	5528	5547	5566
5510	5529	5548	5567
5511	5530	5549	5568
5512	5531	5550	5569
5513	5532	5551	5570
5514	5533	5552	5571
5515	5534	5553	5572
5516	5535	5554	5573
5517	5536	5555	5574
5518	5537	5556	

2-6-0   4300 Class

5306	5321	5334	5351
5307	5322	5335	5353
5310	5323	5336	5355
5311	5324	5337	5356
5312	5325	5338	5357
5313	5326	5339	5358
5314	5328	5341	5360
5315	5330	5344	5361
5317	5331	5345	5362
5318	5332	5347	
5319	5333	5350	

0-6-2T   5600 Class

5600	5602	5604	5606
5601	5603	5605	5607

5608	5631	5654	5677
5609	5632	5655	5678
5610	5633	5656	5679
5611	5634	5657	5680
5612	5635	5658	5681
5613	5636	5659	5682
5614	5637	5660	5683
5615	5638	5661	5684
5616	5639	5662	5685
5617	5640	5663	5686
5618	5641	5664	5687
5619	5642	5665	5688
5620	5643	5666	5689
5621	5644	5667	5690
5622	5645	5668	5691
5623	5646	5669	5692
5624	5647	5670	5693
5625	5648	5671	5694
5626	5649	5672	5695
5627	5650	5673	5696
5628	5651	5674	5697
5629	5652	5675	5698
5630	5653	5676	5699

5786	5790	5794	5798
5787	5791	5795	5799
5788	5792	5796	
5789	5793	5797	

0-4-2T   5800 Class

5800	5805	5810	5815
5801	5806	5811	5816
5802	5807	5812	5817
5803	5808	5813	5818
5804	5809	5814	5819

4-6-0   4900 Class
" Hall "

5900 Hinderton Hall
5901 Hazel Hall
5902 Howick Hall
5903 Keele Hall
5904 Kelham Hall
5905 Knowsley Hall
5906 Lawton Hall
5907 Marble Hall
5908 Moreton Hall
5909 Newton Hall
5910 Park Hall
5911 Preston Hall
5912 Queen's Hall
5913 Rushton Hall
5914 Ripon Hall
5915 Trentham Hall
5916 Trinity Hall
5917 Westminster Hall
5918 Walton Hall
5919 Worsley Hall
5920 Wycliffe Hall
5921 Bingley Hall
5922 Caxton Hall
5923 Colston Hall
5924 Dinton Hall
5925 Eastcote Hall
5926 Grotrian Hall
5927 Guild Hall
5928 Haddon Hall
5929 Hanham Hall
5930 Hannington Hall
5931 Hatherley Hall

0-6-0PT   5700 Class

5701	5722	5743	5765
5702	5723	5744	5766
5703	5724	5745	5767
5704	5725	5746	5768
5705	5726	5747	5769
5706	5727	5748	5770
5707	5728	5749	5771
5708	5729	5750	5772
5709	5730	5751	5773
5710	5731	5752	5774
5711	5732	5753	5775
5712	5733	5754	5776
5713	5734	5755	5777
5714	5735	5756	5778
5715	5736	5757	5779
5716	5737	5758	5780
5717	5738	5759	5781
5718	5739	5760	5782
5719	5740	5761	5783
5720	5741	5763	5784
5721	5742	5764	5785

5932 Haydon Hall	5980 Dingley Hall
5933 Kingsway Hall	5981 Frensham Hall
5934 Kneller Hall	5982 Harrington Hall
5935 Norton Hall	5983 Henley Hall
5936 Oakley Hall	5984 Linden Hall
5937 Stanford Hall	5985 Mostyn Hall
5938 Stanley Hall	5986 Arbury Hall
5939 Tangley Hall	5987 Brocket Hall
5940 Whitbourne Hall	5988 Bostock Hall
5941 Campion Hall	5989 Cransley Hall
5942 Doldowlod Hall	5990 Dorford Hall
5943 Elmdon Hall	5991 Gresham Hall
5944 Ickenham Hall	5992 Horton Hall
5945 Leckhampton Hall	5993 Kirby Hall
5946 Marwell Hall	5994 Roydon Hall
5947 Saint Benet's Hall	5995 Wick Hall
5948 Siddington Hall	5996 Mytton Hall
5949 Trematon Hall	5997 Sparkford Hall
5950 Wardley Hall	5998 Trevor Hall
5951 Clyffe Hall	5999 Wollaton Hall
5952 Cogan Hall	
5953 Dunley Hall	
5954 Faendre Hall	
5955 Garth Hall	
5956 Horsley Hall	**4-6-0 6000 Class**
5957 Hutton Hall	**" King "**
5958 Knolton Hall	
5959 Mawley Hall	6000 King George V
5960 Saint Edmund Hall	6001 King Edward VII
5961 Toynbee Hall	6002 King William IV
5962 Wantage Hall	6003 King George IV
5963 Wimpole Hall	6004 King George III
5964 Wolseley Hall	6005 King George II
5965 Woollas Hall	6006 King George I
5966 Ashford Hall	6007 King William III
5967 Bickmarsh Hall	6008 King James II
5968 Cory Hall	6009 King Charles II
5969 Honington Hall	6010 King Charles I
5970 Hengrave Hall	6011 King James I
5971 Merevale Hall	6012 King Edward VI
5972 Olton Hall	6013 King Henry VIII
5973 Rolleston Hall	6014 King Henry VII
5974 Wallsworth Hall	6015 King Richard III
5975 Winslow Hall	6016 King Edward V
5976 Ashwicke Hall	6017 King Edward IV
5977 Beckford Hall	6018 King Henry VI
5978 Bodinnick Hall	6019 King Henry V
5979 Cruckton Hall	6020 King Henry IV

6021-6679

6021 King Richard II
6022 King Edward III
6023 King Edward II
6024 King Edward I
6025 King Henry III
6026 King John
6027 King Richard I
6028 King George VI
6029 King Edward VIII

6354	6366	6378	6391
6355	6367	6379	6392
6356	6368	6380	6393
6357	6369	6381	6394
6358	6370	6382	6395
6359	6371	6384	6396
6360	6372	6385	6397
6361	6373	6386	6398
6362	6374	6387	6399
6363	6375	6388	
6364	6376	6389	
6365	6377	6390	

2-6-2T   6100 Class

6100	6118	6136	6153
6101	6119	6137	6154
6102	6120	6138	6155
6103	6121	6139	6156
6104	6122	6140	6157
6105	6123	6141	6158
6106	6124	6142	6159
6107	6125	6143	6160
6108	6126	6144	6161
6109	6127	6145	6162
6110	6128	6146	6163
6111	6129	6147	6164
6112	6130	6148	6165
6113	6131	6149	6166
6114	6132	6150	6167
6115	6133	6151	6168
6116	6134	6152	6169
6117	6135		

0-6-0PT   6400 Class

6400	6410	6420	6430
6401	6411	6421	6431
6402	6412	6422	6432
6403	6413	6423	6433
6404	6414	6424	6434
6405	6415	6425	6435
6406	6416	6426	6436
6407	6417	6427	6437
6408	6418	6428	6438
6409	6419	6429	6439

2-6-0   4300 Class

6300	6313	6328	6341
6301	6314	6329	6342
6302	6316	6330	6343
6303	6317	6331	6344
6304	6318	6332	6345
6305	6319	6333	6346
6306	6320	6334	6347
6307	6322	6335	6348
6308	6323	6336	6349
6309	6324	6337	6350
6310	6325	6338	6351
6311	6326	6339	6352
6312	6327	6340	6353

0-6-2T   5600 Class

6600	6620	6640	6660
6601	6621	6641	6661
6602	6622	6642	6662
6603	6623	6643	6663
6604	6624	6644	6664
6605	6625	6645	6665
6606	6626	6646	6666
6607	6627	6647	6667
6608	6628	6648	6668
6609	6629	6649	6669
6610	6630	6650	6670
6611	6631	6651	6671
6612	6632	6652	6672
6613	6633	6653	6673
6614	6634	6654	6674
6615	6635	6655	6675
6616	6636	6656	6676
6617	6637	6657	6677
6618	6638	6658	6678
6619	6639	6659	6679

6680	6685	6690	6695
6681	6686	6691	6696
6682	6687	6692	6697
6683	6688	6693	6698
6684	6689	6694	6699

0-6-0PT   5700 Class

6700	6720	6740	6760
6701	6721	6741	6761
6702	6722	6742	6762
6703	6723	6743	6763
6704	6724	6744	6764
6705	6725	6745	6765
6706	6726	6746	6766
6707	6727	6747	6767
6708	6728	6748	6768
6709	6729	6749	6769
6710	6730	6750	6770
6711	6731	6751	6771
6712	6732	6752	6772
6713	6733	6753	6773
6714	6734	6754	6774
6715	6735	6755	6775
6716	6736	6756	6776
6717	6737	6757	6777
6718	6738	6758	6778
6719	6739	6759	6779

4-6-0   6800 Class
" Grange "

6800 Arlington Grange
6801 Aylburton Grange
6802 Bampton Grange
6803 Bucklebury Grange
6804 Brockington Grange
6805 Broughton Grange
6806 Blackwell Grange
6807 Birchwood Grange
6808 Beenham Grange
6809 Burghclere Grange
6810 Blakemere Grange
6811 Cranbourne Grange
6812 Chesford Grange
6813 Eastbury Grange

6814 Enborne Grange
6815 Frilford Grange
6816 Frankton Grange
6817 Gwenddwr Grange
6818 Hardwick Grange
6819 Highnam Grange
6820 Kingstone Grange
6821 Leaton Grange
6822 Manton Grange
6823 Oakley Grange
6824 Ashley Grange
6825 Llanvair Grange
6826 Nannerth Grange
6827 Llanfrechfa Grange
6828 Trellech Grange
6829 Burmington Grange
6830 Buckenhill Grange
6831 Bearley Grange
6832 Brockton Grange
6833 Calcot Grange
6834 Dummer Grange
6835 Eastham Grange
6836 Estevarney Grange
6837 Forthampton Grange
6838 Goodmoor Grange
6839 Hewell Grange
6840 Hazeley Grange
6841 Marlas Grange
6842 Nunhold Grange
6843 Poulton Grange
6844 Penhydd Grange
6845 Paviland Grange
6846 Ruckley Grange
6847 Tidmarsh Grange
6848 Toddington Grange
6849 Walton Grange
6850 Cleeve Grange
6851 Hurst Grange
6852 Headbourne Grange
6853 Morehampton Grange
6854 Roundhill Grange
6855 Saighton Grange
6856 Stowe Grange
6857 Tudor Grange
6858 Woolston Grange
6859 Yiewsley Grange
6860 Aberporth Grange
6861 Crynant Grange

6862 Derwent Grange
6863 Dolhywel Grange
6864 Dymock Grange
6865 Hopton Grange
6866 Morfa Grange
6867 Peterston Grange
6868 Penrhos Grange
6869 Resolven Grange
6870 Bodicote Grange
6871 Bourton Grange
6872 Crawley Grange
6873 Caradoc Grange
6874 Haughton Grange
6875 Hindford Grange
6876 Kingsland Grange
6877 Llanfair Grange
6878 Longford Grange
6879 Overton Grange

4-6-0   4900 Class
" Hall "

6900 Abney Hall
6901 Arley Hall
6902 Butlers Hall
6903 Belmont Hall
6904 Charfield Hall
6905 Claughton Hall
6906 Chicheley Hall
6907 Davenham Hall
6908 Downham Hall
6909 Frewin Hall
6910 Gossington Hall
6911 Holker Hall
6912 Helmster Hall
6913 Levens Hall
6914 Langton Hall
6915 Mursley Hall
6916 Misterton Hall
6917 Oldlands Hall
6918 Sandon Hall
6919 Tylney Hall
6920 Barningham Hall
6921 Borwick Hall
6922 Burton Hall
6923 Croxteth Hall

6924 Grantley Hall
6925 Hackness Hall
6926 Holkham Hall
6927 Lilford Hall
6928 Underley Hall
6929 Whorlton Hall
6930 Aldersey Hall
6931 Aldborough Hall
6932 Burwarton Hall
6933 Birtles Hall
6934 Beachamwell Hall
6935 Browsholme Hall
6936 Breccles Hall
6937 Conyngham Hall
6938 Corndean Hall
6939 Calveley Hall
6940 Didlington Hall
6941 Fillongley Hall
6942 Eshton Hall
6943 Farnley Hall
6944 Fledborough Hall
6945 Glasfryn Hall
6946 Heatherden Hall
6947 Helmingham Hall
6948 Holbrooke Hall
6949 Haberfield Hall
6950 Kingsthorpe Hall
6951 Impney Hall
6952 Kimberley Hall
6953 Leighton Hall
6954 Lotherton Hall
6955 Lydcott Hall
6956 Mottram Hall
6957 Norcliffe Hall
6958 Oxburgh Hall

4-6-0   6959 Class
" Modified Hall "

6959 Peatling Hall
6960 Raveningham Hall
6961 Stedham Hall
6962 Soughton Hall
6963 Throwley Hall
6964 Thornbridge Hall
6965 Thirlestaine Hall
6966 Witchingham Hall

6967 Willesley Hall
6968 Woodcock Hall
6969 Wraysbury Hall
6970 Whaddon Hall
6971 Athelhampton Hall
6972 Beningbrough Hall
6973 Bricklehampton Hall
6974 Bryngwyn Hall
6975 Capesthorne Hall
6976 Graythwaite Hall
6977 Grundisburgh Hall
6978 Haroldstone Hall
6979 Helperly Hall
6980 Llanrumney Hall
6981 Marbury Hall
6982 Melmerby Hall
6983 Otterington Hall
6984 Owsden Hall
6985 Parwick Hall
6986 Rydal Hall
6987 Shervington Hall
6988 Swithland Hall
6989 Wightwick Hall
6990 Witherslack Hall
6991 Acton Burnell Hall
6992 Arborfield Hall
6993 Arthog Hall
6994 Baggrave Hall
6995 Benthall Hall
6996 Blackwell Hall
6997 Bryn-Ivor Hall
6998 Burton Agnes Hall
6999 Capel Dewi Hall

7009 Athelney Castle
7010 Avondale Castle
7011 Banbury Castle
7012 Barry Castle
7013 Bristol Castle
7014 Caerhays Castle
7015 Carn Brea Castle
7016 Chester Castle
7017 G. J. Churchward
7018 Drysllwyn Castle
7019 Fowey Castle
7020 Gloucester Castle
7021 Haverfordwest Castle
7022 Hereford Castle
7023 Penrice Castle
7024 Powis Castle
7025 Sudeley Castle
7026 Tenby Castle
7027 Thornbury Castle
7028 Cadbury Castle
7029 Clun Castle
7030 Cranbrook Castle
7031 Cromwell's Castle
7032 Denbigh Castle
7033 Hartlebury Castle
7034 Ince Castle
7035 Ogmore Castle
7036 Taunton Castle
7037 Swindon

4-6-0   4073 Class
" Castle "

7000 Viscount Portal
7001 Sir James Milne
7002 Devizes Castle
7003 Elmley Castle
7004 Eastnor Castle
7005 Lamphey Castle
7006 Lydford Castle
7007 Great Western
7008 Swansea Castle

2-8-2T   7200 Class

7200	7214	7228	7242
7201	7215	7229	7243
7202	7216	7230	7244
7203	7217	7231	7245
7204	7218	7232	7246
7205	7219	7233	7247
7206	7220	7234	7248
7207	7221	7235	7249
7208	7222	7236	7250
7209	7223	7237	7251
7210	7224	7238	7252
7211	7225	7239	7253
7212	7226	7240	
7213	7227	7241	

2-6-0 4300 Class

7300	7306	7312	7318
7301	7307	7313	7319
7302	7308	7314	7320
7303	7309	7315	7321
7304	7310	7316	
7305	7311	7317	

0-6-0PT 7400 Class

7400	7413	7426	7438
7401	7414	7427	7439
7402	7415	7428	7440
7403	7416	7429	7441
7404	7417	7430	7442
7405	7418	7431	7443
7406	7419	7432	7444
7407	7420	7433	7445
7408	7421	7434	7446
7409	7422	7435	7447
7410	7423	7436	7448
7411	7424	7437	7449
7412	7425		

0-6-0PT 5700 Class

7700	7721	7742	7763
7701	7722	7743	7764
7702	7723	7744	7765
7703	7724	7745	7766
7704	7725	7746	7767
7705	7726	7747	7768
7706	7727	7748	7769
7707	7728	7749	7770
7708	7729	7750	7771
7709	7730	7751	7772
7710	7731	7752	7773
7711	7732	7753	7774
7712	7733	7754	7775
7713	7734	7755	7776
7714	7735	7756	7777
7715	7736	7757	7778
7716	7737	7758	7779
7717	7738	7759	7780
7718	7739	7760	7781
7719	7740	7761	7782
7720	7741	7762	7783

7784	7788	7792	7796
7785	7789	7793	7797
7786	7790	7794	7798
7787	7791	7795	7799

4-6-0 7800 Class
"Manor"

7800 Torquay Manor
7801 Anthony Manor
7802 Bradley Manor
7803 Barcote Manor
7804 Baydon Manor
7805 Broome Manor
7806 Cockington Manor
7807 Compton Manor
7808 Cookham Manor
7809 Childrey Manor
7810 Draycott Manor
7811 Dunley Manor
7812 Erlestoke Manor
7813 Freshford Manor
7814 Fringford Manor
7815 Fritwell Manor
7816 Frilsham Manor
7817 Garsington Manor
7818 Granville Manor
7819 Hinton Manor
7820 Dinmore Manor
7821 Ditcheat Manor
7822 Foxcote Manor
7823 Hook Norton Manor
7824 Iford Manor
7825 Lechlade Manor
7826 Longworth Manor
7827 Lydham Manor
7828 Odney Manor
7829 Ramsbury Manor

4-6-0 6959 Class
"Modified Hall"

7900 Saint Peter's Hall
7901 Dodington Hall
7902 Eaton Mascot Hall
7903 Foremarke Hall
7904 Fountains Hall

Top: 7200 Class 2-8-2T No. 7234
[*Brian E. Morrison*

Centre: 7200 Class 2-8-2T No. 7212 (with raised footplating over cylinders)
[*C. G. Pearson*

Right: 3100 Class 2-6-2T No. 3103
[*C. G. Pearson*

6100 Class 2-6-2T No. 6122

4500 Class 2-6-2T No. 4574

4500 Class 2-6-2T No. 5541 (with sloping side tanks)

1000 Class 4-6-0 No. 1022 *County of Northampton* (with double chimney)   [*P. H. Wells*

1000 Class 4-6-0 No. 1000 *County of Middlesex* (with earlier style of double chimney)
[*G. Wheeler*

4000 Class 4-6-0 No. 4061 *Glastonbury Abbey*   [*G. Wheeler*

4900 Class 4-6-0 No. 6904 *Charfield Hall* [*G. Wheeler*

6959 Class 4-6-0 No. 7908 *Henshall Hall* [*A. E. Brown*

6800 Class 4-6-0 No. 6854 *Roundhill Grange* [*A. E. Brown*

7800 Class 4-6-0 No. 7823 *Hook Norton Manor* [*A. E. Brown*

4300 Class 2-6-0 No. 6378 [*A. A. Cameron*

4300 Class 2-6-0 No. 9309 (with side-window cab) [*A. E. Brown*

2800 Class 2-8-0 No. 2825   [G. Wheeler

!800 Class 2-8-0 No. 3834 (with side-window cab)   [C. G. Pearso

4700 Class 2-8-0 No. 4706   [C. G. Pearson

R.O.D. Class 2-8-0 No. 3028

[P. H. Wells

Class 0-6-0 No. 2294

[A. E. Brown

9000 Class 4-4-0 No. 9028

[P. H. Wells

4200 Class 2-8-0T No. 5254 (with outside steam pipes)   [*A. R. Carpenter*

4200 Class 2-8-0T No. 4270   [*G. Wheeler*

4200 Class 2-8-0T No. 5202 (with raised footplating over cylinders) [*A. R. Carpenter*

7905	Fowey Hall		
7906	Fron Hall		
7907	Hart Hall		
7908	Henshall Hall		
7909	Heveningham Hall		
7910	Hown Hall		
7911	Lady Margaret Hall		
7912	Little Linford Hall		
7913	Little Wyrley Hall		
7914	Lleweni Hall		
7915	Mere Hall		
7916	Mobberley Hall		
7917	North Aston Hall		
7918	Rhose Wood Hall		
7919	Runter Hall		
7920	Coney Hall		
7921	Edstone Hall		
7922	Salford Hall		
7923	Speke Hall		
7924	Thornycroft Hall		
7925	Westol Hall		
7926	Willey Hall		
7927	Willington Hall		
7928	Wolf Hall		
7929	Wyke Hall		

8456	8467	8478	8489
8457	8468	8479	8490
8458	8469	8480	8491
8459	8470	8481	8492
8460	8471	8482	8493
8461	8472	8483	8494
8462	8473	8484	8495
8463	8474	8485	8496
8464	8475	8486	8497
8465	8476	8487	8498
8466	8477	8488	8499

0-6-0PT   5700 Class

8700	8725	8750	8775
8701	8726	8751	8776
8702	8727	8752	8777
8703	8728	8753	8778
8704	8729	8754	8779
8705	8730	8755	8780
8706	8731	8756	8781
8707	8732	8757	8782
8708	8733	8758	8783
8709	8734	8759	8784
8710	8735	8760	8785
8711	8736	8761	8786
8712	8737	8762	8787
8713	8738	8763	8788
8714	8739	8764	8789
8715	8740	8765	8790
8716	8741	8766	8791
8717	8742	8767	8792
8718	8743	8768	8793
8719	8744	8769	8794
8720	8745	8770	8795
8721	8746	8771	8796
8722	8747	8772	8797
8723	8748	8773	8798
8724	8749	8774	8799

2-6-2T   8100 Class

8100	8103	8106	8108
8101	8104	8107	8109
8102	8105		

0-6-0PT   9400 Class

8400	8414	8428	8442
8401	8415	8429	8443
8402	8416	8430	8444
8403	8417	8431	8445
8404	8418	8432	8446
8405	8419	8433	8447
8406	8420	8434	8448
8407	8421	8435	8449
8408	8422	8436	8450
8409	8423	8437	8451
8410	8424	8438	8452
8411	8425	8439	8453
8412	8426	8440	8454
8413	8427	8441	8455

4-4-0   9000 Class

9004	9012	9018	9025
9005	9013	9020	9026
9008	9014	9021	9027
9009	9015	9022	9028
9010	9016	9023	
9011	9017	9024	

2-6-0   4300 Class

9300	9305	9310	9315
9301	9306	9311	9316
9302	9307	9312	9317
9303	9308	9313	9318
9304	9309	9314	9319

0-6-0PT   9400 Class

9400	9425	9450	9475
9401	9426	9451	9476
9402	9427	9452	9477
9403	9428	9453	9478
9404	9429	9454	9479
9405	9430	9455	9480
9406	9431	9456	9481
9407	9432	9457	9482
9408	9433	9458	9483
9409	9434	9459	9484
9410	9435	9460	9485
9411	9436	9461	9486
9412	9437	9462	9487
9413	9438	9463	9488
9414	9439	9464	9489
9415	9440	9465	9490
9416	9441	9466	9491
9417	9442	9467	9492
9418	9443	9468	9493
9419	9444	9469	9494
9420	9445	9470	9495
9421	9446	9471	9496
9422	9447	9472	9497
9423	9448	9473	9498
9424	9449	9474	9499

0-6-0PT   5700 Class

9600	9610	9620	9630
9601	9611	9621	9631
9602	9612	9622	9632
9603	9613	9623	9633
9604	9614	9624	9634
9605	9615	9625	9635
9606	9616	9626	9636
9607	9617	9627	9637
9608	9618	9628	9638
9609	9619	9629	9639

9640	9676	9729	9765
9641	9677	9730	9766
9642	9678	9731	9767
9643	9679	9732	9768
9644	9680	9733	9769
9645	9681	9734	9770
9646	9682	9735	9771
9647	9700	9736	9772
9648	9701	9737	9773
9649	9702	9738	9774
9650	9703	9739	9775
9651	9704	9740	9776
9652	9705	9741	9777
9653	9706	9742	9778
9654	9707	9743	9779
9655	9708	9744	9780
9656	9709	9745	9781
9657	9710	9746	9782
9658	9711	9747	9783
9659	9712	9748	9784
9660	9713	9749	9785
9661	9714	9750	9786
9662	9715	9751	9787
9663	9716	9752	9788
9664	9717	9753	9789
9665	9718	9754	9790
9666	9719	9755	9791
9667	9720	9756	9792
9668	9721	9757	9793
9669	9722	9758	9794
9670	9723	9759	9795
9671	9724	9760	9796
9672	9725	9761	9797
9673	9726	9762	9798
9674	9727	9763	9799
9675	9728	9764	

SERVICE LOCOMOTIVES

Petrol

22, 23, 24, 26 and 27

Total 5

BRITISH RAILWAYS STANDARD LOCOMOTIVES

Chief Officer (Mechanical Engineering)

R. C. BOND

4-6-2   Class 7P6F

Introduced 1951. Designed at Derby.

Weight: Loco.   94 tons 0 cwt.
         Tender (see page 58).

Pressure: 250 lb. Su.

Cyls.: (O) 20″ × 28″.

Driving Wheels: 6′ 2″.

T.E.: 32,150 lb.

Walschaerts gear.   P.V.

70000	Britannia
70001	Lord Hurcomb
70002	Geoffrey Chaucer
70003	John Bunyan
70004	William Shakespeare
70005	John Milton
70006	Robert Burns
70007	Coeur-de-Lion
70008	Black Prince
70009	Alfred the Great
70010	Owen Glendower
70011	Hotspur
70012	John of Gaunt
70013	Oliver Cromwell
70014	Iron Duke
70015	Apollo
70016	Ariel
70017	Arrow
70018	Flying Dutchman
70019	Lightning
70020	Mercury
70021	Morning Star
70022	Tornado
70023	Venus
70024	Vulcan
70025	Western Star
70026	Polar Star
70027	Rising Star
70028	Royal Star
70029	Shooting Star
70030	William Wordsworth
70031	Byron
70032	Tennyson
70033	Charles Dickens
70034	Thomas Hardy
70035	Rudyard Kipling
70036	Boadicea
70037	Hereward the Wake
70038	Robin Hood
70039	Sir Christopher Wren
70040	Clive of India
70041	Sir John Moore
70042	Lord Roberts
70043	
70044	
70045	
70046	
70047	
70048	
70049	
70050	Firth of Clyde
70051	Firth of Forth
70052	Firth of Tay
70053	Moray Firth
70054	Dornoch Firth

Total 55

4-6-2   Class 8P

Introduced 1954. Designed at Derby.

Weight: Loco.   101 tons 5 cwt.
         Tender (see page 58).

Pressure: 250 lb. Su.

Cyls.: (3) 18″ × 28″.

Driving Wheels: 6′ 2″

T.E.: 39,080 lb.

Caprotti valve gear.

71000 Duke of Gloucester

Total 1

4-6-2   Class 6P5F

Introduced 1952. Designed at Derby.
Weight: Loco. 86 tons 19 cwt.
    Tender (see page 58).
Pressure: 225 lb. Su.
Cyls.: (O) 19¼″ × 28″.
Driving Wheels: 6′ 2″.
T.E.: 27,520 lb.
Walschaerts gear. P.V.

72000	Clan Buchanan
72001	Clan Cameron
72002	Clan Campbell
72003	Clan Fraser
72004	Clan Macdonald
72005	Clan Macgregor
72006	Clan Mackenzie
72007	Clan Mackintosh
72008	Clan Macleod
72009	Clan Stewart

Total 10

4-6-0   Class 5

Introduced 1951. Designed at Doncaster.
Introduced 1956. Fitted with Caprotti valve gear.
Weight: Loco. 76 tons 4 cwt.
    Tender (see page 58).
Pressure: 225 lb. Su.
Cyls.: (O) 19″ × 28″.
Driving Wheels: 6′ 2″.
T.E.: 26,120 lb.
Walschaerts gear. P.V.

73000	73014	73028	73042
73001	73015	73029	73043
73002	73016	73030	73044
73003	73017	73031	73045
73004	73018	73032	73046
73005	73019	73033	73047
73006	73020	73034	73048
73007	73021	73035	73049
73008	73022	73036	73050
73009	73023	73037	73051
73010	73024	73038	73052
73011	73025	73039	73053
73012	73026	73040	73054
73013	73027	73041	73055

73056	73085	73114	73143*
73057	73086	73115	73144*
73058	73087	73116	73145
73059	73088	73117	73146
73060	73089	73118	73147
73061	73090	73119	73148
73062	73091	73120	73149
73063	73092	73121	73150
73064	73093	73122	73151
73065	73094	73123	73152
73066	73095	73124	73153
73067	73096	73125*	73154
73068	73097	73126*	73155
73069	73098	73127*	73156
73070	73099	73128*	73157
73071	73100	73129*	73158
73072	73101	73130*	73159
73073	73102	73131*	73160
73074	73103	73132*	73161
73075	73104	73133*	73162
73076	73105	73134*	73163
73077	73106	73135*	73164
73078	73107	73136*	73165
73079	73108	73137*	73166
73080	73109	73138*	73167
73081	73110	73139*	73168
73082	73111	73140*	73169
73083	73112	73141*	73170
73084	73113	73142*	73171

Engines of this class are still being delivered.

4-6-0   Class 4

Introduced 1951. Designed at Brighton.
Weight: Loco. 69 tons 0 cwt.
    Tender (see page 58).
Pressure: 225 lb. Su.
Cyls.: (O) 18″ × 28″.
Driving Wheels: 5′ 8″.
T.E.: 25,100 lb.
Walschaerts gear. P.V.

75000	75008	75016	75024
75001	75009	75017	75025
75002	75010	75018	75026
75003	75011	75019	75027
75004	75012	75020	75028
75005	75013	75021	75029
75006	75014	75022	75030
75007	75015	75023	75031

75032	75047	75062	75077
75033	75048	75063	75078
75034	75049	75064	75079
75035	75050	75065	75080
75036	75051	75066	75081
75037	75052	75067	75082
75038	75053	75068	75083
75039	75054	75069	75084
75040	75055	75070	75085
75041	75056	75071	75086
75042	75057	75072	75087
75043	75058	75073	75088
75044	75059	75074	75089
75045	75060	75075	
75046	75061	75076	

Engines of this class are still being delivered.

2-6-0   Class 4

Introduced 1953. Designed at Doncaster.
Weight: Loco. 59 tons 2 cwt.
          Tender (see page 58).
Pressure: 225 lb. Su.
Cyls.: (O) $17\frac{1}{2}'' \times 26''$.
Driving Wheels: 5' 3".
T.E.: 24,170 lb.
Walschaerts gear. P.V.

76000	76017	76034	76051
76001	76018	76035	76052
76002	76019	76036	76053
76003	76020	76037	76054
76004	76021	76038	76055
76005	76022	76039	76056
76006	76023	76040	76057
76007	76024	76041	76058
76008	76025	76042	76059
76009	76026	76043	76060
76010	76027	76044	76061
76011	76028	76045	76062
76012	76029	76046	76063
76013	76030	76047	76064
76014	76031	76048	76065
76015	76032	76049	76066
76016	76033	76050	76067

76068	76080	76092	76104
76069	76081	76093	76105
76070	76082	76094	76106
76071	76083	76095	76107
76072	76084	76096	76108
76073	76085	76097	76109
76074	76086	76098	76110
76075	76087	76099	76111
76076	76088	76100	76112
76077	76089	76101	76113
76078	76090	76102	76114
76079	76091	76103	

Engines of this class are still being delivered.

2-6-0   Class 3

Introduced 1954. Designed at Swindon
Weight: Loco. 57 tons 9 cwt.
          Tender (see page 58).
Pressure: 200 lb. Su.
Cyls.: (O) $17\frac{1}{2}'' \times 26''$.
Driving Wheels: 5' 3".
T.E.: 21,490 lb.
Walschaerts gear. P.V.

77000	77007	77014	77021
77001	77008	77015	77022
77002	77009	77016	77023
77003	77010	77017	77024
77004	77011	77018	
77005	77012	77019	
77006	77013	77020	

Engines of this class are still being delivered.

2-6-0   Class 2

Introduced 1953. Designed at Derby.
Weight: Loco. 49 tons 5 cwt.
          Tender (see page 58).
Pressure: 200 lb. Su.
Cyls.: (O) $16\frac{1}{2}'' \times 24''$.
Driving Wheels: 5' 0"
T.E.: 18,515 lb.
Walschaerts gear. P.V

78000	78007	78014	78021
78001	78008	78015	78022
78002	78009	78016	78023
78003	78010	78017	78024
78004	78011	78018	78025
78005	78012	78019	78026
78006	78013	78020	78027

78028	78038	78048	78058
78029	78039	78049	78059
78030	78040	78050	78060
78031	78041	78051	78061
78032	78042	78052	78062
78033	78043	78053	78063
78034	78044	78054	78064
78035	78045	78055	
78036	78046	78056	
78037	78047	78057	

Engines of this class are still being delivered.

2-6-4T Class 4

Introduced 1951. Designed at Brighton.
Weight: 88 tons 10 cwt.
Pressure: 225 lb. Su.
Cyls.: (O) 18″ × 28″.
Driving Wheels: 5′ 8″.
T.E.: 25,100 lb.
Walschaerts gear. P.V.

80000	80026	80052	80078
80001	80027	80053	80079
80002	80028	80054	80080
80003	80029	80055	80081
80004	80030	80056	80082
80005	80031	80057	80083
80006	80032	80058	80084
80007	80033	80059	80085
80008	80034	80060	80086
80009	80035	80061	80087
80010	80036	80062	80088
80011	80037	80063	80089
80012	80038	80064	80090
80013	80039	80065	80091
80014	80040	80066	80092
80015	80041	80067	80093
80016	80042	80068	80094
80017	80043	80069	80095
80018	80044	80070	80096
80019	80045	80071	80097
80020	80046	80072	80098
80021	80047	80073	80099
80022	80048	80074	80100
80023	80049	80075	80101
80024	80050	80076	80102
80025	80051	80077	80103

80104	80117	80130	80143
80105	80118	80131	80144
80106	80119	80132	80145
80107	80120	80133	80146
80108	80121	80134	80147
80109	80122	80135	80148
80110	80123	80136	80149
80111	80124	80137	80150
80112	80125	80138	80151
80113	80126	80139	80152
80114	80127	80140	80153
80115	80128	80141	80154
80116	80129	80142	

Engines of this class are still being delivered.

2-6-2T Class 3

Introduced 1952. Designed at Swindon.
Weight: 73 tons 10 cwt.
Pressure: 200 lb. Su.
Cyls.: (O) 17½″ × 26″.
Driving Wheels: 5′ 3″.
T.E.: 21,490 lb.
Walschaerts gear. P.V.

82000	82012	82024	82036
82001	82013	82025	82037
82002	82014	82026	82038
82003	82015	82027	82039
82004	82016	82028	82040
82005	82017	82029	82041
82006	82018	82030	82042
82007	82019	82031	82043
82008	82020	82032	82044
82009	82021	82033	
82010	82022	82034	
82011	82023	82035	

Total 45

2-6-2T Class 2

Introduced 1953. Designed at Derby.
Weight: 63 tons 5 cwt.
Pressure: 200 lb. Su.
Cyls.: (O) 16½″ × 24″.
Driving Wheels: 5′ 0″.
T.E.: 18,515 lb.
Walschaerts gear. P.V.

84000	84002	84004	84006
84001	84003	84005	84007

84008	84014	84020	84026
84009	84015	84021	84027
84010	84016	84022	84028
84011	84017	84023	84029
84012	84018	84024	
84013	84019	84025	

Engines of this class are still being delivered.

2-8-0   8F   Class WD

Ministry of Supply " Austerity " 2-8-0 locomotives purchased by British Railways, 1948.

Introduced 1943. Riddles M.o.S. design.

Weight: Loco.   70 tons 5 cwt.
　　　　Tender 55 tons 10 cwt.

Pressure: 225 lb. Su.

Cyls.: (O) 19″ × 28″.

Driving Wheels: 4′ 8½″.

T.E.: 34,215 lb.

Walschaerts gear.   P.V.

90000	90026	90052	90078
90001	90027	90053	90079
90002	90028	90054	90080
90003	90029	90055	90081
90004	90030	90056	90082
90005	90031	90057	90083
90006	90032	90058	90084
90007	90033	90059	90085
90008	90034	90060	90086
90009	90035	90061	90087
90010	90036	90062	90088
90011	90037	90063	90089
90012	90038	90064	90090
90013	90039	90065	90091
90014	90040	90066	90092
90015	90041	90067	90093
90016	90042	90068	90094
90017	90043	90069	90095
90018	90044	90070	90096
90019	90045	90071	90097
90020	90046	90072	90098
90021	90047	90073	90099
90022	90048	90074	90100
90023	90049	90075	90101
90024	90050	90076	90102
90025	90051	90077	90103

90104	90152	90200	90248
90105	90153	90201	90249
90106	90154	90202	90250
90107	90155	90203	90251
90108	90156	90204	90252
90109	90157	90205	90253
90110	90158	90206	90254
90111	90159	90207	90255
90112	90160	90208	90256
90113	90161	90209	90257
90114	90162	90210	90258
90115	90163	90211	90259
90116	90164	90212	90260
90117	90165	90213	90261
90118	90166	90214	90262
90119	90167	90215	90263
90120	90168	90216	90264
90121	90169	90217	90265
90122	90170	90218	90266
90123	90171	90219	90267
90124	90172	90220	90268
90125	90173	90221	90269
90126	90174	90222	90270
90127	90175	90223	90271
90128	90176	90224	90272
90129	90177	90225	90273
90130	90178	90226	90274
90131	90179	90227	90275
90132	90180	90228	90276
90133	90181	90229	90277
90134	90182	90230	90278
90135	90183	90231	90279
90136	90184	90232	90280
90137	90185	90233	90281
90138	90186	90234	90282
90139	90187	90235	90283
90140	90188	90236	90284
90141	90189	90237	90285
90142	90190	90238	90286
90143	90191	90239	90287
90144	90192	90240	90288
90145	90193	90241	90289
90146	90194	90242	90290
90147	90195	90243	90291
90148	90196	90244	90292
90149	90197	90245	90293
90150	90198	90246	90294
90151	90199	90247	90295

90296	90344	90392	90440	90488	90536	90584	90632
90297	90345	90393	90441	90489	90537	90585	90633
90298	90346	90394	90442	90490	90538	90586	90634
90299	90347	90395	90443	90491	90539	90587	90635
90300	90348	90396	90444	90492	90540	90588	90636
90301	90349	90397	90445	90493	90541	90589	90637
90302	90350	90398	90446	90494	90542	90590	90638
90303	90351	90399	90447	90495	90543	90591	90639
90304	90352	90400	90448	90496	90544	90592	90640
90305	90353	90401	90449	90497	90545	90593	90641
90306	90354	90402	90450	90498	90546	90594	90642
90307	90355	90403	90451	90499	90547	90595	90643
90308	90356	90404	90452	90500	90548	90596	90644
90309	90357	90405	90453	90501	90549	90597	90645
90310	90358	90406	90454	90502	90550	90598	90646
90311	90359	90407	90455	90503	90551	90599	90647
90312	90360	90408	90456	90504	90552	90600	90648
90313	90361	90409	90457	90505	90553	90601	90649
90314	90362	90410	90458	90506	90554	90602	90650
90315	90363	90411	90459	90507	90555	90603	90651
90316	90364	90412	90460	90508	90556	90604	90652
90317	90365	90413	90461	90509	90557	90605	90653
90318	90366	90414	90462	90510	90558	90606	90654
90319	90367	90415	90463	90511	90559	90607	90655
90320	90368	90416	90464	90512	90560	90608	90656
90321	90369	90417	90465	90513	90561	90609	90657
90322	90370	90418	90466	90514	90562	90610	90658
90323	90371	90419	90467	90515	90563	90611	90659
90324	90372	90420	90468	90516	90564	90612	90660
90325	90373	90421	90469	90517	90565	90613	90661
90326	90374	90422	90470	90518	90566	90614	90662
90327	90375	90423	90471	90519	90567	90615	90663
90328	90376	90424	90472	90520	90568	90616	90664
90329	90377	90425	90473	90521	90569	90617	90665
90330	90378	90426	90474	90522	90570	90618	90666
90331	90379	90427	90475	90523	90571	90619	90667
90332	90380	90428	90476	90524	90572	90620	90668
90333	90381	90429	90477	90525	90573	90621	90669
90334	90382	90430	90478	90526	90574	90622	90670
90335	90383	90431	90479	90527	90575	90623	90671
90336	90384	90432	90480	90528	90576	90624	90672
90337	90385	90433	90481	90529	90577	90625	90673
90338	90386	90434	90482	90530	90578	90626	90674
90339	90387	90435	90483	90531	90579	90627	90675
90340	90388	90436	90484	90532	90580	90628	90676
90341	90389	90437	90485	90533	90581	90629	90677
90342	90390	90438	90486	90534	90582	90630	90678
90343	90391	90439	90487	90535	90583	90631	90679

90680	90694	90708	90722
90681	90695	90709	90723
90682	90696	90710	90724
90683	90697	90711	90725
90684	90698	90712	90726
90685	90699	90713	90727
90686	90700	90714	90728
90687	90701	90715	90729
90688	90702	90716	90730
90689	90703	90717	90731
90690	90704	90718	90732
90691	90705	90719	Vulcan
90692	90706	90720	
90693	90707	90721	

Total 733

2-10-0 8F Class WD

Ministry of Supply "Austerity" 2-10-0 locomotives purchased by British Railways, 1948.

Introduced 1943, Riddles M.o.S. design.

Weight: Loco.   78 tons 6 cwt.
       Tender 55 tons 10 cwt.

Pressure: 225 lb. Su.

Cyls.: (O) 19″ × 28″.

Driving Wheels: 4′ 8½″.

T.E.: 34,215 lb.

Walschaerts gear.   P.V.

90750	90757	90764	90771
90751	90758	90765	90772
90752	90759	90766	90773
90753	90760	90767	90774
90754	90761	90768	
90755	90762	90769	
90756	90763	90770	

Total 25

2-10-0 Class 9F

Introduced 1954. Designed at Brighton.

*Introduced 1955. Fitted with Crosti boiler.

Weight: Loco. { 86 tons 14 cwt.
              { 90 tons 4 cwt.*
       Tender (see page 58).

Pressure: 250 lb. Su.

Cyls.: (O) 20″ × 28″.

Driving Wheels: 5′ 0″.

T.E.: 39,670 lb.

Walschaerts gear.   P.V.

92000	92043	92086	92129
92001	92044	92087	92130
92002	92045	92088	92131
92003	92046	92089	92132
92004	92047	92090	92133
92005	92048	92091	92134
92006	92049	92092	92135
92007	92050	92093	92136
92008	92051	92094	92137
92009	92052	92095	92138
92010	92053	92096	92139
92011	92054	92097	92140
92012	92055	92098	92141
92013	92056	92099	92142
92014	92057	92100	92143
92015	92058	92101	92144
92016	92059	92102	92145
92017	92060	92103	92146
92018	92061	92104	92147
92019	92062	92105	92148
92020*	92063	92106	92149
92021*	92064	92107	92150
92022*	92065	92108	92151
92023*	92066	92109	92152
92024*	92067	92110	92153
92025*	92068	92111	92154
92026*	92069	92112	92155
92027*	92070	92113	92156
92028*	92071	92114	92157
92029*	92072	92115	92158
92030	92073	92116	92159
92031	92074	92117	92160
92032	92075	92118	92161
92033	92076	92119	92162
92034	92077	92120	92163
92035	92078	92121	92164
92036	92079	92122	92165
92037	92080	92123	92166
92038	92081	92124	92167
92039	92082	92125	92168
92040	92083	92126	92169
92041	92084	92127	92170
92042	92085	92128	92171

92172	92177	92182	92187	92192	92195	92198	92201
92173	92178	92183	92188	92193	92196	92199	92202
92174	92179	92184	92189	92194	92197	92200	
92175	92180	92185	92190				
92176	92181	92186	92191				

Engines of this class are still being delivered.

BRITISH RAILWAYS STANDARD TENDERS

N.B.—These pairings are not permanent and are liable to alteration with changed operating conditions.

| Type | Capacity | | Weight in Full W.O. | | Locos to which Allocated |
	Water galls.	Coal tons	tons	cwt.	
BR1	4,250	7	49	3	70000–24/30–44 72000–9 73000–49
BR1A	5,000	7	52	10	73025–29
BR1B	4,725	7	50	5	73080–89 73100–09/20–34 73145–71 75065–79 76053–69 92020–29/60–6 92097–9
BR1C	4,725	9	53	5	73065–79/90–9 73135–44 92015–9/45–59 92077–86 92100–39/50–67
BR1D	4,725	9	54	10	70045–54
BR1E	4,725	10	55	10	71000
BR1F	5,625	7	55	5	73110–19 92010–14/30–44 92067–76 92087–96 92140–9 92168–92202
BR1G	5,000	7	52	10	73050–52 92000–9
BR1H	4,250	7	49	3	73053–64
BR2	3,500	6	42	3	75000–49 76000–44
BR2A	3,500	6	42	3	75050–64/80–9 76045–52 76070–76114 77000–24
BR3	3,000	4	36	17	78000–64

POWER AND WEIGHT CLASSIFICATION

Since 1920 Western Region locomotives have been classified for power and weight by a letter on a coloured disc on the cab side. The letter represents the power of the locomotive, and is approximately proportional to the tractive effort as under :

Power class	Tractive effort lb.	Power class	Tractive effort lb.
Special	Over 38,000	B	18,501–20,500
E	33,001–38,000	A	16,500–18,500
D	25,001–33,000	Un-grouped	
C	20,501–25,000		Below 16,500

The colour of the circle represents the routes over which the engine may work. Red engines are limited to the main lines and lines capable of carrying the heaviest locomotives ; blue engines are allowed over additional routes, yellow engines over nearly the whole system and uncoloured engines are more or less unrestricted. The double red circles on the " King " class represent special restrictions for these engines.

Class	Power Class	Route Restriction Colour	Class	Power Class	Route Restriction Colour
4-6-0			**0-6-2T**		
1000	D	Red	5600	D	Red
4000	D	Red	(35)	D	Red
4073	D	Red	(304)	C	Red
4900	D	Red			
6000	Special	Double Red	**0-6-0T**		
6800	D	Red	850	—	—
6959	D	Red	1351	—	—
7800	D	Blue	1366	—	—
4-4-0			1500	C	Red
9000	B	Yellow	1600	A	—
2-8-0			2021	A	—
2800	E	Blue	5400	—	Yellow
R.O.D.	D	Blue	5700	C	Yellow
4700	D	Red	9700–10	C	Blue
2-6-0			6400	A	Yellow
4300	D	Blue	7400	A	Yellow
930019	D	Red	9400	C	Red
0-6-0			(2198)	—	—
2251	B	Yellow	(822)	—	—
2301	A	—			
2-8-2T			**0-4-2T**		
7200	E	Red	1400	—	—
2-8-0T			5800	—	—
4200	E	Red			
2-6-2T			**0-4-0T**		
3100	D	Red	1101	B	Red
4500	C	Yellow	(1338)	—	—
5100	D	Blue	(1151)	—	—
6100	D	Blue	(1140)	—	—
8100	D	Blue	(1143)	—	Blue
(7)	—	—	(1144)	—	Yellow
			(1142)	A	Yellow

DIESEL MULTIPLE UNIT TRAINS

The following abbreviations are used, and although based on the British Railways standard rolling stock code, are not necessarily those carried on the vehicles, all of which are of the open, centre or off centre corridor type :—

BOGIE VEHICLES

Fitted with a driving compartment at one end and gangway connections at the other end.

Motor BS—Motor Brake Second.
Motor S—Motor Second.
Motor C—Motor Composite.
Motor CL—Motor Composite (lavatory fitted).
Driving SL—Driving Trailer Second (lavatory fitted).
Driving CL—Driving Trailer Composite (lavatory fitted).

Non driving, non motor vehicles, gangway fitted at both ends.

BSL—Trailer Brake Second (lavatory fitted).
SL—Trailer Second (lavatory fitted).

4-WHEEL VEHICLES

Motor coaches fitted with a driving compartment at each end. None are gangway fitted.

Motor S—Motor Second.   **Motor BS**—Motor Brake Second.   **S**—Trailer Second.

FORMATION. Nearly all are formed into two coach sets as under:—

Motor BS–Motor CL (Bradford area).
Motor BS–Driving CL (Majority).
Motor BS–Driving SL (East Anglian area).
Newcastle–Middlesbrough units are formed into four coach sets:—
Motor C–BSL–SL–Motor S.

The 4-wheel vehicles are made up to three coach sets and are used on the Watford–St. Albans Branch:—
Motor BS–S–Motor S.

BOGIE VEHICLES

Motor BS:—

E79000	M79017	E79034	E79051*	E79068*	M79120	E79137	M79173
E79001	M79018	E79035	E79052*	E79069*	M79121	E79138	M79174
E79002	M79019	E79036	E79053*	E79070*	M79122	E79139	M79175
E79003	M79020	E79037	E79054*	E79071*	M79123	E79140	M79176
E79004	E79021	E79038	E79055*	E79072*	M79124	M79141	M79177
E79005	E79022	E79039	E79056*	E79073*	M79125	M79142	M79178
E79006	E79023	E79040	E79057*	E79074*	M79126	M79143	M79179
E79007	E79024	E79041	E79058*	E79075*	M79127	M79144	M79180
M79008	E79025	E79042	E79059*	M79076*	M79128	M79145	M79181
M79009	E79026	E79043	E79060*	M79077*	M79129	M79146	M79184
M79010	E79027	E79044	E79061*	M79078*	M79130	M79147	M79185
M79011	E79028	E79045	E79062*	M79079*	M79131	M79148	M79186
M79012	E79029	E79046	E79063*	M79080*	M79132	M79149	M79900‡
M79013	E79030	E79047*	E79064*	M79081*	M79133	M79169	
M79014	E79031	E79048*	E79065*	M79082*	M79134	M79170	
M79015	E79032	E79049*	E79066*	M79118	M79135	M79171	
M79016	E79033	E79050*	E79067*	M79119	M79136	M79172	

Motor S:—

E79150, E79151, E79152, E79153, E79154.

Driving SL :—

E79250	E79256	E79262	E79268*	E79274*	E79280*	E79285*	E79290*
E79251	E79257	E79263*	E79269*	E79275*	E79281*	E79286*	E79291*
E79252	E79258	E79264*	E79270*	E79276*	E79282*	E79287*	
E79253	E79259	E79265*	E79271*	E79277*	E79283*	E79288*	
E79254	E79260	E79266*	E79272*	E79278*	E79284*	E79289*	
E79255	E79261	E79267*	E79273*	E79279*			

BSL:—

E79325, E79326, E79327, E79328, E79329.

SL:—

E79400, E79401, E79402, E79403, E79404.

Motor CL:—

M79189, M79190, M79191, E79500, E79501, E79502, E79503, E79504, E79505, E79506, E79507.

Motor C:—

E79508, E79509, E79510, E79511, E79512.

Driving CL:—

M79600	M79610	E79620	M79630*	M79646	M79656	M79666	M79676
M79601	M79611	E79621	M79631*	M79647	M79657	M79667	M79677
M79602	M79612	E79622	M79632*	M79648	E79658	M79668	M79678
M79603	E79613	E79623	M79639	M79649	E79659	M79669	M79679
M79604	E79614	E79624	M79640	M79650	E79660	M79670	M79680
M79605	E79615	E79625	M79641	M79651	E79661	M79671	M79681
M79606	E79616	M79626*	M79642	M79652	M79662	M79672	M79682
M79607	E79617	M79627*	M79643	M79653	M79663	M79673	M79683
M79608	E79618	M79628*	M79644	M79654	M79664	M79674	M79684
M79609	E79619	M79629*	M79645	M79655	M79665	M79675	

4-WHEEL VEHICLES

Motor S	Motor BS	S
M79740†	M79742†	M79741†
M79745†	M79743†	M79746†
	M79744†	M79747†

* Built by Metro-Cammel C. & W. Co.

† Built by British United Traction Co.
  Remainder built by British Railways at Derby.

‡ *Single Unit—non gangwayed, driving compartment both ends.*

NUMBERING OF W.R. PASSENGER TRAINS—WINTER, 1956-57

CERTAIN passenger trains, and any relief trains run thereto, bear a number for identification purposes for the whole or part of the journey over the Western Region, as shown in the following list. In a few instances through trains to and from the Southern Region carry the identification number during their journey over that Region also.

The number allotted to each train is displayed in a metal frame carried on the smoke-box of the engine.

The numbers shown in this list refer to ordinary trains only : those carried by relief or duplicate trains are shown only in the Western Region's official working notices, as required, and do not appear in this list.

NUMBERING OF PASSENGER TRAINS

** Weekdays & Suns. § Every weekday. * Sats. exc.
† Sats. only. ‡ Fris. only. ‡‡ Suns. only. †† Mons. only.
M—Mons., Weds. & Fris. only.
T—Tues., Thurs. & Sats. only.
W—Weds., Fris. & Suns. only.
a—† from 1/6/57.
b—* from 27/5. 57.
c—† from 25/5/57.
d—§ from 25/5/57.

Train No.	Time	From	To
38	10.45 a.m. ††	Manchester (L.R.)	Cardiff
100	5.30 a.m.§	Paddington	Penzance
107	7.30 a.m.§	"	Paignton
113	8.20 a.m.a	"	Weymouth
115	8.20 a.m.b	"	"
115	8.30 a.m.c	"	"
116	8.45 a.m.*	"	Bristol
119	9.05 a.m.§	"	"
122	9.30 a.m.§	"	Plymouth
130	10.30 a.m.§	"	Penzance
131	10.35 a.m.§	"	"
142	11.15 a.m.§	"	Weston-super-Mare
146	12.00 nn.§	"	Kingswear

Train No.	Time	From	To
153	3.30 p.m.§	Paddington	Penzance
154	4.15 p.m.§	"	Plymouth
155	5.00 p.m.§	"	Weston-super-Mare
157	5.30 p.m.§	"	Plymouth
159	6.30 p.m.§	"	Weston-super-Mare
163	8.55 a.m.§	"	Pembroke Dock
164	9.55 a.m.*	"	Swansea
165	10.55 a.m.§	"	Pembroke Dock
166	11.35 a.m.†	"	Carmarthen
167	11.55 a.m.†	"	Pembroke Dock
168	1.50 p.m.†	"	Carmarthen
169	1.55 p.m.§	"	Pembroke Dock
171	3.55 p.m.§	"	Fishguard Harbour
172	4.55 p.m.§	"	Cheltenham
173	5.55 p.m.§	"	Carmarthen
174	5.50 p.m.§	"	Swansea
176	6.35 p.m.§	"	Cheltenham
178	6.55 p.m.§	"	Fishguard Harbour
180	9.00 a.m.§	"	Birkenhead
181	10.10 a.m.§	"	Wolverhampton
183	10.10 a.m.§	"	Aberystwyth
185	11.45 a.m.§	"	Hereford
186	1.45 p.m.§	"	Birkenhead
187	4.10 p.m.§	"	Hereford
189	4.45 p.m.*	"	Wolverhampton
192	5.10 p.m.*	"	Birkenhead
195	6.10 p.m.§	"	

Train No.	Time	From	To
196	6.08 p.m.§	Paddington	Wolverhampton
198	6.45 p.m.§	"	Hereford
205	12.00 nn.§	"	Crewe
208	9.10 a.m.‡‡	"	Plymouth
210	10.40 a.m.‡‡	Penzance	Swansea
215	9.10 a.m.**	Liverpool	Liverpool
217	12.05 a.m.**	"	Manchester (L.R.)
228	4.50 p.m.§	Manchester (L.R.)	Plymouth
240	12.10 a.m.††	Cardiff	Cardiff
241	11.45 a.m.§	Penzance	Bristol
246	2.55 p.m.§	Bristol	Manchester (L.R.)
248	3.10 p.m.‡‡	Manchester (L.R.)	Cardiff
257	8.55 a.m.§	"	Bristol
262	8.33 p.m.§	Cardiff "	Manchester (L.R.)
263	8.20 p.m.§	Crewe	Penzance
265	4.40 p.m.§	Manchester (L.R.)	Plymouth
273	12.35 a.m.§	Crewe	Crewe
277	1.40 a.m.‡‡	Plymouth	"
280	8.00 a.m.§	"	Manchester (L.R.)
283	8.45 a.m.‡‡	Swansea	"
285	11.50 a.m.§	Cardiff	Crewe
	12.40 p.m.‡‡	Penzance	Cardiff
	7.30 a.m.§	Hereford	Manchester (L.R.)
	7.55 p.m.§	Crewe	Liverpool
	1.25 a.m.**	Bristol	
	8.15 a.m.§	Plymouth	
	1.10 p.m.§		

63

Train No.	Time	From	To
289	6.15 p.m.††	Cardiff	Crewe
301	6.47 p.m.§	Bristol	Paddington
350	6.45 a.m.§	Wolverhampton	Paddington
353	7.30 a.m.§	Shrewsbury	"
355	6.35 a.m.	Hereford	"
360	8.19 a.m.§	Kidderminster	"
363	7.25 a.m.*	Wolverhampton	"
365	11.15 a.m.§	Aberstwyth	"
370	4.35 p.m.	Wolverhampton	"
375	2.35 p.m.§	Birkenhead	"
376	5.20 p.m.+‡	Wolverhampton	"
387	3.45 p.m.d	Weymouth	Plymouth
419	6.25 a.m.§	Bristol	Paddington
450	7.00 a.m.§	Weston-super-Mare	"
455	8.20 a.m.§	"	"
460	11.45 a.m.§	Bristol	"
463	1.50 p.m.§	"	"
470	6.25 p.m.*	"	"
473	4.30 p.m.*	Weston-super-Mare	"
475	4.35 p.m.§	Kingswear	"
520	11.25 a.m.§	Plymouth	"
600	7.15 a.m.§	"	"
605	8.30 a.m.§	Penzance	"
608	6.25 a.m.§	"	"
635	10.00 a.m.§	"	"
636	12.15 p.m.§	Plymouth	"
644	3.35 p.m.‡	"	Stapleton Road

Train No.	Time	From	To
675	10.10 a.m.§	Penzance	Wolverhampton
676	2.11 p.m.§	Exeter	Paddington
711	3.55 a.m.W	Fishguard Harbour	"
715	6.30 a.m.§	Swansea	"
716	7.45 a.m.§	Cardiff	"
718	4.55 a.m.T	Fishguard Harbour	"
719	8.15 a.m.M	Cardiff	"
720	9.45 a.m.§	"	"
724	7.30 a.m.§	Carmarthen	"
725	7.05 a.m.§	Cheltenham	"
740	7.55 a.m.§	"	"
745	11.10 a.m.§	Milford Haven	"
753	12.05 p.m.§	Pembroke Dock	"
755	1.05 p.m.§	Neyland	"
758	2.30 p.m.§	Swansea	"
825	4.35 a.m.*	Wolverhampton	"
826	9.00 a.m.§	"	Penzance
850	9.10 a.m.§	"	Kingswear
877	8.00 a.m.	Birmingham	Weymouth
965	3.45 p.m.	"	Swansea
	9.30 a.m.§	Bournemouth (W)	Birkenhead

THE abc OF
BRITISH RAILWAYS
LOCOMOTIVES

PART 2—Nos. 10000-39999

also S.R. Electric Train Units and Pullman Cars.

WINTER
1956/7
EDITION

LONDON :

Ian Allan Ltd

NOTES ON THE USE OF THIS BOOK

1. This book lists and describes British Railways locomotives numbered between 10000 and 39999, Southern Region electric units and Pullman Cars allocated to the Southern Region. Some British Railways standard locomotives numbered between 70000 and 99999 are in service on the Southern Region and are listed in Parts 1, 3 or 4 of the *ABC of British Railways Locomotives*. The following notes are a guide to the system of reference marks and other details given in the lists of dimensions shown for each class in the alphabetical list of classes.

   (a) In the lists of dimensions "Su" after the boiler pressure details indicates a superheated class.

   (b) Locomotives are fitted with two inside cylinders, slide valves and Stephenson link motion, except where otherwise shown, *e.g.*, (O) indicates outside cylinders and "P.V." piston valves.

   (c) The letter "S" following a number indicates a Service Locomotive. On the S.R. (only) this marking appears on the locomotive.

   (d) (W) before a number indicates an Isle of Wight locomotive. The "W" is no longer painted on the locomotives, but may still be seen on the bunker numberplate of some of them.

   (e) The date on which a design of locomotive first appeared or was modified is indicated by "Introduced." Difference between subdivisions of a class can be followed by tracing the appropriate reference mark throughout the details given for that class.

   (f) The code given in smaller bold type at the head of each class, *e.g.*, "2P2F" denotes its British Railways power classification.

2. Southern electric units are listed on pp. 56-62 and Pullman Cars on pp. 63/4.

3. The details given in this book are correct to **August 31st, 1956.**

BRITISH RAILWAYS
MOTIVE POWER DEPOTS AND CODES

(ALL B.R. LOCOMOTIVES CARRY THE CODE OF THEIR HOME DEPOT ON A SMALL PLATE AFFIXED TO THE SMOKEBOX DOOR.)

LONDON MIDLAND REGION

1A	**Willesden**	9A	**Longsight**	19A	Sheffield
1B	Camden	9B	Stockport	19B	Millhouses
1C	Watford		**(Edgeley)**	19C	Canklow
1D	Devons Road (Bow)	9C	Macclesfield		
1E	Bletchley	9D	Buxton	*20A	**Leeds (Holbeck)**
		9E	Trafford Park	*20B	Stourton
2A	**Rugby**	9F	Heaton Mersey	*20C	Royston
2B	Nuneaton	9G	Northwich	*20D	Normanton
2C	Warwick			*20E	Manningham
2D	Coventry	10A	**Springs Branch**	*20F	Skipton
2E	Northampton		**(Wigan)**	20G	Hellifield
2F	Market Harboro'	10B	Preston		
		10C	Patricroft	21A	**Saltley**
3A	**Bescot**	10D	Sutton Oak	21B	Bournville
3B	Bushbury			21C	Bromsgrove
3C	Walsall	11A	**Carnforth**		
3D	Aston	11B	Barrow	22A	**Bristol**
3E	Monument Lane	11C	Oxenholme	22B	Gloucester
		11D	Tebay		
5A	**Crewe North**	11E	Lancaster	24A	**Accrington**
5B	Crewe South			24B	Rose Grove
5C	Stafford	12A	**Carlisle**	24C	Lostock Hall
5D	Stoke		**(Upperby)**	24D	Lower Darwen
5E	Alsager	12B	Penrith	24E	Blackpool
5F	Uttoxeter	12C	Workington	24F	Fleetwood
6A	**Chester**	14A	**Cricklewood**	*25A	**Wakefield**
6B	Mold Junction	14B	Kentish Town	*25B	Huddersfield
6C	Birkenhead	14C	St. Albans	*25C	Goole
6D	Chester			*25D	Mirfield
	(Northgate)	15A	**Wellingborough**	*25E	Sowerby Bridge
6E	Wrexham	15B	Kettering	*25F	Low Moor
6F	Bidston	15C	Leicester	*25G	Farnley Junction
6G	Llandudno	15D	Bedford		
	Junction			26A	**Newton Heath**
6H	Bangor	16A	**Nottingham**	26B	Agecroft
6J	Holyhead	16B	Kirkby	26C	Bolton
6K	Rhyl	16C	Mansfield	26D	Bury
				26E	Lees
8A	**Edge Hill**	17A	**Derby**		
8B	Warrington	17B	Burton	27A	**Bank Hall**
8C	Speke Junction	17C	Coalville	27B	Aintree
8D	Widnes	17D	Rowsley	27C	Southport
8E	Brunswick (L'pool)	18A	**Toton**	27D	Wigan (L. & Y.)
		18B	Westhouses	27E	Walton
		18C	Hasland		
		18D	Staveley		

* See N.E. Region Codes 53, 55 and 56.

3

MOTIVE POWER DEPOTS AND CODES—continued

EASTERN REGION

30A	**Stratford**	32F	Yarmouth Beach	36D	Barnsley
30B	Hertford East	32G	Melton Constable	36E	Retford
30C	Bishops Stortford				
30D	Southend (Victoria)	33A	**Plaistow**	38A	**Colwick**
30E	Colchester	33B	Tilbury	38B	Annesley
30F	Parkeston	33C	Shoeburyness	38C	Leicester
31A	**Cambridge**	34A	**Kings Cross**	38D	Staveley
31B	March	34B	Hornsey	38E	Woodford Halse
31C	Kings Lynn	34C	Hatfield		
31D	South Lynn	34D	Hitchin	39A	**Gorton**
31E	Bury St. Edmunds	34E	Neasden		
32A	**Norwich**			40A	**Lincoln**
32B	Ipswich	35A	**New England**	40B	Immingham
32C	Lowestoft	35B	Grantham	40C	Louth
32D	Yarmouth	35C	Peterborough	40D	Tuxford
	(South Town)		(Spital)	40E	Langwith Junction
32E	Yarmouth	36A	**Doncaster**	40F	Boston
	(Vauxhall)	36B	Mexborough	41A	**Sheffield**
		36C	Frodingham		(Darnall)

NORTH EASTERN REGION

50A	**York**	52B	Heaton	†55A	**Leeds (Holbeck)**
50B	Leeds (Neville Hill)	52C	Blaydon		(20A)
50C	Selby	52D	Tweedmouth	†55B	Stourton (20B)
50D	Starbeck	52E	Percy Main	†55C	Farnley Junction
50E	Scarborough	52F	North Blyth		(25G)
50F	Malton			†55D	Royston (20C)
50G	Whitby	53A	**Hull**	†55E	Normanton (20D)
51A	**Darlington**		(Dairycoates)	†55F	Manningham (20E)
51B	Newport (Yorks.)	53B	Hull	†55G	Huddersfield (25B)
51C	West Hartlepool		(Botanic Gardens)		
51D	Middlesbrough	53C	Hull (Springhead)	†56A	Wakefield (25A)
51E	Stockton	53D	Bridlington	56B	Ardsley (37A)
51F	West Auckland	†53E	Goole (25C)	56C	Copley Hill (37B)
51G	Haverton Hill			†56D	Mirfield (25D)
51H	Kirkby Stephen	54A	**Sunderland**	†56E	Sowerby Bridge
51J	Northallerton	54B	Tyne Dock		(25E)
51K	Saltburn	54C	Borough Gardens	†56F	Low Moor (25F)
52A	**Gateshead**	54D	Consett	56G	Bradford (37C)

† *Altered Shed Codes in course of adoption, former Code in brackets.*

SCOTTISH REGION

60A	**Inverness**	64A	**St. Margarets**	65I	Balloch
60B	Aviemore		(Edinburgh)	65J	Fort William
60C	Helmsdale	64B	Haymarket	66A	**Polmadie**
60D	Wick	64C	Dalry Road		(Glasgow)
60E	Forres	64D	Carstairs	66B	Motherwell
		64E	Polmont	66C	Hamilton
61A	**Kittybrewster**	64F	Bathgate	66D	Greenock
61B	Aberdeen	64G	Hawick	67A	**Corkerhill**
	(Ferryhill)				(Glasgow)
61C	Keith	65A	**Eastfield**	67B	Hurlford
62A	**Thornton**		(Glasgow)	67C	Ayr
62B	Dundee	65B	St. Rollox	67D	Ardrossan
	(Tay Bridge)	65C	Parkhead	68A	**Carlisle**
62C	Dunfermline	65D	Dawsholm		(Kingmoor)
63A	**Perth South**	65E	Kipps	68B	Dumfries
63B	Stirling South	65F	Grangemouth	68C	Stranraer
63C	Forfar	65G	Yoker	68D	Beattock
63D	Oban	65H	Helensburgh	68E	Carlisle (Canal)

4

MOTIVE POWER DEPOTS AND CODES—*continued*

SOUTHERN REGION

70A	**Nine Elms**		72B	Salisbury
70B	Feltham		72C	Yeovil
70C	Guildford		72D	Plymouth
70D	Basingstoke			Callington
70E	Reading		72E	Barnstaple Junction
70F	Fratton			Ilfracombe
70G	Newport (I.O.W.)			Torrington
70H	Ryde (I.O.W.)		72F	Wadebridge
71A	**Eastleigh**		73A	**Stewarts Lane**
	Andover Junction		73B	Bricklayers' Arms
	Lymington		73C	Hither Green
	Winchester		73D	Gillingham (Kent)
71B	Bournemouth		73E	Faversham
	Branksome			
71G	Bath (S. & D.)		74A	**Ashford (Kent)**
	Radstock		74B	Ramsgate
71H	Templecombe		74C	Dover
71I	Southampton Docks			Folkestone
71J	Highbridge		74D	Tonbridge
			74E	St. Leonards
			75A	**Brighton**
72A	**Exmouth Junction**			Newhaven
	Bude		75B	Redhill
	Exmouth		75C	Norwood Junction
	Lyme Regis		75D	Horsham
	Okehampton		75E	Three Bridges
	Seaton		75F	Tunbridge Wells West

WESTERN REGION

81A	**Old Oak**	84B	Oxley		86J	Aberdare
	Common	84C	Banbury		86K	Tredegar
81B	Slough	84D	Leamington Spa		87A	**Neath**
81C	Southall	84E	Tyseley		87B	Duffryn Yard
81D	Reading	84F	Stourbridge Junc.		87C	Danygraig
81E	Didcot	84G	Shrewsbury		87D	Swansea
81F	Oxford	84H	Wellington (Salop			(East Dock)
82A	**Bristol (Bath Rd.)**	84J	Croes Newydd		87E	Landore
82B	Bristol	84K	Chester		87F	Llanelly
	(St. Philip's Marsh)	85A	**Worcester**		87G	Carmarthen
82C	Swindon	85B	Gloucester		87H	Neyland
82D	Westbury	85C	Hereford		87J	Goodwick
82E	Yeovil	85D	Kidderminster		87K	Swansea (Victoria)
82F	Weymouth	86A	**Newport**		88A	**Cardiff (Cathays)**
83A	**Newton Abbot**		**(Ebbw Jcn.)**		88B	Cardiff East Dock
83B	Taunton	86B	Newport (Pill)		88C	Barry
83C	Exeter	86C	Cardiff (Canton)		88D	Merthyr
83D	Laira (Plymouth)	86D	Llantrisant		88E	Abercynon
83E	St. Blazey	86E	Severn Tunnel		88F	Treherbert
83F	Truro		Junction		89A	**Oswestry**
83G	Penzance	86F	Tondu		89B	Brecon
84A	**Wolverhampton**	86G	Pontypool Road		89C	Machynlleth
	(Stafford Road)	86H	Aberbeeg			

BRITISH RAILWAYS NON-STEAM LOCOMOTIVE CLASSES

INTERNAL COMBUSTION LOCOMOTIVES

Co-Co 5P/5F Diesel Electric

Introduced 1947: English Electric Co. and H. G. Ivatt, main line passenger design for L.M.S.R.
Weight: 121 tons 10 cwt.
Driving Wheels: 3′ 6″.
T.E.: 41,400 lb.
Engine: English Electric Co. 16 cyls. 1,600 h.p.
Motors: Six nose-suspended motors, single reduction gear drive.

| 10000 | 10001 | **Total 2** |

2-D-2 6P/5F Diesel Mechanical

Introduced 1951: H. G. Ivatt and Fell design for L.M.S.R.
Engines: Four 500 h.p., 12-cylinder.
Transmission: Fell patent differential drive and fluid couplings.
Weight : 120 tons.
Driving Wheels : 4′ 3″.
T.E. : 25,000 lb.

| 10100 | **Total 1** |

1-Co-Co-1 $\left\{ \begin{array}{l} 10201/2 \ 5P/5F \\ 10203 \ \ \ \ 6P/6F \end{array} \right\}$ Diesel Elec.

Introduced 1951: English Electric Co. and Bulleid main line passenger design for S.R.
*Introduced 1954: Modernised version of above.
Engine : English Electric Co. 16 cyls. 1,750 h.p. (2,000 h.p.*)
Weight : 135 tons.
Driving Wheels . 3′ 7′.
T.E. : $\left\{ \begin{array}{l} 48,000 \ \text{lb}. \\ 50,000 \ \text{lb}.* \end{array} \right.$

| 10201 | 10202 | *10203 |
| | | **Total 3** |

Bo-Bo 3 Diesel Electric

Introduced 1950: N.B. Loco. Co., B.T.H. Co. and H. G. vatt, branch line design for L.M.S.R.
Weight: 69 tons 16 cwt.
Driving Wheels: 3′ 6″
T.E.: 34,500 lb.
Engine: Davey Paxman 16 cyls. 827 h.p.
Motors: Four nose-suspended motors, single reduction gear drive.

| 10800 | **Total 1** |

0-6-0 Diesel Mechanical

introduced 1950: Bulleid S.R. design for shunting and transfer work.
Weight: 49 tons 9 cwt.
Driving Wheels: 4′ 6″.
T.E.: 33,500 lb. (max. in low gear).
Engine: Davey Paxman 12 cyls. 500 h.p.
Transmission: S.S.S. Powerflow three-speed gearbox and fluid coupling.

| 11001 | **Total 1** |

0-6-0 Diesel Mechanical

Introduced 1952 : 200 h.p. locomotives. Built by various contractors and at Swindon. On the E. & N.E. Regions these locomotives are classified as follows :
Nos. 11100-15 : Drewry : DJ12/1.
Nos. 11121-35/49-60 : Drewry (with 3′ 6″ Driving Wheels) : DJ12/2.
Nos. 11136-43/61-72 : Hunslet Engineering Co. : DJ13.
Nos. 11177-86 : Andrew Barclay DJ14.

11100	11110	11119	11128
11101	11111	11120	11129
11102	11112	11121	11130
11103	11113	11122	11131
11105	11114	11123	11132
11106	11115	11124	11133
11107	11116	11125	11134
11108	11117	11126	11135
11109	11118	11127	11136

11137	11162	11187	11212
11138	11163	11188	11213
11139	11164	11189	11214
11140	11165	11190	11215
11141	11166	11191	11216
11142	11167	11192	11217
11143	11168	11193	11218
11144	11169	11194	11219
11145	11170	11195	11220
11146	11171	11196	11221
11147	11172	11197	11222
11148	11173	11198	11223
11149	11174	11199	11224
11150	11175	11200	11225
11151	11176	11201	11226
11152	11177	11202	11227
11153	11178	11203	11228
11154	11179	11204	11229
11155	11180	11205	11230
11156	11181	11206	11231
11157	11182	11207	11232
11158	11183	11208	11233
11159	11184	11209	11234
11160	11185	11210	11235
11161	11186	11211	11236

N.B.—Locos of this type are still being delivered.

0-4-0 Diesel Mechanical
Introduced 1955. 153 h.p. locomotives for E.R. Built by Hunslet and classified **DY1** by the E. & N.E.R.

11500   11501   11502   11503
Total 4

0-4-0 Diesel Mechanical
Introduced 1956. 153 h.p. locomotives for E.R. Built by Andrew Barclay, Kilmarnock and classified **DY2** by the E. & N.E.R.

11504   11505   11506
Total 3

0-4-0 Diesel Mechanical
Introduced 1956. 165 h.p. locomotives. Built by Ruston & Hornsby and classified **DY5** by the E. & N.E.R.

11507   11508   **Total 2**

0-4-0 Diesel Hydraulic
Introduced 1953 : N.B. Loco. Co. design for N.E. and Scottish Regions and classified **DY11** by the E. & N.E.R.
Engine Davey Paxman G.R.P.H.L. 200 h.p.
Weight 32 tons.
Driving Wheels : 3' 6".
T.E. : 22,000 lb.

11700	11705	11710	11715
11701	11706	11711	11716
11702	11707	11712	11717
11703	11708	11713	11718
11704	11709	11714	11719

N.B.—Locos of this type are still being delivered

0-6-0 Diesel Electric
Introduced 1936: English Electric Hawthorn Leslie design for L.M.S.R.
Weight: 51 tons.
Driving Wheels: 4' 0½".
T.E.: 30,000 lb.
Engine: English Electric 6 cyls. 350 h.p.
Motors: Two nose-suspended motors single reduction gear drive.

12000   12001   **Total 2**

0-6-0 Diesel Electric
Introduced 1939: English Electric and Stanier design for L.M.S.R., development of previous design with jackshaft drive.
Weight: 54 tons 16 cwt.
Driving Wheels: 4' 3".
T.E.: 33,000 lb.
Engine: English Electric, 6 cyls. 350 h.p.
Motors: Single motor; jackshaft drive.

12003	12011	12019	12027
12004	12012	12020	12028
12005	12013	12021	12029
12006	12014	12022	12030
12007	12015	12023	12031
12008	12016	12024	12032
12009	12017	12025	
12010	12018	12026	

Total 30

12033-13139

0-6-0   Diesel Electric

Introduced 1945: English Electric and Fairburn design for L.M.S.R., development of previous design with double reduction gear drive. Classified DEJ3 by the E. and N.E.R.
Weight: 50 tons.
Driving Wheels: 4′ 0½″.
T.E.: 33,000 lb.
Engine: English Electric, 6 cyls. 350 h.p.
Motors: Two nose-suspended motors double reduction gear drive.

These locomotives are variously engined and equipped. Those on the E. & N.E. Regions are classified as follows : English Electric as DEJ4; G.E.C.—Blackstone DEJ5; B.T.H.—Blackstone DEJ6.

Motors : Two nose-suspended motors, double reduction gear drive.

12033	12060	12087	12114
12034	12061	12088	12115
12035	12062	12089	12116
12036	12063	12090	12117
12037	12064	12091	12118
12038	12065	12092	12119
12039	12066	12093	12120
12040	12067	12094	12121
12041	12068	12095	12122
12042	12069	12096	12123
12043	12070	12097	12124
12044	12071	12098	12125
12045	12072	12099	12126
12046	12073	12100	12127
12047	12074	12101	12128
12048	12075	12102	12129
12049	12076	12103	12130
12050	12077	12104	12131
12051	12078	12105	12132
12052	12079	12106	12133
12053	12080	12107	12134
12054	12081	12108	12135
12055	12082	12109	12136
12056	12083	12110	12137
12057	12084	12111	12138
12058	12085	12112	
12059	12086	12113	

Total 106

0-6-0   Diesel Electric

Introduced 1953: B.R. standard design.
Weight : 49 tons.
Driving Wheels : 4′ 6″.
T.E. : 35,000 lb.
Engine : 6 cyls. 400 h.p.

13000	13035	13070	13105
13001	13036	13071	13106
13002	13037	13072	13107
13003	13038	13073	13108
13004	13039	13074	13109
13005	13040	13075	13110
13006	13041	13076	13111
13007	13042	13077	13112
13008	13043	13078	13113
13009	13044	13079	13114
13010	13045	13080	13115
13011	13046	13081	13116
13012	13047	13082	13117
13013	13048	13083	13118
13014	13049	13084	13119
13015	13050	13085	13120
13016	13051	13086	13121
13017	13052	13087	13122
13018	13053	13088	13123
13019	13054	13089	13124
13020	13055	13090	13125
13021	13056	13091	13126
13022	13057	13092	13127
13023	13058	13093	13128
13024	13059	13094	13129
13025	13060	13095	13130
13026	13061	13096	13131
13027	13062	13097	13132
13028	13063	13098	13133
13029	13064	13099	13134
13030	13065	13100	13135
13031	13066	13101	13136
13032	13067	13102	13137
13033	13068	13103	13138
13034	13069	13104	13139

13140	13184	13228	13272
13141	13185	13229	13273
13142	13186	13230	13274
13143	13187	13231	13275
13144	13188	13232	13276
13145	13189	13233	13277
13146	13190	13234	13278
13147	13191	13235	13279
13148	13192	13236	13280
13149	13193	13237	13281
13150	13194	13238	13282
13151	13195	13239	13283
13152	13196	13240	13284
13153	13197	13241	13285
13154	13198	13242	13286
13155	13199	13243	13287
13156	13200	13244	13288
13157	13201	13245	13289
13158	13202	13246	13290
13159	13203	13247	13291
13160	13204	13248	13292
13161	13205	13249	13293
13162	13206	13250	13294
13163	13207	13251	13295
13164	13208	13252	13296
13165	13209	13253	13297
13166	13210	13254	13298
13167	13211	13255	13299
13168	13212	13256	13300
13169	13213	13257	13301
13170	13214	13258	13302
13171	13215	13259	13303
13172	13216	13260	13304
13173	13217	13261	13305
13174	13218	13262	13306
13175	13219	13263	13307
13176	13220	13264	13308
13177	13221	13265	13309
13178	13222	13266	13310
13179	13223	13267	13311
13180	13224	13268	13312
13181	13225	13269	13313
13182	13226	13270	13314
13183	13227	13271	13315

13316	13322	13328	13334
13317	13323	13329	13335
13318	13324	13330	13336
13319	13325	13331	
13320	13326	13332	
13321	13327	13333	

N.B.—Locos of this class are still being delivered.

0-6-0 Diesel Electric

Introduced 1944: English Electric and Thompson design for L.N.E.R., (L.N.E.R. version of L.M.S. 12033 series). Classified **DEJI** by the E. & N.E.R.
Weight: 51 tons.
Driving Wheels: 4' 0".
T.E.: 32,000 lb.
Engine: English Electric, 6 cyls. 350 h.p.
Motors: Two nose-suspended motors, double reduction gear drive.

15000   15001   15002   15003
Total 4

0-6-0 Diesel Electric

Introduced 1949: Brush design for E.R. Classified **DEJ2** by the E. & N.E.R.
Weight: 51 tons.
Driving Wheels: 4' 0".
T.E.: 32,000 lb.
Engine: Petter 4 cyls. 360 h.p.

15004   **Total 1**

0-4-0   Petrol   Class Y11

Introduced 1921: Motor, Rail and Tram Car Co., design (purchased by N.B.R. and L.N.E.R.).
Weight: 8 tons.
Driving Wheels: 3' 1".
Engine: 4 cyls. 40 h.p. petrol.
Drive: Chains and two-speed gear box.

15098   15099   **Total 2**

15100--18100

0-6-0   Diesel Electric

Introduced 1936: Hawthorn Leslie and
   English Electric design for G.W.R.
   (G.W.R. version of L.M.S.R. Nos.
   12000/1).
Weight: 51 tons 10 cwt.
Driving Wheels: 4' 1".
T.E.: 30,000 lb.
Engine: English Electric 6 cyls. 350 h.p.
Motors: Two nose-suspended motors
   single reduction gear drive.

15100   **Total 1**

0-6-0   Diesel Electric

Introduced 1948: English Electric and
   Hawksworth design for Western
   Region (W.R. version of L.M.S.
   12033 series).
Weight: 46 tons 9 cwt.
Driving Wheels: 4' 0½".
T.E.: 33,500 lb.
Engine: English Electric 6 cyls. 350 h.p.
Motors: Two nose-suspended motors.
   single reduction gear drive.

15101	15103	15105	
15102	15104	15106	**Total 6**

0-6-0   Diesel Electric

Introduced 1949: Brush design for
   W.R.
15107   **Total 1**

0-6-0   Diesel Electric

Introduced 1937: English Electric and
   Bulleid design for S.R.
Weight: 55 tons 5 cwt.
Driving Wheels: 4' 6".
T.E.: 30,000 lb.
Engine: English Electric 6 cyls. 350 h.p.
Motors: Two nose-suspended motors,
   single reduction gear drive.
15201   15202   15203   **Total 3**

0-6-0   Diesel Electric

Introduced 1949: English Electric and
   Bulleid design for S.R. (S.R. version
   of L.M.S.R. 12033 series, but designed
   for higher speeds).
Weight: 49 tons.
Driving Wheels: 4' 6".
T.E.: 24,000 lb.
Engine: English Electric 6 cyls. 350 h.p.
Motors: Two nose-suspended motors,
   double reduction gear drive.

15211	15218	15225	15232
15212	15219	15226	15233
15213	15220	15227	15234
15214	15221	15228	15235
15215	15222	15229	15236
15216	15223	15230	
15217	15224	15231	

Total 26

AIA-AIA   Gas Turbine

Introduced 1949: Brown Boveri
   (Switzerland) design for G.W.R.
Weight: 115 tons.
Driving Wheels: 4' 0½".
T.E.: 31,500 lb. at 21 m.p.h.
Engine: 2,500 h.p. gas turbine.
Motors: Four independently mounted
   motors with spring drive.

18000   **Total 1**

Co-Co   Gas Turbine

Introduced 1951:
Metropolitan-Vickers and Hawksworth
   design for G.W.R.
Weight: 129 tons 10 cwt.
Driving Wheels: 3' 8".
T.E.: maximum 60,000 lb. Continuous
   rating : 30,000 lb
Motors: Six nose-suspended motors
   with single reduction gear drive.

18100   **Total 1**

ELECTRIC LOCOMOTIVES

Co-Co 7P/5F Class CC

*Introduced 1941: Raworth & Bulleid design for S.R.
†Introduced 1948: Later design with detail differences.
Weight: { 99 tons 14 cwt.*
{ 104 tons 14 cwt.†
Driving Wheels: 3' 7"
T.E.: { 40,000 lb.*
{ 45,000 lb.†
Voltage: 660 D.C.
Current Collection: Overhead and third rail, with flywheel-driven generator for gaps in third rail.

20001*   20002*   20003†
Total 3

Bo-Bo Class EM1

*Introduced 1941: Metropolitan-Vickers and Gresley design for L.N.E.R.
Remainder. Introduced 1950.
Production design with detail alterations.
Weight: 87 tons 18 cwt.
Driving Wheels: 4' 2".
T.E.: 45,000 lb.   Voltage: 1,500 D.C.
Current Collection : Overhead.

26000*	26015	26030	26045
26001	26016	26031	26046
26002	26017	26032	26047
26003	26018	26033	26048
26004	26019	26034	26049
26005	26020	26035	26050
26006	26021	26036	26051
26007	26022	26037	26052
26008	26023	26038	26053
26009	26024	26039	26054
26010	26025	26040	26055
26011	26026	26041	26056
26012	26027	26042	26057
26013	26028	26043	**Total**
26014	26029	26044	**58**

*26000 named *Tommy*

Bo-Bo Class ES1

Built 1902: Brush & Thomson-Houston shunting design for N.E.R.
Weight: 46 tons.
Voltage: 600 D.C.   T.E.: 25,000 lb.
Current collection : Overhead and third rail.

26500   26501   **Total 2**

Bo-Bo Class EB1

Introduced 1946: L.N.E.R. rebuild of N.E.R. Raven freight design (Introduced 1914) for banking work on Manchester-Wath line.
Weight: 74 tons 8 cwt.
Driving Wheels: 4' 0".
T.E.: 37,600 lb.   Voltage: 1,500 D.C.
Current collection: Overhead.

26510   **Total 1**

Co-Co Class EM2

Introduced 1954: Metropolitan-Vickers and L.N.E.R. design. development of EM1 with six **axles** and higher speed range
Weight 102 tons.
Driving Wheels: 4' 2".
T.E.: 45,000 lb.   Voltage: 1,500 D.C.
Current Collection: Overhead.

27000	27002	27004	27006
27001	27003	27005	

Total 7

SUMMARY OF SOUTHERN REGION STEAM LOCOMOTIVE CLASSES
IN ALPHABETICAL ORDER
WITH HISTORICAL NOTES AND DIMENSIONS

Classes

0-6-0T 0P A1 & A1X

*A1 Introduced 1872: Stroudley L.B.S.C. "Terrier," later fitted with Marsh boiler. retaining original type smokebox.

†A1X Introduced 1911: Rebuild o. A1 with Marsh boiler and extended smokebox.

‡A1X Loco. with increased cylinder diameter.

Weight: $\begin{cases} 27 \text{ tons } 10 \text{ cwt.}^* \\ 28 \text{ tons } 5 \text{ cwt.}†‡ \end{cases}$

Pressure: 150 lb. Cyls. $\begin{cases} 12'' \times 20''.^*† \\ 14\frac{3}{16}'' \times 20''.‡ \end{cases}$

Driving Wheels: 4' 0"

T.E.: $\begin{cases} 7,650 \text{ lb.}^*† \\ 10,695 \text{ lb.}‡ \end{cases}$

*DS680

†DS377 DS681, 32640/6/50/5/61 /2/70/7/8.

‡32636

Total: A1   1
        A1X 12

0-4-0T 1F Class B4

*Introduced 1891: Adams L.S.W. design for dock shunting.

†Introduced 1908: Drummond K14 locos., with smaller boiler and detail alterations.

‡Adams loco. fitted with Drummond boiler.

§Drummond loco. fitted with Adams boiler.

Weight: $\begin{cases} 33 \text{ tons } 9 \text{ cwt.}^*‡ \\ 32 \text{ tons } 18 \text{ cwt.}†§ \end{cases}$

Pressure: 140 lb. Cyls. (O): 16" × 22".
Driving Wheels: 3' 9¾".
T.E.: 14,650 lb.

*30086/7/9/93/4/6, 30102.
†30082/3   ‡30088   §30084

Total 11

0-6-0 2F Class C

Introduced 1900: Wainwright S.E.C. design.
Weight: Loco. 43 tons 16 cwt.
Pressure: 160 lb. Cyls.: 18½" × 26"
Driving Wheels: 5' 2"
T.E.: 19,520 lb.

31004/18/33/7/54/9 / 61 / 8/ 71 / 86, 31102/12/3/50/91, 31218/9 /21/3/7 / 9/42–5/52/3 / 5 / 6 / 67 /8/70–2/80/ 7 /93 / 7/ 8, 31317, 31461/80/1/95/8, 31508/10/73/5 /6/8/9, 81–5/8–90/2/3, 31681–4/ 6/8–95, 31711/2/4–7/9–25.

Total 88

0-6-0 2F Class C2X

Introduced 1908: Marsh rebuild of R. J. Billinton L.B.S.C. C2 with larger C3-type boiler, extended smokebox, etc.
Weight: Loco. 45 tons 5 cwt.
Pressure: 170 lb.
Cyls.: 17½" × 26".
Driving Wheels: 5' 0".
T.E.: 19,175 lb.

32434/7/8/40–51, 32521–9/32/4– 41/3–54.

Total 45

0-4-0T 0P Class C14

Introduced 1923: Urie rebuild as shunting 'ocos. of Drummond L.S.W. motor-train 2-2-0T (originally introduced 1906).
Weight: 25 tons 15 cwt.
Pressure: 150 lb.
Cyls.: (O) 14" × 14".
Driving Wheels: 3' 0".
T.E.: 9,720 lb.
Walschaerts gear.

DS77, 30588/9.   Total 3

Classes D & DI

4-4-0 {2P D / 3P DI} Classes D & DI

*D Introduced 1901: Wainwright S.E.C. design, with round-top firebox, some later fitted with extended smokebox.

†DI Introduced 1921: Maunsell rebuild of Class D, with larger superheated boiler, Belpaire firebox and long-travel piston valves.

Weight: Loco. { 50 tons.* / 52 tons 4 cwt.†

Pressure: { 175 lb.* / 180 lb. Su.†

Cyls.: 19″ × 26″.
Driving Wheels: 6′ 3″.

T.E.: { 17,450 lb.* / 17,950 lb.†

*31075, 31549/74/7, 31737.
†31145,   31246/7,   31470/87/9/ 92/4, 31505/9/45, 31727/35/9/ 41/3/9.

Total: Class D 5
Class DI 17

4-4-0 3P Class EI

Introduced 1919 : Maunsell rebuild of Wainwright E. with larger superheated boiler, Belpaire firebox and long-travel piston valves.
Weight: Loco. 53 tons 9 cwt.
Pressure: 180 lb.
Cyls.: 19″ × 26″.
Driving Wheels: 6′ 6″.
T.E.: 18,410 lb.

31019/67,   31165,   31497,
31504/6/7.

Total: 7

0-6-0T 2F Class EI

Introduced 1874: Stroudley L.B.S.C design, reboilered by Marsh.
Weight: 44 tons 3 cwt.
Pressure: 170 lb. Cyls.: 17″ × 24″.
Driving Wheels: 4′ 6″.
T.E. 18,560 lb.

32113/38/9/51,   32689/94.
  (W) 1-4.

Total 10

0-6-2T IP2F Class EI/R

Introduced 1927: Maunsell rebuild of Stroudley EI, with radial trailing axle and larger bunker for passenger service in West of England.
Weight: 50 tons 5 cwt.
Pressure: 170 lb. Cyls.: 17″ × 24″.
Driving Wheels: 4′ 6″.
T.E.: 18,560 lb.

32095/6, 32124/35, 32608/95/7

Total 7

0-6-0T 3F Class E2

*Introduced 1913: L. B. Billinton L.B.S.C. design.

†Introduced 1915: Later locos. with tanks extended forward.

Weight: { 52 tons 15 cwt.* / 53 tons 10 cwt.†
Pressure: 170 lb. Cyls.: 17½″ × 26″.
Driving Wheels: 4′ 6″.
T.E : 21,305 lb.

*32100-4.
†32105-9.

Total 10

0-6-2T 2F Class E3

Introduced 1894: R. J. Billinton L.B.S.C. design, development of Stroudley "West Brighton" (introduced 1891), reboilered and fitted with extended smokebox, 1918 onwards; cylinder diameter reduced from 18″ by S.R.
Weight: 56 tons 10 cwt.
Pressure: { 160 lb. / 170 lb *
Cyls.: 17½″ × 26″.
Driving Wheels 4 6″
T.E.: { 20,055 lb. / 21,305 lb.*

*32165/6/70.
32454-6 8, 61/2

Total 9

13

Classes E4 & E4X–H

Classes E4 & E4X

0-6-2T 2P2F

*E4 Introduced 1897: R. J. Billinton
  L.B.S.C. design, development of E3
  with larger wheels, reboilered with
  Marsh boiler and extended smokebox,
  cylinder diameter reduced from 18"
  by S.R.
†E4X Introduced 1909: E4 reboilered
  with larger 12 4-4-2T type boiler.

Weight: { 57 tons 10 cwt.*
         { 59 tons 5 cwt.†
Pressure: 170 lb. Cyls.: 17½" × 26".
Driving Wheels: 5' 0".
T.E.: 19,175 lb.

*32463/7–76/9–81/4–8/91–5/7–9,
32500/2–12/4/5/7/9/20/56–60/2–6
/77–82.

†32466/77.

                Total: E4 60
                       E4X 2

Classes E6 & E6X

0-6-2T 3F

*‡E6 Introduced 1904: R. J. Billinton
  L.B.S.C. design, development of E5
  with smaller wheels, some with
  higher pressure.
†E6X Introduced 1911. E6 reboilered
  with larger C3-type boiler.

Weight: { 61 tons.*‡
        { 63 tons.†
Pressure: { 160 lb.*
          { 175 lb.‡
          { 170 lb.†
Cyls. 18" × 26".
Driving Wheels: 4' 6".
T.E.: { 21,215 lb.*
      { 23,205 lb.‡
      { 22,540 lb.†

*‡32408–10/2–8.   †32407/11.

                Total: E6 10
                       E6X 2

Class G6

0-6-0T 2F

*Introduced 1894: Adams L.S.W. design,
  later additions by Drummond, but
  with Adams type boiler.
†Introduced 1925: Fitted with Drum-
  mond type boiler.
Weight: 47 tons 13 cwt.
Pressure: 160 lb. Cyls.: 17½" × 24".
Driving Wheels: 4' 10".
T.E.: 17,235 lb.

*30162, 30238/58/60/6/70/7,
  30349, DS3152.
†30160, 30274.

                        Total 11

Class G16

4-8-0T 8F

Introduced 1921: Urie L.S.W. " Hump "
  loco.
Weight: 95 tons 2 cwt.
Pressure: 180 lb. Su.
Cyls. (O): 22" × 28".
Driving Wheels: 5' 1".
T.E. 33,990 lb.
Walschaerts gear. P.V.

30492–5   Total 4

Class H

0-4-4T 1P

Introduced 1904: Wainwright S.E.C.
  design.
*Introduced 1949: Fitted for push-and-
  pull working.
Weight: 54 tons 8 cwt.
Pressure: 160 lb. Cyls.: 18" × 26"
Driving Wheels: 5' 6".
T.E.: 17,360 lb.

31005, 31259/61/3/5/6,
  31305–7/21/4/6/8,
  31500/3/33/40/2/50–3.

*31161/2/4/77/84/93, 31239/
  69/74/6/8/9/95, 31308/10/9/22/
  7/9,31512/7–23/30/43/4/8/54.

                        Total 54

14

4-4-2 4P Class H2

Introduced 1911: Marsh L.B.S.C.
design, superheated development of
H1 with larger cylinders.
Weight: Loco. 68 tons 5 cwt.
Pressure: 200 lb. Su.
Cyls.: (O) 21" × 26".
Driving Wheels: 6' 7½".
T.E.: 24,520 lb.
P.V.

32422/4/5.   **Total 3**

4-6-0 4P5F Class H15

*Introduced 1914: Urie L.S.W. design,
fitted with " Maunsell " superheater
from 1927, replacing earlier types.

†Introduced 1915: Urie rebuild with
two outside cylinders of Drummond
E14, 4 cyl. 4-6-0 introduced 1907, retaining original boiler retubed and
fitted with superheater

‡Introduced 1924:   Maunsell locos
with N15 type boiler and smaller
tender.

§Introduced 1924: Maunsell rebuild of
Drummond F13 4-cyl 4-6-0 introduced 1905, with **detail** differences
from rebuild of E14.

¶Introduced 1927: Urie loco. (built
1914 saturated) rebuilt with later
N15 type boiler, with smaller
firebox.

Weight: Loco. {81 tons 5 cwt.*
{82 tons 1 cwt.†
{79 tons 19 cwt.‡¶
{80 tons 11 cwt.§

Pressure: {180 lb. Su.*‡¶
{175 lb. Su.†§
Cyls.: (O) 21" × 28".
Driving Wheels: 6' 0".
T.E.: {26,240 lb.*‡¶
{25,510 lb.†§
Walschaerts gear. P.V.

*30482-4/6-9
†30335
‡30473-8, 30521-4
§30330-4
¶30491   **Total 24**

4-6-2T 6F Class H16

Introduced 1921: Urie L.S.W. design
for heavy freight traffic.
Weight: 96 tons 8 cwt.
Pressure: 180 lb. Su.
Cyls.: (O) 21" × 28".
Driving Wheels: 5' 7 .
T.E.: 28,200 lb.
Walschaerts valve gear. P.V.

30516-20   **Total 5**

2-6-0 4P5F Class K

Introduced 1913: L. B. Billinton
L.B.S.C. design.
Weight: Loco. 63 tons 15 cwt.
Pressure: 180 lb. Su.
Cyls.: (O) 21" × 26".
Driving Wheels: 5' 6".
T.E.: 26,580 lb.
P.V.

32337-53   **Total 17**

4-4-0 3P Class L

Introduced 1914. Wainwright S.E.C.
design, with detail alterations by
Maunsell.
Weight: Loco. 57 tons 9 cwt.
Pressure: 160 lb. Su.
Cyls.: 20½" × 26".
Driving Wheels: 6' 8".
T.E.: 18,575 lb.
P.V.

31760-8/70-81   **Total 21**

4-4-0 3P Class L1

Introduced 1926: Post-grouping devel-
opment of L, with long-travel valves,
side window cab and detail alterations.
Weight: Loco. 57 tons 16 cwt.
Pressure: 180 lb. Su.
Cyls: 19½" × 26".
Driving Wheels: 6' 8".
T.E.: 18,910 lb.
P.V.

31753-9/82-9   **Total 15**

15

Classes LN–N & NI

4-6-0   7P   Class LN

*Introduced 1926: Maunsell design cylinders and tender modified by Bulleid from 1938, and fitted with multiple-jet blastpipe and large chimney.

†Introduced 1929: Loco. fitted experimentally with smaller driving wheels.

‡Introduced 1929: Loco. fitted experimentally with longer boiler.

Weight: Loco. $\begin{cases} 83 \text{ tons } 10 \text{ cwt.}*† \\ 84 \text{ tons } 16 \text{ cwt.}‡ \end{cases}$

Pressure: 220 lb. Su.

Cyls.: (4) $16\frac{1}{2}'' \times 26''$

Driving Wheels: $\begin{cases} 6' \ 7''.*‡ \\ 6' \ 3''.† \end{cases}$

T.E.: $\begin{cases} 33,510 \text{ lb.}*† \\ 35,300 \text{ lb.}† \end{cases}$

Walschaerts gear. P.V.

*30850–8/61–5.

†30859   ‡30860

Total 16

0-4-4T   2P   Class M7

*Introduced 1897: Drummond L.S.W. M7 design.

†Introduced 1903: Drummond X14 design, with increased front overhang, steam reverser and detail alterations, now classified M7 (30254 originally M7).

‡Introduced 1925 : X14 design fitted for push-and-pull working.

Weight: $\begin{cases} 60 \text{ tons } 4 \text{ cwt.}* \\ 60 \text{ tons } 3 \text{ cwt.}† \\ 62 \text{ tons } 0 \text{ cwt.}‡ \end{cases}$

Pressure: 175 lb.

Cyls.: $18\frac{1}{2}'' \times 26''$

Driving Wheels: 5′ 7″.

T.E.: 19,755 lb.

*30022–6/31–44, 30112, 30241–53/5/6, 30318–24/56/7, 30667–71/3–6.

†30030, 30123/4/7/30/2/3, 30254, 30374–8, 30479.

‡30021/7/8/9/45–60, 30104–11/25/8/9/31, 30328/79, 30480/1.

Total 103

4-6-2   8P   Class MN

*Introduced 1941 : Bulleid design originally with 280 lb. pressure, multiple-jet blastpipe and Bulleid valve gear.

†Introduced 1956 : Rebuilt with Walschaerts valve gear, modified details and air-smoothed casing removed.

Weight: Loco. $\begin{cases} 94 \text{ tons } 15 \text{ cwt.}* \\ 97 \text{ tons } 18 \text{ cwt.}† \end{cases}$

Pressure : 250 lb.

Cyls. : (3) $18'' \times 24''$.

Driving Wheels : 6′ 2″.

T.E. : 33,495 lb. P.V.

*35001–12/5–7/9/21/3–30.

†35013/4/8/20/2.

Total 30

Classes N & NI

2-6-0   4P5F

*N Introduced 1917: Maunsell S.E.C. mixed traffic design.

†NI Introduced 1922: 3-cylinder development of N.

Weight: Loco. $\begin{cases} 61 \text{ tons } 4 \text{ cwt.}* \\ 64 \text{ tons } 5 \text{ cwt.}† \end{cases}$

Pressure: 200 lb. Su.

Cyls.: $\begin{cases} (O) \ 19'' \times 28''.* \\ (3) \ 16'' \times 28''.† \end{cases}$

Driving Wheels: 5′ 6″

T.E.: $\begin{cases} 26,035 \text{ lb.}* \\ 27,695 \text{ lb.}† \end{cases}$

Walschaerts gear. P.V.

*31400–14, 31810–21/3–75

†31822/76–80

Total: Class N 80

Class NI 6

Above: Class B4 0-4-0T
No. 30094
[A. R. Carpenter

Right: Class C14 0-4-0T
No. 77S (departmental)
[W. M. J. Jackson

Below: Class P 0-6-0T
No. 31323
[A. R. Carpenter

Class M7 0-4-4T No. 30242
[R. K. Evans

Class H 0-4-4T No. 31520
[P. H. Groom

Class U.S.A. 0-6-0T No. 30071
[Brian E. Morrison

Class G6 0-6-0T No. 30162   [R. K. Evans

Class O2 0-4-4T No. 30177   [G. Wheeler

Class O2 0-4-4T No. 36 *Carisbrooke* (Westinghouse brake fitted, and larger bunker for I.O.W. ; push-and-pull fitted)   [E. Gamblin

Class 0415 4-4-2T No. 30584   *[R. E. Vincent*

Class 0298 2-4-0WT No. 30587   *[R. C. Riley*

Class 757 0-6-2T No. 30757 *Earl of Mount Edgcumbe*   *[C. P. Boocock*

Class O1 0-6-0 No. 31064

[A. R. Carpenter

Class C 0-6-0 No. 31037

[D. Penney

Class K 2-6-0 No. 32338

[R. J. Buckley

Class D 4-4-0 No. 31574   [*B. I. Nathan*

Class D1 4-4-0 No. 31470   [*P. H. Groom*

Class L 4-4-0 No. 31776   [*P. H. Groom*

Class L1 4-4-0 No. 31753   [D. Penney

Class T9 4-4-0 No. 30707   [A. E. Brown

Class H2 4-4-2 No. 32421 *South Foreland* (now withdrawn)   [E. Gamblin

Class N 2-6-0 No. 31407

[P. H. Groom

Class N 2-6-0 No. 31848 (with modified front end including outside steam pipes, new cylinders but without smoke deflectors)

[D. Penney

Class U 2-6-0 No. 31806

[A. E. Brown

4-6-0   5P   Class N15

*Introduced 1918: Urie L.S.W. design.
†Introduced 1928: Urie Locos. modified with cylinders of reduced diameter.
‡Introduced 1925: Maunsell Locos. with long-travel valves, increased boiler pressure smaller fireboxes, and tenders from Drummond G14 4-6-0's.
§Introduced 1925: Later locos. with detail alterations and increased weight.
||Introduced 1925: Locos. with modified cabs to suit Eastern Section, and new bogie tenders.
¶Introduced 1926. Locos. with detail alterations and six-wheeled tenders for Central Section.

Weight: Loco. $\begin{cases} 80 \text{ tons } 7 \text{ cwt.}^{*}† \\ 79 \text{ tons } 18 \text{ cwt.}‡ \\ 80 \text{ tons } 19 \text{ cwt.}§ \\ 81 \text{ tons } 17 \text{ cwt.}¶ \end{cases}$

Pressure: $\begin{cases} 180 \text{ lb. Su.}^{*}† \\ 200 \text{ lb. Su.}‡||¶ \end{cases}$

Cyls.: $\begin{cases} (O) \ 22'' \times 28''.^{*} \\ (O) \ 21'' \times 28''.† \\ (O) \ 20\frac{1}{2}'' \times 28''.‡§||¶ \end{cases}$

Driving Wheels: 6′ 7″.

T.E.: $\begin{cases} 26,245 \text{ lb.}^{*} \\ 23,915 \text{ lb.}† \\ 25,320 \text{ lb.}§‡||¶ \end{cases}$

Walschaerts gear.   P.V

NOTE: Nos. 30736/55 are fitted with multiple jet blastpipe and large diameter chimney.

*30755   †30736/8/9/42/7–51/3
‡30453–7   §30448–52
||30763–92   ¶30793–30806

Total 65

4-6-0   4P   Class N15X

Introduced 1934: Maunsell rebuild of L. B. Billinton L.B.S.C. Class L 4-6-4T (introduced 1914).
Weight: Loco. 73 tons 2 cwt.
Pressure: 180 lb. Su.
Cyls.: (O) 21″ × 28″.
Driving Wheels: 6′ 9″.
T.E.: 23,325 lb.
Walschaerts gear.   P.V.

32331.   **Total 1**

0-6-0   2F   Class O1

*Introduced 1903: Wainwright rebuild with domed boiler and new cab of Stirling S.E. Class O 0–6–0 (introduced 1878).
†Introduced 1903 : Loco. with smaller driving wheels.
Weight: Loco. 41 tons 1 cwt.
Pressure: 150 lb. Cyls.: 18″ × 26″.
Driving Wheels: $\begin{cases} 5' \ 2''.^{*} \\ 5' \ 1''.† \end{cases}$
T.E.: $\begin{cases} 17,325 \text{ lb.}^{*} \\ 17,610 \text{ lb.}† \end{cases}$

*31064/5,   31258,   31370,   31425/30/4
†31048

Total 8

0-4-4T   0P   Class O2

*Introduced 1889: Adams L.S.W design.
†Introduced 1923: Fitted with Westinghouse brake for I.O.W bunker. enlarged from 1932.
‡Fitted with Drummond-type boiler
§Fitted for push-and-pull working.
Weight: $\begin{cases} 46 \text{ tons } 18 \text{ cwt.}^{*}‡ \\ 48 \text{ tons } 8 \text{ cwt.}† \end{cases}$
Pressure: 160 lb. Cyls.: 17½″ × 24″.
Driving Wheels: 4′ 10″.
T.E.: 17,235 lb.

*30177/9/92/3/9   30200/12/6/24/5/9/32/6.
†(W)14/6–8/20–2/4–33.
‡§(W)35/6.
‡30223/33.
‡§30182/3, 30207.

Total 37

0-6-0T   Unclass   Class P

Introduced 1909: Wainwright S.E.C. design for push-and-pull work, now used for shunting.
Weight: 28 tons 10 cwt.
Pressure: 160 lb. Cyls.: 12″ × 18″
Driving Wheels: 3′ 9⅝″.
T.E.: 7,810 lb.

31027, 31178, 31323/5, 31556–8.

Total 7

Classes Q–T9

0-6-0   4F   Class Q

Introduced 1938: Maunsell design, later
fitted with multiple-jet blastpipe and
large diameter chimney.
Weight: Loco. 49 tons 10 cwt.
Pressure: 200 lb. Su
Cyls.: 19″ × 26″.
Driving Wheels: 5′ 1″
T.E.: 26,160 lb.
P.V.

30530–49   **Total 20**

0-6-0   5F   Class Q1

Introduced 1942: Bulleid " Austerity "
design.
Weight: Loco. 51 tons 5 cwt.
Pressure: 230 lb. Su.
Cyls.: 19″ × 26″.
Driving Wheels: 5′ 1″.
T.E.: 30,080 lb.
P.V.

33001–40   **Total 40**

0-6-0T   2F   Class R1

*Introduced 1888: Stirling S.E. design
later rebuilt with domed boiler.
†Introduced 1938: Fitted with Urie
type short chimney for Whitstable
branch, and fitted with or retaining
original Stirling-type cab.
‡ Introduced 1952. Rebuilt with
domed boiler but retaining Stirling
cab.
Weight: $\begin{cases} 46 \text{ tons } 15 \text{ cwt.}^* \\ 46 \text{ tons } 8 \text{ cwt.}\dagger\ddagger \end{cases}$
Pressure: 160 lb. Cyls.: 18″ × 26″.
Driving Wheels: $\begin{cases} 5′ 2″.^* \\ 5′ 1″.\dagger\ddagger \end{cases}$
T.E.: $\begin{cases} 18,480 \text{ lb.}^* \\ 18,780 \text{ lb.}\dagger\ddagger \end{cases}$

*31047, 31107/28/74,
  31337/40
†31010, 31147, 31339
‡31069

                   Total 10

4-6-0   6F   Class S15

*Introduced 1920: Urie L.S.W. design,
development of N15 for mixed traffic
work.
†Introduced 1927: Maunsell design,
with higher pressure. smaller grate,
modified footplating and other detail
differences. 30833-7 with 6-wheel
tenders for Central Section.
‡Introduced 1936: Later locos. with
detail differences and reduced weight.
Weight: Loco. $\begin{cases} 79 \text{ tons } 16 \text{ cwt.}^* \\ 80 \text{ tons } 14 \text{ cwt.}\dagger \\ 79 \text{ tons } 5 \text{ cwt.}\ddagger \end{cases}$
Pressure: $\begin{cases} 180 \text{ lb. Su.}^* \\ 200 \text{ lb. Su.}\dagger\ddagger \end{cases}$
Cyls.: $\begin{cases} (O) 21″ × 28″.^* \\ (O) 20\frac{1}{2}″ × 28″.\dagger\ddagger \end{cases}$
Driving Wheels: 5′ 7″.
T.E.: $\begin{cases} 28,200 \text{ lb.}^* \\ 29,855 \text{ lb.}\dagger\ddagger \end{cases}$
Walschaerts gear.   P.V.

*30496–30515   †30823–37
‡30838–47

                   Total 45

4-4-0   3P   Class T9

*Introduced 1899: Drummond L.S.W.
design. fitted with superheater and
larger cylinders by Urie from 1922.
†Introduced 1899: Locos. with detail
differences (originally fitted with firebox watertubes).
‡Introduced 1900: Locos. with wider
cab and splashers, without coupling rod splashers and originally
fitted with firebox watertubes.
Weight: Loco. $\begin{cases} 51 \text{ tons } 18 \text{ cwt.}^* \\ 51 \text{ tons } 16 \text{ cwt.}\dagger \\ 51 \text{ tons } 7 \text{ cwt.}\ddagger \end{cases}$
Pressure: 175 lb. Su.
Cyls.: 19″ × 26″.
Driving Wheels: 6′ 7″.
T.E.: 17,675 lb.

*30117/20, 30283–5/7–9
†30702/5–12/5/7–9/21/4/6–30/2
‡30300/1/4/10/3/37/8

                   Total 36

Classes
2-6-0 4P3F U & UI

*U Introduced 1928: Rebuild of
  Maunsell S.E.C. Class K (" River ")
  2-6-4T (introduced 1917).
†U Introduced 1928: Locos. built as
  Class U, with smaller splashers and
  detail alterations.
‡UI Introduced 1928: 3-cylinder
  development of Class U (prototype
  31890, rebuilt from 2-6-4T, originally
  built 1925).

Weight: Loco. $\begin{cases} 63 \text{ tons.*} \\ 62 \text{ tons 6 cwt.†} \\ 65 \text{ tons 6 cwt.‡} \end{cases}$

Pressure: 200 lb. Su.
Cyls.: $\begin{cases} (O) \ 19'' \times 28''.*† \\ (3) \ 16'' \times 28''.‡ \end{cases}$
Driving Wheels: 6' 0".
T.E.: $\begin{cases} 23,865 \text{ lb.*†} \\ 25,385 \text{ lb.‡} \end{cases}$
Walschaerts gear. P.V.

*31790–31809   †31610–39
‡31890–31910

Total: Class U 50
Class UI 21

0-6-0T 3F Class USA

Introduced 1942: U.S. Army Trans-
portation Corps design, purchased by
S.R. 1946, and fitted with modified cab
and bunker and other detail altera-
tions.
Weight: 46 tons 10 cwt.
Pressure: 210 lb.
Cyls.: (O) 16½" × 24".
Driving Wheels: 4' 6".
T.E.: 21,600 lb.
Walschaerts gear. P.V

30061–74   Total 14

4-4-0 5P Class V

*Introduced 1930: Maunsell design.
†Introduced 1938: Fitted with multiple
  jet blastpipe and large diameter
  chimney by Bulleid.
Weight: Loco. 67 tons 2 cwt.
Pressure: 220 lb. Su.
Cyls.: (3) 16½" × 26".
Driving Wheels: 6' 7".
T.E.: 25,135 lb.
Walschaerts gear. P.V.

Classes U & UI-Z

*30902–6/8/10–2/6/22/3/5–8/32/5
  /6.
†30900/1/7/9/13–5/7–21/4/29–31/
  3/4/7–9.

Total 40

2-6-4T 6F Class W

Introduced 1931: Maunsell design
developed from Class NI 2-6-0.
Weight: 90 tons 14 cwt.
Pressure: 200 lb. Su.
Cyls.: (3) 16½" × 28".
Driving Wheels: 5' 6".
T.E.: 29,450 lb.
Walschaerts gear. P.V.

31911–25   Total 15

4-6-2 7P5F
Classes WC & BB

*Introduced 1945: Bulleid " West
  Country " Class.
†Introduced 1946: Bulleid " Battle of
  Britain " Class.
‡Introduced 1948: Locos. with larger
  tenders.
Weight: Loco. 86 tons 0 cwt.
Pressure: 250 lb. Su.
Cyls.: (3) 16⅜" × 24".
Driving Wheels: 6' 2".
T.E.: 27,715 lb.
Bulleid valve gear. P.V.
*34001–48   †34049–70
††34071–90, 34109/10
*‡34091–34108   Total 110

0-8-0T 6F Class Z

Introduced 1929: Maunsell design for
heavy shunting.
Weight: 71 tons 12 cwt.
Pressure: 180 lb. Cyls.: (3) 16" × 18".
Driving Wheels: 4' 8".
T.E.: 29,375 lb.
Walschaerts gear. P.V

30950–7   Total 8

27

0-6-0   3F   Class 700

Introduced 1897: Drummond L.S.W.
design, superheated from 1921.
Weight: Loco. 46 tons 14 cwt.
Pressure: 180 lb. Su.
Cyls.: 19″ × 26″
Driving Wheels: 5′ 1″.
T.E.: 23,540 lb.

30306/8/9/15–7/25–7/39/46/50/2/
5/68, 30687–30701.

Total 30

0-6-2T   IP2F   Class 757

Introduced 1907: Hawthorn Leslie
design for P.D.S.W.J.
Weight: 49 tons 19 cwt.
Pressure: 170 lb.
Cyls.: (O) 16″ × 24″.
Driving Wheels: 4′ 0″.
T.E.: 18,495 lb.

30757/8

Total 2

2-4-0WT   0P   Class 0298

Introduced 1874: Beattie L.S.W.
design, rebuilt by Adams (1884-92),
Urie (1921-2) and Maunsell (1931-5)
Weight: 37 tons 16 cwt.
Pressure: 160 lb.
Cyls.: (O) 16½″ × 20″.
Driving Wheels: 5′ 7″
T.E.: 11,050 lb.

30585–7

Total 3

0-6-0   2F   Class 0395

*Introduced 1881 Adams L.S.W.
design.
†Introduced 1885: Adams " 496 "
class with longer front overhang.
‡Introduced 1928: Reboilered with
ex-L.C. & D. Class M3 4–4–0 boiler.
Weight: Loco. $\begin{cases} 37 \text{ tons } 12 \text{ cwt.}^{*}† \\ 38 \text{ tons } 14 \text{ cwt.}†‡ \end{cases}$
Pressure: $\begin{cases} 140 \text{ lb.}^{*}† \\ 150 \text{ lb.}‡ \end{cases}$
Driving Wheels: 5′ 1″.
T.E.: $\begin{cases} 15,535 \text{ lb.}^{*}† \\ 16,645 \text{ lb.}‡ \end{cases}$

*30568/70/2/4/5/8
†30566   *‡30567/73
†‡30564/80

Total 11

4-4-2T   IP   Class 0415

Introduced 1882: Adams L.S.W.
design, later reboilered.
Weight: 55 tons 2 cwt.
Pressure: 160 lb.
Cyls.: (O) 17½″ × 24″.
Driving Wheels: 5′ 7″.
T.E.: 14,920 lb.

30582–4

Total 3

BRITISH RAILWAYS LOCOMOTIVES
Nos. 30021-35030, W1-36

Named Engines are indicated by an asterisk (*)

No.	Class	No.	Class	No.	Class	No.	Class
30021	M7	30056	M7	30109	M7	30233	O2
30022	M7	30057	M7	30110	M7	30236	O2
30023	M7	30058	M7	30111	M7	30238	G6
30024	M7	30059	M7	30112	M7	30241	M7
30025	M7	30060	M7	30117	T9	30242	M7
30026	M7	30061	U.S.A.	30120	T9	30243	M7
30027	M7	30062	U.S.A.	30123	M7	30244	M7
30028	M7	30063	U.S.A.	30124	M7	30245	M7
30029	M7	30064	U.S.A.	30125	M7	30246	M7
30030	M7	30065	U.S.A.	30127	M7	30247	M7
30031	M7	30066	U.S.A.	30128	M7	30248	M7
30032	M7	30067	U.S.A.	30129	M7	30249	M7
30033	M7	30068	U.S.A.	30130	M7	30250	M7
30034	M7	30069	U.S.A.	30131	M7	30251	M7
30035	M7	30070	U.S.A.	30132	M7	30252	M7
30036	M7	30071	U.S.A.	30133	M7	30253	M7
30037	M7	30072	U.S.A.	30160	G6	30254	M7
30038	M7	30073	U.S.A.	30162	G6	30255	M7
30039	M7	30074	U.S.A.	30177	O2	30256	M7
30040	M7	30082	B4	30179	O2	30258	G6
30041	M7	30083	B4	30182	O2	30260	G6
30042	M7	30084	B4	30183	O2	30266	G6
30043	M7	30086	B4	30192	O2	30270	G6
30044	M7	30087	B4	30193	O2	30274	G6
30045	M7	30088	B4	30199	O2	30277	G6
30046	M7	30089	B4	30200	O2	30283	T9
30047	M7	30093	B4	30207	O2	30284	T9
30048	M7	30094	B4	30212	O2	30285	T9
30049	M7	30096	B4	30216	O2	30287	T9
30050	M7	30102	B4	30223	O2	30288	T9
30051	M7	30104	M7	30224	O2	30289	T9
30052	M7	30105	M7	30225	O2	30300	T9
30053	M7	30106	M7	30229	O2	30301	T9
30054	M7	30107	M7	30232	O2	30304	T9
30055	M7	30108	M7	30232	O2	30306	700

No.	Class	No.	Class	No.	Class	No.	Class
30308	700	30450*	N15	30510	S15	30574	0395
30309	700	30451*	N15	30511	S15	30575	0395
30310	T9	30452*	N15	30512	S15	30578	0395
30313	T9	30453*	N15	30513	S15	30580	0395
30315	700	30454*	N15	30514	S15	30582	0415
30316	700	30455*	N15	30515	S15	30583	0415
30317	700	30456*	N15	30516	H16	30584	0415
30318	M7	30457*	N15	30517	H16	30585	0298
30319	M7	30473	H15	30518	H16	30586	0298
30320	M7	30474	H15	30519	H16	30587	0298
30321	M7	30475	H15	30520	H16	30588	C14
30322	M7	30476	H15	30521	H15	30589	C14
30323	M7	30477	H15	30522	H15	30667	M7
30324	M7	30478	H15	30523	H15	30668	M7
30325	700	30479	M7	30524	H15	30669	M7
30326	700	30480	M7	30530	Q	30670	M7
30327	700	30481	M7	30531	Q	30671	M7
30328	M7	30482	H15	30532	Q	30673	M7
30330	H15	30483	H15	30533	Q	30674	M7
30331	H15	30484	H15	30534	Q	30675	M7
30332	H15	30486	H15	30535	Q	30676	M7
30333	H15	30487	H15	30536	Q	30687	700
30334	H15	30488	H15	30537	Q	30688	700
30335	H15	30489	H15	30538	Q	30689	700
30337	T9	30491	G16	30539	Q	30690	700
30338	T9	30492	G16	30540	Q	30691	700
30339	700	30493	G16	30541	Q	30692	700
30346	700	30494	G16	30542	Q	30693	700
30349	G6	30495	G16	30543	Q	30694	700
30350	700	30496	S15	30544	Q	30695	700
30352	700	30497	S15	30545	Q	30696	700
30355	700	30498	S15	30546	Q	30697	700
30356	M7	30499	S15	30547	Q	30698	700
30357	M7	30500	S15	30548	Q	30699	700
30368	700	30501	S15	30549	Q	30700	700
30374	M7	30502	S15	30564	0395	30701	700
30375	M7	30503	S15	30566	0395	30702	T9
30376	M7	30504	S15	30567	0395	30705	T9
30377	M7	30505	S15	30568	0395	30706	T9
30378	M7	30506	S15	30570	0395	30707	T9
30379	M7	30507	S15	30572	0395	30708	T9
30448*	N15	30508	S15	30573	0395	30709	T9
30449*	N15	30509	S15			30710	T9

No.	Class	No.	Class	No.	Class	No.	Class
30711	T9	30778*	N15	30837	S15	30916*	V
30712	T9	30779*	N15	30838	S15	30917*	V
30715	T9	30780*	N15	30839	S15	30918*	V
30717	T9	30781*	N15	30840	S15	30919*	V
30718	T9	30782*	N15	30841	S15	30920*	V
30719	T9	30783*	N15	30842	S15	30921*	V
30721	T9	30784*	N15	30843	S15	30922*	V
30724	T9	30785*	N15	30844	S15	30923*	V
30726	T9	30786*	N15	30845	S15	30924*	V
30727	T9	30787*	N15	30846	S15	30925*	V
30728	T9	30788*	N15	30847	S15	30926*	V
30729	T9	30789*	N15	30850*	LN	30927*	V
30730	T9	30790*	N15	30851*	LN	30928*	V
30732	T9	30791*	N15	30852*	LN	30929*	V
30736*	N15	30792*	N15	30853*	LN	30930*	V
30738*	N15	30793*	N15	30854*	LN	30931*	V
30739*	N15	30794*	N15	30855*	LN	30932*	V
30742*	N15	30795*	N15	30856*	LN	30933*	V
30747*	N15	30796*	N15	30857*	LN	30934*	V
30748*	N15	30797*	N15	30858*	LN	30935*	V
30749*	N15	30798*	N15	30859*	LN	30936*	V
30750*	N15	30799*	N15	30860*	LN	30937*	V
30751*	N15	30800*	N15	30861*	LN	30938*	V
30753*	N15	30801*	N15	30862*	LN	30939*	V
30755*	N15	30802*	N15	30863*	LN	30950	Z
30757	757	30803*	N15	30864*	LN	30951	Z
30758	757	30804*	N15	30865*	LN	30952	Z
30763*	N15	30805*	N15	30900*	V	30953	Z
30764*	N15	30806*	N15	30901*	V	30954	Z
30765*	N15	30823	S15	30902*	V	30955	Z
30766*	N15	30824	S15	30903*	V	30956	Z
30767*	N15	30825	S15	30904*	V	30957	Z
30768*	N15	30826	S15	30905*	V	31004	C
30769*	N15	30827	S15	30906*	V	31005	H
30770*	N15	30828	S15	30907*	V	31010	RI
30771*	N15	30829	S15	30908*	V	31018	C
30772*	N15	30830	S15	30909*	V	31019	EI
30773*	N15	30831	S15	30910*	V	31027	P
30774*	N15	30832	S15	30911*	V	31033	C
30775*	N15	30833	S15	30912*	V	31037	C
30776*	N15	30834	S15	30913*	V	31047	RI
30777*	N15	30835	S15	30914*	V	31048	OI
		30836	S15	30915*	V	31054	C

No.	Class	No.	Class	No.	Class	No.	Class
31059	C	31255	C	31370	OI	31520	H
31061	C	31256	C	31400	N	31521	H
31064	OI	31258	OI	31401	N	31522	H
31065	OI	31259	H	31402	N	31523	H
31067	EI	31261	H	31403	N	31530	H
31068	C	31263	H	31404	N	31533	H
31069	RI	31265	H	31405	N	31540	H
31071	C	31266	H	31406	N	31542	H
31075	D	31267	C	31407	N	31543	H
31086	C	31268	C	31408	N	31544	H
31102	C	31269	H	31409	N	31545	DI
31107	RI	31270	C	31410	N	31548	H
31112	C	31271	C	31411	N	31549	D
31113	C	31272	C	31412	N	31550	H
31128	RI	31274	H	31413	N	31551	H
31145	DI	31276	H	31414	N	31552	H
31147	RI	31278	H	31425	OI	31553	H
31150	C	31279	H	31430	OI	31554	H
31161	H	31280	C	31434	OI	31556	P
31162	H	31287	C	31461	C	31557	P
31164	H	31293	C	31470	DI	31558	P
31165	EI	31295	H	31480	C	31573	C
31174	RI	31297	C	31481	C	31574	D
31177	H	31298	C	31487	DI	31575	C
31178	P	31305	H	31489	DI	31576	C
31184	H	31306	H	31492	DI	31577	D
31191	C	31307	H	31494	DI	31578	C
31193	H	31308	H	31495	C	31579	C
31218	C	31310	H	31497	EI	31581	C
31219	C	31317	C	31498	C	31582	C
31221	C	31319	H	31500	H	31583	C
31223	C	31321	H	31503	H	31584	C
31227	C	31322	H	31504	EI	31585	C
31229	C	31323	P	31505	DI	31588	C
31239	H	31324	H	31506	EI	31589	C
31242	C	31325	P	31507	EI	31590	C
31243	C	31326	H	31508	C	31592	C
31244	C	31327	H	31509	DI	31593	C
31245	C	31328	H	31510	C	31610	U
31246	DI	31329	H	31512	H	31611	U
31247	DI	31337	RI	31517	H	31612	U
31252	C	31339	RI	31518	H	31613	U
31253	C	31340	RI	31519	H	31614	U

No.	Class	No.	Class	No.	Class	No.	Class
31615	U	31717	C	31782	LI	31825	N
31616	U	31719	C	31783	LI	31826	N
31617	U	31720	C	31784	LI	31827	N
31618	U	31721	C	31785	LI	31828	N
31619	U	31722	C	31786	LI	31829	N
31620	U	31723	C	31787	LI	31830	N
31621	U	31724	C	31788	LI	31831	N
31622	U	31725	C	31789	LI	31832	N
31623	U	31727	DI	31790	U	31833	N
31624	U	31735	DI	31791	U	31834	N
31625	U	31737	D	31792	U	31835	N
31626	U	31739	DI	31793	U	31836	N
31627	U	31741	DI	31794	U	31837	N
31628	U	31743	DI	31795	U	31838	N
31629	U	31749	DI	31796	U	31839	N
31630	U	31753	LI	31797	U	31840	N
31631	U	31754	LI	31798	U	31841	N
31632	U	31755	LI	31799	U	31842	N
31633	U	31756	LI	31800	U	31843	N
31634	U	31757	LI	31801	U	31844	N
31635	U	31758	LI	31802	U	31845	N
31636	U	31759	LI	31803	U	31846	N
31637	U	31760	L	31804	U	31847	N
31638	U	31761	L	31805	U	31848	N
31639	U	31762	L	31806	U	31849	N
31681	C	31763	L	31807	U	31850	N
31682	C	31764	L	31808	U	31851	N
31683	C	31765	L	31809	U	31852	N
31684	C	31766	L	31810	N	31853	N
31686	C	31767	L	31811	N	31854	N
31688	C	31768	L	31812	N	31855	N
31689	C	31770	L	31813	N	31856	N
31690	C	31771	L	31814	N	31857	N
31691	C	31772	L	31815	N	31858	N
31692	C	31773	L	31816	N	31859	N
31693	C	31774	L	31817	N	31860	N
31694	C	31775	L	31818	N	31861	N
31695	C	31776	L	31819	N	31862	N
31711	C	31777	L	31820	N	31863	N
31712	C	31778	L	31821	N	31864	N
31714	C	31779	L	31822	NI	31865	N
31715	C	31780	L	31823	N	31866	N
31716	C	31781	L	31824	N	31867	N

No.	Class	No.	Class	No.	Class	No.	Class
31868	N	31920	W	32352	K	32470	E4
31869	N	31921	W	32353	K	32471	E4
31870	N	31922	W	32407	E6X	32472	E4
31871	N	31923	W	32408	E6	32473	E4
31872	N	31924	W	32409	E6	32474	E4
31873	N	31925	W	32410	E6	32475	E4
31874	N	32095	E1/R	32411	E6X	32476	E4
31875	N	32096	E1/R	32412	E6	32477	E4X
31876	N1	32100	E2	32413	E6	32479	E4
31877	N1	32101	E2	32414	E6	32480	E4
31878	N1	32102	E2	32415	E6	32481	E4
31879	N1	32103	E2	32416	E6	32484	E4
31880	N1	32104	E2	32417	E6	32485	E4
31890	U1	32105	E2	32418	E6	32486	E4
31891	U1	32106	E2	32422*	H2	32487	E4
31892	U1	32107	E2	32424*	H2	32488	E4
31893	U1	32108	E2	32425*	H2	32491	E4
31894	U1	32109	E2	32434	C2X	32492	E4
31895	U1	32113	E1	32437	C2X	32493	E4
31896	U1	32124	E1/R	32438	C2X	32494	E4
31897	U1	32135	E1/R	32440	C2X	32495	E4
31898	U1	32138	E1	32441	C2X	32497	E4
31899	U1	32139	E1	32442	C2X	32498	E4
31900	U1	32151	E1	32443	C2X	32499	E4
31901	U1	32165	E3	32444	C2X	32500	E4
31902	U1	32166	E3	32445	C2X	32502	E4
31903	U1	32170	E3	32446	C2X	32503	E4
31904	U1	32331*	N15X	32447	C2X	32504	E4
31905	U1	32337	K	32448	C2X	32505	E4
31906	U1	32338	K	32449	C2X	32506	E4
31907	U1	32339	K	32450	C2X	32507	E4
31908	U1	32340	K	32451	C2X	32508	E4
31909	U1	32341	K	32454	E3	32509	E4
31910	U1	32342	K	32455	E3	32510	E4
31911	W	32343	K	32456	E3	32511	E4
31912	W	32344	K	32458	E3	32512	E4
31913	W	32345	K	32461	E3	32514	E4
31914	W	32346	K	32462	E3	32515	E4
31915	W	32347	K	32463	E4	32517	E4
31916	W	32348	K	32466	E4X	32519	E4
31917	W	32349	K	32467	E4	32520	E4
31918	W	32350	K	32468	E4	32521	C2X
31919	W	32351	K	32469	E4	32522	C2X

No.	Class	No.	Class	No.	Class	No.	Class
32523	C2X	32582	E4	33028	Q1	34031*	WC
32524	C2X	32608	E1/R	33029	Q1	34032*	WC
32525	C2X	32636	A1X	33030	Q1	34033*	WC
32526	C2X	32640	A1X	33031	Q1	34034*	WC
32527	C2X	32646	A1X	33032	Q1	34035*	WC
32528	C2X	32650	A1X	33033	Q1	34036*	WC
32529	C2X	32655	A1X	33034	Q1	34037*	WC
32532	C2X	32661	A1X	33035	Q1	34038*	WC
32534	C2X	32662	A1X	33036	Q1	34039*	WC
32535	C2X	32670	A1X	33037	Q1	34040*	WC
32536	C2X	32677	A1X	33038	Q1	34041*	WC
32537	C2X	32678	A1X	33039	Q1	34042*	WC
32538	C2X	32689	E1	33040	Q1	34043*	WC
32539	C2X	32694	E1	34001*	WC	34044*	WC
32540	C2X	32695	E1/R	34002*	WC	34045*	WC
32541	C2X	32697	E1/R	34003*	WC	34046*	WC
32543	C2X	33001	Q1	34004*	WC	34047*	WC
32544	C2X	33002	Q1	34005*	WC	34048*	WC
32545	C2X	33003	Q1	34006*	WC	34049*	BB
32546	C2X	33004	Q1	34007*	WC	34050*	BB
32547	C2X	33005	Q1	34008*	WC	34051*	BB
32548	C2X	33006	Q1	34009*	WC	34052*	BB
32549	C2X	33007	Q1	34010*	WC	34053*	BB
32550	C2X	33008	Q1	34011*	WC	34054*	BB
32551	C2X	33009	Q1	34012*	WC	34055*	BB
32552	C2X	33010	Q1	34013*	WC	34056*	BB
32553	C2X	33011	Q1	34014*	WC	34057*	BB
32554	C2X	33012	Q1	34015*	WC	34058*	BB
32556	E4	33013	Q1	34016*	WC	34059*	BB
32557	E4	33014	Q1	34017*	WC	34060*	BB
32558	E4	33015	Q1	34018*	WC	34061*	BB
32559	E4	33016	Q1	34019*	WC	34062*	BB
32560	E4	33017	Q1	34020*	WC	34063*	BB
32562	E4	33018	Q1	34021*	WC	34064*	BB
32563	E4	33019	Q1	34022*	WC	34065*	BB
32564	E4	33020	Q1	34023*	WC	34066*	BB
32565	E4	33021	Q1	34024*	WC	34067*	BB
32566	E4	33022	Q1	34025*	WC	34068*	BB
32577	E4	33023	Q1	34026*	WC	34069*	BB
32578	E4	33024	Q1	34027*	WC	34070*	BB
32579	E4	33025	Q1	34028*	WC	34071*	BB
32580	E4	33026	Q1	34029*	WC	34072*	BB
32581	E4	33027	Q1	34030*	WC	34073*	BB

No.	Class	No.	Class	No.	Class	No.	Class
34074*	BB	34097*	WC	35010*	MN	Isle of Wight	
34075*	BB	34098*	WC	35011*	MN	Locomotives	
34076*	BB	34099*	WC	35012*	MN		
34077*	BB	34100*	WC	35013*	MN	W1*	E1
34078*	BB	34101*	WC	35014*	MN	W2*	E1
34079*	BB	34102*	WC	35015*	MN	W3*	E1
34080*	BB	34103*	WC	35016*	MN	W4*	E1
34081*	BB	34104*	WC	35017*	MN	W14*	O2
34082*	BB	34105*	WC	35018*	MN	W16*	O2
34083*	BB	34106*	WC	35019*	MN	W17*	O2
34084*	BB	34107*	WC	35020*	MN	W18*	O2
34085*	BB	34108*	WC	35021*	MN	W20*	O2
34086*	BB	34109*	BB	35022*	MN	W21*	O2
34087*	BB	34110*	BB	35023*	MN	W22*	O2
34088*	BB	35001*	MN	35024*	MN	W24*	O2
34089*	BB	35002*	MN	35025*	MN	W25*	O2
34090*	BB	35003*	MN	35026*	MN	W26*	O2
34091*	WC	35004*	MN	35027*	MN	W27*	O2
34092*	WC	35005*	MN	35028*	MN	W28*	O2
34093*	WC	35006*	MN	35029*	MN	W29*	O2
34094*	WC	35007*	MN	35030*	MN	W30*	O2
34095*	WC	35008*	MN			W31*	O2
34096*	WC	35009*	MN			W32*	O2
						W33*	O2
						W35*	O2
						W36*	O2

SOUTHERN REGION SERVICE LOCOMOTIVES

No.	Old No.	Class	Station
*DS 74	—	Bo-Bo	Durnsford Road Power Station
*DS 75	—	Bo	Waterloo & City
DS 77	0745	C14	Redbridge Sleeper Depot
†DS 377	2635	A1X	Brighton Works
DS 600	—	0-4-0 Diese	Eastleigh Carriage Works
DS 680	L.B.S.C. 654 S.E.C. 751	A1	Lancing Carriage Works
DS 681	L.B.S.C. 659 I.W.9	A1X	Lancing Carriage Works
DS 1173	2217	0-6-0 Diesel	Engineer's Department
DS 3152	30272	G6	Meldon Quarry

* Electric   † Repainted 1947 in Stroudley livery

BRITISH RAILWAYS LOCOMOTIVES

Nos. 26000-35030 and W1-W36

NAMED LOCOMOTIVES

CLASS EMI BO-BO ELECTRIC

26000 Tommy

CLASS NI5 " KING ARTHUR " 4-6-0

30448	Sir Tristram	30453	King Arthur
30449	Sir Torre	30454	Queen Guinevere
30450	Sir Kay	30455	Sir Launcelot
30451	Sir Lamorak	30456	Sir Galahad
30452	Sir Meliagrance	30457	Sir Bedivere

CLASS NI5 " KING ARTHUR " 4-6-0

30736	Excalibur	30749	Iseult
30738	King Pellinore	30750	Morgan le Fay
30739	King Leodegrance	30751	Etarre
30742	Camelot	30753	Melisande
30747	Elaine	30755	The Red Knight
30748	Vivien		

CLASS 757 0-6-2T

30757 Earl of Mount Edgcumbe | 30758 Lord St. Levan

CLASS NI5 " KING ARTHUR " 4-6-0

30763	Sir Bors de Ganis	30768	Sir Balin
30764	Sir Gawain	30769	Sir Balan
30765	Sir Gareth	30770	Sir Prianius
30766	Sir Geraint	30771	Sir Sagramore
30767	Sir Valence	30772	Sir Percivale

30773	Sir Lavaine	30790	Sir Villiars
30774	Sir Gaheris	30791	Sir Uwaine
30775	Sir Agravaine	30792	Sir Hervis de Revel
30776	Sir Galagars	30793	Sir Ontzlake
30777	Sir Lamiel	30794	Sir Ector de Maris
30778	Sir Pelleas	30795	Sir Dinadan
30779	Sir Colgrevance	30796	Sir Dodinas le Savage
30780	Sir Persant	30797	Sir Blamor de Ganis
30781	Sir Aglovale	30798	Sir Hectimere
30782	Sir Brian	30799	Sir Ironside
30783	Sir Gillemere	30800	Sir Meleaus de Lile
30784	Sir Nerovens	30801	Sir Meliot de Logres
30785	Sir Mador de la Porte	30802	Sir Durnore
30786	Sir Lionel	30803	Sir Harry le Fise Lake
30787	Sir Menadeuke	30804	Sir Cador of Cornwall
30788	Sir Urre of the Mount	30805	Sir Constantine
30789	Sir Guy	30806	Sir Galleron

CLASS LN " LORD NELSON " 4-6-0

30850	Lord Nelson	30858	Lord Duncan
30851	Sir Francis Drake	30859	Lord Hood
30852	Sir Walter Raleigh	30860	Lord Hawke
30853	Sir Richard Grenville	30861	Lord Anson
30854	Howard of Effingham	30862	Lord Collingwood
30855	Robert Blake	30863	Lord Rodney
30856	Lord St. Vincent	30864	Sir Martin Frobisher
30857	Lord Howe	30865	Sir John Hawkins

CLASS V " SCHOOLS " 4-4-0

30900	Eton	30910	Merchant Taylors
30901	Winchester	30911	Dover
30902	Wellington	30912	Downside
30903	Charterhouse	30913	Christ's Hospital
30904	Lancing	30914	Eastbourne
30905	Tonbridge	30915	Brighton
30906	Sherborne	30916	Whitgift
30907	Dulwich	30917	Ardingly
30908	Westminster	30918	Hurstpierpoint
30909	St. Paul's	30919	Harrow

NAMED LOCOMOTIVES—cont.

30920	Rugby	30930	Radley
30921	Shrewsbury	30931	King's Wimbledon
30922	Marlborough	30932	Blundells
30923	Bradfield	30933	King's Canterbury
30924	Haileybury	30934	St. Lawrence
30925	Cheltenham	30935	Sevenoaks
30926	Repton	30936	Cranleigh
30927	Clifton	30937	Epsom
30928	Stowe	30938	St. Olave's
30929	Malvern	30939	Leatherhead

CLASS N15X " REMEMBRANCE " 4-6-0
32331 Beattie

CLASS H2 4-4-2

32422	North Foreland	32425	Trevose Head
32424	Beachy Head		

CLASSES WC & BB 4-6-2
" WEST COUNTRY " and " BATTLE OF BRITAIN "

34001	Exeter	34019	Bideford
34002	Salisbury	34020	Seaton
34003	Plymouth	34021	Dartmoor
34004	Yeovil	34022	Exmoor
34005	Barnstaple	34023	Blackmore Vale
34006	Bude	34024	Tamar Valley
34007	Wadebridge	34025	Whimple
34008	Padstow	34026	Yes Tor
34009	Lyme Regis	34027	Taw Valley
34010	Sidmouth	34028	Eddystone
34011	Tavistock	34029	Lundy
34012	Launceston	34030	Watersmeet
34013	Okehampton	34031	Torrington
34014	Budleigh Salterton	34032	Camelford
34015	Exmouth	34033	Chard
34016	Bodmin	34034	Honiton
34017	Ilfracombe	34035	Shaftesbury
34018	Axminster	34036	Westward Ho

34037	Clovelly	34075	264 Squadron
34038	Lynton	34076	41 Squadron
34039	Boscastle	34077	603 Squadron
34040	Crewkerne	34078	222 Squadron
34041	Wilton	34079	141 Squadron
34042	Dorchester	34080	74 Squadron
34043	Combe Martin	34081	92 Squadron
34044	Woolacombe	34082	615 Squadron
34045	Ottery St. Mary	34083	605 Squadron
34046	Braunton	34084	253 Squadron
34047	Callington	34085	501 Squadron
34048	Crediton	34086	219 Squadron
34049	Anti-Aircraft Command	34087	145 Squadron
34050	Royal Observer Corps	34088	213 Squadron
34051	Winston Churchill	34089	602 Squadron
34052	Lord Dowding	34090	Sir Eustace Missenden, Southern Railway
34053	Sir Keith Park		
34054	Lord Beaverbrook	34091	Weymouth
34055	Fighter Pilot	34092	City of Wells
34056	Croydon	34093	Saunton
34057	Biggin Hill	34094	Mortehoe
34058	Sir Frederick Pile	34095	Brentor
34059	Sir Archibald Sinclair	34096	Trevone
34060	25 Squadron	34097	Holsworthy
34061	73 Squadron	34098	Templecombe
34062	17 Squadron	34099	Lynmouth
34063	229 Squadron	34100	Appledore
34064	Fighter Command	34101	Hartland
34065	Hurricane	34102	Lapford
34066	Spitfire	34103	Calstock
34067	Tangmere	34104	Bere Alston
34068	Kenley	34105	Swanage
34069	Hawkinge	34106	Lydford
34070	Manston	34107	Blandford Forum
34071	601 Squadron	34108	Wincanton
34072	257 Squadron	34109	Sir Trafford Leigh-Mallory
34073	249 Squadron		
34074	46 Squadron	34110	66 Squadron

CLASS MN " MERCHANT NAVY " 4-6-2

35001	Channel Packet	35006	Peninsular & Oriental S.N. Co.
35002	Union Castle		
35003	Royal Mail	35007	Aberdeen Commonwealth
35004	Cunard White Star		
35005	Canadian Pacific	35008	Orient Line

Class U1 2-6-0 No. 31893   [K. R. Pirt

Class Z 0-8-0T No. 30952   [D. Penney

Class W 2-6-4T No. 31914   [R. K. Evans

Rebuilt Class MN 4-6-2 No. 35018 *British India Line* [*A. E. Brown*

Class WC 4-6-2 No. 34105 *Swanage* [*G. Wheeler*

Class V 4-4-0 No. 30923 *Bradfield* [*G. Wheeler*

Class LN 4-6-0 No. 30852 *Sir Walter Raleigh* (with modified double chimney) [*J. A. Young*

Class LN 4-6-0 No. 30863 *Lord Rodney* (with shortened smokebox) [*P. H. Groom*

Class N15 4-6-0 No. 30755 *The Red Knight* (Urie loco ; with multiple jet blast pipe and double chimney) [*G. Wheeler*

Class N15 4-6-0 No. 30788 *Sir Urre of the Mount* (Maunsell loco with modified cab)
[*L. Elsey*

Class H15 (Urie) 4-6-0 No. 30483
[*R. Russell*

Class H15 4-6-0 No. 30491 (Urie loco with Maunsell taper boiler)
[*C. P. Boocock*

Class H15 (Maunsell) 4-5-0 No. 30478   [L. Elsey]

Class S15 (Urie) 4-6-0 No. 30511   [A. E. Brown]

Class S15 (Maunsell) 4-6-0 No. 30826   [J. Robertson]

Class 700 0-6-0 No. 30368   [D. Penney

Class Q1 0-6-0 No. 33028   [R. E. Vincent

Class C2X 0-6-0 No. 32532   [A. R. Carpenter

Right: Class A1X 0-6-0T
No. 32640
[R. J. Buckley

Centre: Class E1 0-6-0T
No. 32606 (fitted with
two-way radio tele-
phone equipment;
engine now with-
drawn)
[W. M. J. Jackson

Bottom: Class E1/R
0-6-2T No. 32608
[J. A. Young

Top: Class E4 0-6-2T
No. 32485
[R. J. Buckley

Centre: Class E6 0-6-2T
No. 32408 [D. Penney

Left: Class E4X 0-6-2T
No. 32477
[A. R. Carpenter

NAMED LOCOMOTIVES—*cont.*

35009	Shaw Savill
35010	Blue Star
35011	General Steam Navigation
35012	United States Line
35013	Blue Funnel
35014	Nederland Line
35015	Rotterdam Lloyd
35016	Elders Fyffes
35017	Belgian Marine
35018	British India Line
35019	French Line CGT
35020	Bibby Line
35021	New Zealand Line
35022	Holland-America Line
35023	Holland-Afrika Line
35024	East Asiatic Company
35025	Brocklebank Line
35026	Lamport & Holt Line
35027	Port Line
35028	Clan Line
35029	Ellerman Lines
35030	Elder Dempster Lines

CLASS E1 0-6-0T

W 1	Medina
W 2	Yarmouth
W 3	Ryde
W 4	Wroxall

CLASS O2 0-4-4T

W14	Fishbourne	W24	Calbourne	W31	Chale
W16	Ventnor	W25	Godshill	W32	Bonchurch
W17	Seaview	W26	Whitwell	W33	Bembridge
W18	Ningwood	W27	Merstone	W35	Freshwater
W20	Shanklin	W28	Ashey	W36	Carisbrooke
W21	Sandown	W29	Alverstone		
W22	Brading	W30	Shorwell		

SOME S.R. LOCOMOTIVE HEADCODES

This list is not complete and gives only the principal one, two and three disc (or lamp) codes.

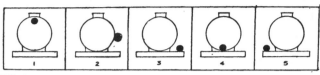

NO. 1

Victoria and Dover via Chatham
Victoria and Norwood Yard via Selhurst
Loughborough Sidings to Holborn
Ashford and Hastings
Reading and Margate via Redhill
Eastleigh and Bulford via Chandlers Ford and Andover
Southampton Terminus and Brockenhurst and Weymouth via Wimborne
Plymouth Friary and Tavistock
Woking and Reading via Virginia Water West Curve
Exeter Central and Ilfracombe
Bodmin and Wadebridge
Petersfield and Midhurst
Exeter Central and Exmouth

NO. 2

Victoria or Clapham Junction and Holborn (L.L.)
London Bridge or Bricklayers' Arms and Portsmouth via Quarry line and Horsham
Via Mid Kent Line and Beckenham Junction
Ashford and Eastbourne direct
Waterloo or Nine Elms and Southampton Terminus, direct (not boat trains)
Willesden and Feltham Yard via Gunnersbury
Waterloo or Nine Elms and Windsor via Twickenham
Southampton Central to Lymington
Yeovil Junction and Yeovil Town
Seaton Junction and Seaton
Barnstaple Junction and Torrington
Halwill and Bude

NO. 3

Victoria or Clapham Junction and Holborn
London Bridge or Bricklayers' Arms and Brighton via Quarry Line
Tonbridge and Brighton via Eridge
Hastings via Mid Kent Line, Oxted, Crowhurst Junction and Tonbridge
Dunton Green and Westerham
Ashford and Margate via Canterbury West
Lydd Branch
Folkestone Junction and Folkestone Harbour
Crowhurst and Bexhill West
Swanley Junction and Gravesend West
Sittingbourne and Sheerness
Deal and Kearsney
Gravesend Central and Allhallows-on-Sea or Port Victoria
All stations to Feltham (except via Mortlake)

Weymouth and Portland and Easton (goods trains)
Bournemouth West and Brockenhurst via Wimborne

NO. 4

Victoria or Battersea Yard and Brighton via Redhill
Oxted and Eastbourne via Eridge
London Bridge and New Cross via Bricklayers' Arms Junction
Horsham and Brighton
Alton and Fareham
Bentley and Bordon
Salisbury and Bulford
Axminster and Lyme Regis
Tipton St. John's and Exmouth
Wareham and Swanage
Brockenhurst and Lymington Pier
Bere Alston and Callington

NO. 5

Victoria or Stewarts Lane and Clapham Junction
Oxted and Tunbridge Wells West via East Grinstead (H.L.)
Pulborough, Midhurst and Chichester
Havant and Hayling Island
London Bridge and Bricklayers' Arms
Tonbridge and Maidstone West
Ashford (Kent) and Dover via Minster and Deal
Stewarts Lane to Victoria
Southampton Docks and Nine Elms via main line (market goods, fruit or potato
    train)

NO. 6

London Bridge or Bricklayers' Arms and Dover or Ramsgate via East Croydon
    Oxted and Tonbridge
Tonbridge and Hawkhurst
Battersea Yard and Kensington
Waterloo or Nine Elms and Reading via Twickenham
Willesden and Feltham Yard via Kew East Junction
Exeter Central and Sidmouth
Plymouth Friary and Turnchapel
Eastleigh or Southampton and Fawley
Bournemouth Central and Brockenhurst via Wimborne
Torrington and Halwill

NO. 7

Victoria or Battersea Yard and Portsmouth via Quarry Line and Horsham
Via Maidstone East line to Victoria or Holborn
Waterloo or Nine Elms and Southampton Docks via Brentford, Chertsey and
    Woking

NO. 8

London Bridge or Bricklayers' Arms and Eastbourne or Hastings via Quarry line
Victoria or West London line and Ramsgate via Herne Hill or Catford Loop
London Bridge or Bricklayers' Arms and Hastings via Chislehurst and Tunbridge
    Wells Central

51

| 11 | 12 | 13 | 14 | 15 |

West London line to East Croydon via Crystal Palace (L.L.)
Special boat trains Waterloo and Southampton Docks via Northam
Special boat trains from Southampton Docks to Waterloo via Millbrook
Southampton and Andover via Redbridge

NO. 9

Victoria or Battersea Yard and Eastbourne or Hastings via Quarry line
London and Hither Green Sidings
Victoria and Folkestone Harbour or Dover Marine via Swanley, Otford and
Tonbridge
Waterloo or Nine Elms and Plymouth
Bournemouth Central and Dorchester goods trains
Battersea Yard and Brent via New Kew Junction
Southampton Terminus and Portsmouth Harbour via Netley

NO. 10

London Bridge or Bricklayers' Arms and Portsmouth via Redhill and Horsham
Victoria or Battersea Yard and Norwood Yard via Crystal Palace (L.L.)
London Bridge and New Cross Gate to Eardley Sidings via Peckham Rye
Deptford Wharf and New Cross Gate
London Bridge or Bricklayers' Arms and Folkestone or Dover via Chislehurst
Tonbridge and Ashford
Dover and Margate via Deal and Minster Loop
Special boat trains Waterloo to Southampton Docks via Millbrook
Feltham to Durnsford Road via Chertsey

NO. 11

Victoria or Battersea Yard and Portsmouth via Redhill and Horsham
Via Dartford Loop line
Victoria or Holborn and Hastings line via Orpington Loop and Tunbridge
Wells Central
Bricklayers' Arms and Guildford via Leatherhead and Effingham Junction
Waterloo or Nine Elms and Southampton Terminus via Alton
Salisbury and Bournemouth West via Wimborne
Fareham and Gosport
Ballast trains to Meldon Quarry from Exeter Central and stations West thereof

NO. 12

Victoria or Battersea Yard and Portsmouth via Mitcham Junction
London Bridge or Bricklayers' Arms and Eastbourne or Hastings via Redhill
Victoria, Stewarts Lane or Holborn to North Kent line via Nunhead line
Nine Elms and Feltham via Mortlake
Exeter Central to Nine Elms (market goods and fish)
Down main line goods terminating at Woking
Southampton Docks and Salisbury via Eastleigh

NO. 13

London Bridge or Bricklayers' Arms and Brighton via Redhill
Oxted and Brighton via East Grinstead (L.L.) and Lewes
Three Bridges and Tunbridge Wells West
West London line to Norwood Yard via Thornton Heath
Victoria or Holborn to Dover via Nunhead line and Maidstone East
Parcels and empty trains Waterloo to Clapham Junction (Kensington sidings)

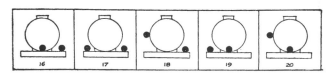

| 16 | 17 | 18 | 19 | 20 |

Feltham Yard and Neasden via Kew East Junction
Portsmouth Harbour or Portsmouth and Southsea to Fratton Loco. Depot
Exeter Central and Exmouth Junction
Bournemouth West to Dorchester
Southampton and Salisbury via Redbridge

NO. 14

London Bridge and Portsmouth via Mitcham Junction
London Bridge, Oxted and Tunbridge Wells West via Hever
Oxted and Lewes or Seaford or Eastbourne via Haywards Heath and Keymer
    Junction (change to No. 5 or No. 21 code at Lewes)
London Bridge or Bricklayers' Arms and Dover via Chislehurst Loop and
    Maidstone East
Waterloo or Nine Elms and Brockenhurst and Bournemouth West via Sway

NO. 15

Via Bexleyheath line
Victoria, Stewar_s Lane or Holborn via Nunhead line and Bexleyheath
Oxted and Brighton via Haywards Heath
Waterloo or Nine Elms and Reading via Loop line
All trains terminating at Portsmouth and Southsea (trains from Salisbury to
    carry No. 17 to Eastleigh)
Exeter Central and Padstow
Light engines, Bournemouth Central or Bournemouth West to Bournemouth
    Central via triangle to turn
Light engines Eastleigh Loco. to Portsmouth and Southsea
Light engines to Guildford Loco. via Woking (except via Staines

NO. 16

London Bridge or Bricklayers' Arms and Portsmouth via West Croydon
Victoria or Battersea Yard and Eastbourne or Hastings via Redhill
Oxted and Brighton via Eridge
London Bridge or Bricklayers' Arms and Ramsgate via Tonbridge and Canter-
    bury West
Waterloo or Nine Elms and Woking via Richmond and Chertsey
Milk and empty trains to Clapham Junction via Byfleet curve and Richmond

NO. 17

London Bridge or Bricklayers' Arms and Tonbridge or Reading via East Croydon
    and Redhill (also Tonbridge and Reading
Brighton and Hove via Preston Park Spur
Three Bridges and Eridge
Victoria or Holborn and Folkestone or Dover via Orpington Loop, Tonbridge
    and Ashford
London Bridge or Bricklayers Arms and Gillingham, Faversham, Ramsgate or
    Dover via Chislehurst Loop and Chatham
Waterloo or Nine Elms and Clapham Junction (empty trains and light engines)
Passenger trains Bournemouth Central and Weymouth

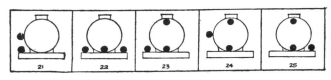

| 21 | 22 | 23 | 24 | 25 |

NO. 18

London Bridge or Bricklayers' Arms and Dover, Ramsgate or Hastings via Chislehurst, Swanley, Otford and Sevenoaks
Victoria, Oxted and Tunbridge Wells West via Hever
Holborn and Ramsgate via Herne Hill or Catford Loop
Light engines and trains requiring to run to up main loop, Clapham Junction, from stations westward
Southampton and Andover via Eastleigh
Light engines or engines with vehicles attached running round the triangle at Bournemouth West to turn

NO. 19

Victoria or Battersea Yard and Brighton via Quarry line
London Bridge or New Cross Gate and Norwood Yard
Tunbridge Wells West and Eastbourne
Victoria or Holborn and Ramsgate, Dover or Hastings via Nunhead line and Tonbridge
Horsham and Guildford
Waterloo or Nine Elms and Southampton Docks via East Putney
Salisbury and Portsmouth Harbour via Eastleigh
Portsmouth and Southsea to Salisbury via Eastleigh

NO. 20

Victoria, Stewarts Lane or Holborn to Ramsgate via Nunhead line, Chislehurst and Chatham
London Bridge or Bricklayers' Arms and North Kent line via Greenwich
Via Streatham Spur
Feltham Yard and Brent via Kew East Junction
Clapham Junction and Kensington
Portsmouth and Southsea to Salisbury via Redbridge
Salisbury and Portsmouth Harbour via Redbridge

NO. 21

Victoria and Newhaven Harbour
Victoria or Holborn to Ramsgate via Nunhead line and Maidstone East
Waterloo or Nine Elms and Portsmouth via Woking and Guildford
Light engines from all stations to Feltham Loco.
Light engines from all stations west of Basingstoke to Eastleigh Loco.

NO. 22

Waterloo and Portsmouth Harbour via Eastleigh
Feltham and Brent via Richmond
S.R. and W.R. trains Hither Green Sidings, Stewarts Lane or South Lambeth to Old Oak Common
L.M. (Western Division) trains between Willesden and Redhill via Clapham Junction
L.M. (Midland Division) and E.R. (G.N.) trains to or from Hither Green Sidings
W.R. trains, Norwood Yard to Old Oak Common
W.R. trains Cattewater Junction and Plymstock

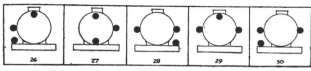

| 26 | 27 | 28 | 29 | 30 |

NO. 23

Nine Elms and Willesden via New Kew Junction
Brighton and Salisbury via Southampton Central
Eastleigh and Micheldever or Basingstoke (light engines for testing)
Windsor and Hastings Excursion trains
Windsor and Margate or Dover Excursion trains or between Windsor and Redhill
W.R. trains to South Lambeth
E.R. trains to or from Lower Sydenham

NO. 24

Waterloo and Guildford via Leatherhead (except light engines Nine Elms to Raynes Park)
Southampton and Willesden via Richmond and Gunnersbury
Southampton or Salisbury and Willesden via Chertsey and Kew East Junction (or from Basingstoke)
Reading to Willesden via Feltham

NO. 25

Nine Elms and Brent via New Kew Junction
Kingston and Shepperton
Brighton and Salisbury through trains via Eastleigh
Windsor and Bognor Regis Excursion trains
To L.M.R. via West London line

NO. 26

Brighton and Bournemouth
Waterloo and Wimbledon Park Sidings via East Putney (empty trains and light engines
Merstham and Staines Moor via Guildford, Byfleet Junction and Staines
Victoria (E. or C.), Stewarts Lane, Clapham Junction or Holborn and Eardley Sidings via Herne Hill

NO. 27

Hither Green Sidings and Feltham via Brentford
Feltham to Wimbledon West Yard
London Bridge or Bricklayers' Arms and Brighton via Oxted, Eridge and Lewes

NO. 28

Hither Green Sidings and Feltham via Richmond
London Bridge or Bricklayers' Arms and Brighton via Oxted, East Grinstead and Lewes

NO. 29

Plumstead and Feltham via Brentford
Victoria or Battersea Yard and Brighton via Oxted, Eridge and Lewes

NO. 30

Plumstead and Feltham via Richmond
Victoria or Battersea Yard and Brighton via Oxted, East Grinstead and Lewes

NUMERICAL LIST OF SOUTHERN REGION ELECTRIC MOTOR UNITS

(Number to be seen on front and rear of each set)

TWO-CAR NON-CORRIDOR MOTOR UNITS
(2-NOL.)

1813*	1832*	1851	1873
1814*	1833*	1852	1874
1815*	1834*	1854	1875
1816*	1835*	1856	1876
1817*	1836*	1857	1879
1818*	1837*	1858	1880
1819*	1839*	1859	1881
1820*	1840*	1860	1882
1821*	1841*	1861	1883†
1822*	1842*	1862	1884†
1823*	1843*	1863	1885†
1824*	1844*	1864	1886†
1825*	1845*	1865	1887†
1826*	1846*	1866	1888†
1827*	1847*	1867	1889†
1829*	1848*	1868	1890†
1830*	1849*	1869	
1831*	1850*	1872	

* With 1st and 2nd class compartments.

† With electro-pneumatic control gear.

TWO-CAR MOTOR LAVATORY UNITS
(2-BIL.)

2001†	2006†	2011	2017
2002†	2007†	2012	2018
2003†	2008†	2013	2019
2004†	2009†	2015	2020
2005†	2010†	2016	2021

2022	2054	2086	2120
2023	2055	2087	2121
2024	2056*	2088*	2122
2025	2057	2089	2123
2026	2058	2090	2124
2027	2059	2091	2125
2028	2060	2092	2126
2029	2061	2093	2127
2030	2062	2094	2128
2031	2063	2095	2129
2032	2064	2096	2130
2033	2065	2097	2132
2034	2066	2098	2133*
2035	2067	2099	2134
2036	2068	2100*	2135
2037	2069*	2101	2136
2038	2070	2103	2137
2039	2071	2104	2138
2040	2072	2105	2139
2041	2073	2106	2140
2042	2074	2107	2141
2043	2075	2108	2142
2044	2076	2109	2143
2045	2077	2110	2144
2046	2078	2111	2145
2047	2079	2112	2146
2048	2080	2113	2147
2049	2081	2114	2148
2050	2082	2115	2149
2051	2083	2116	2150
2052	2084	2117	2151
2053	2085	2118	2152

†88 2nd seats instead of 84 and all-electric control gear.

*BIL Motor Coach and HAL trailer.

TWO-CAR MOTOR LAVATORY UNITS

(with one corridor and one non-corridor coach).

(2-HAL.)

2601	2626	2652	2677
2602	2627	2653	2678
2603	2628	2654	2679
2604	2629	2655	2681
2605	2630	2656	2682
2606	2631	2657	2683
2607	2632	2658	2684
2608	2633	2659	2685
2609	2634	2660	2686
2610	2635	2661	2687
2611	2636	2662	2688
2612	2637	2663	2689
2613	2638	2664	2690
2614	2639	2665	2691
2615	2640	2666	2692
2616	2641	2667	2693
2617	2642	2668	2694
2618	2643	2669	2695
2619	2644	2670	2696
2620	2645	2671	2697
2621	2647	2672	2698
2622	2648	2673	2699
2623	2649	2674	2700
2624	2650	2675	
2625	2651	2676	

FOUR-CAR MOTOR LAVATORY UNITS

(with two 2nd and one 1st/2nd non-corridor coaches and one 1st/2nd corridor coach).

(4-LAV.)

2921	2928	2935	2942
2922	2929	2936	2943
2923	2930	2937	2944
2924	2931	2938	2945
2925	2932	2939	2946
2926*	2933	2940	2947
2927	2934	2941	2948

2949	2951	2953	2955†
2950	2952	2954†	

*One motor coach with electro-pneumatic control gear.
†With electro-pneumatic control gear.

SIX-CAR MOTOR CORRIDOR UNITS *(with Pullman Car)*

(6-PUL.)

3001	3007	3013	3019
3002	3008	3014	3020
3003	3009	3015	3041*
3004	3010	3016	3042*
3005	3011	3017	3043*
3006	3012	3018	

*Ex-" 6-CIT " Units.

SIX-CAR MOTOR CORRIDOR UNITS *(with Pantry Car)*

(6-PAN.)

3021	3026	3030	3034
3022	3027	3031	3035
3023	3028	3032	3036
3024	3029	3033	3037
3025			

FIVE-CAR PULLMAN MOTOR UNITS

(For "Brighton Belle" Service)

(5-BEL.)

3051	3052	3053

FOUR-CAR KITCHEN CORRIDOR MOTOR UNITS

(4-RES.)

3054	3059	3065	3069
3055	3061	3066	3070
3056	3062	3067	3071
3057	3064	3068	3072

FOUR-CAR BUFFET CORRIDOR MOTOR UNITS
(4-BUF.)

3073	3077	3080	3083
3074	3078	3081	3084
3075	3079	3082	3085
3076			

FOUR-CAR CORRIDOR MOTOR UNITS
(4-COR.)

3101	3116	3131	3145
3102	3117	3132	3146
3103	3118	3133	3147
3104	3119	3134	3148
3105	3120	3135	3149
3106	3121	3136	3150
3107	3122	3137	3151
3108	3123	3138	3152
3109	3124	3139	3153
3110	3125	3140	3154
3111	3126	3141	3155
3112	3127	3142	3156
3113	3128	3143	3157
3114	3129	3144	3158
3115	3130		

FOUR-CAR DOUBLE DECK SUBURBAN UNITS
(4-DD.)

4001	4002

FOUR-CAR NON-CORRIDOR SUBURBAN UNITS
(4-SUB.)

4101	4105	4109	4113
4102	4106	4110	4114
4103	4107	4111	4115
4104	4108	4112	4116

4117	4307	4354	4535
4118	4308	4355	4538
4119	4309	4356	4541
4120	4310	4357	4543
4121	4311	4358	4544
4122	4312	4359	4545
4123	4313	4360	4547
4124	4314	4361	4548
4125	4315	4362	4550
4126	4316	4363	4551
4127	4317	4364	4552
4128	4318	4365	4554
4129	4319	4366	4555
4130	4320	4367	4556
4251	4321	4368	4557
4277	4322	4369	4558
4278	4323	4370	4579
4279	4324	4371	4601
4280	4325	4372	4602
4281	4326	4373	4603
4282	4327	4374	4604
4283	4328	4375	4605
4284	4329	4376	4606
4285	4330	4377	4607
4286	4331	4378	4621
4287	4332	4379	4622
4288	4333	4380	4623
4289	4334	4381	4624
4290	4335	4382	4625
4291	4336	4383	4626
4292	4337	4384	4627
4293	4338	4385	4628
4294	4340	4386	4629
4295	4341	4387	4630
4296	4342	4501	4631
4297	4343	4502	4632
4298	4344	4503	4633
4299	4345	4504	4634
4300	4346	4505	4635
4301	4347	4528	4636
4302	4348	4529	4637
4303	4349	4530	4638
4304	4351	4531	4639
4305	4352	4532	4640
4306	4353	4533	

4641	4670	4699	4728	5033	5125	5170	5215
4642	4671	4700	4729	5034	5126	5171	5216
4643	4672	4701	4730	5035	5127	5172	5217
4644	4673	4702	4731	5036	5128	5173	5218
4645	4674	4703	4732	5037	5129	5174	5219
4646	4675	4704	4733	5038	5130	5175	5220
4647	4676	4705	4734	5039	5131	5176	5221
4648	4677	4706	4735	5040	5132	5177	5222
4649	4678	4707	4736	5041	5133	5178	5223
4650	4679	4708	4737	5042	5134	5179	5224
4651	4680	4709	4738	5043	5135	5180	5225
4652	4681	4710	4739	5044	5136	5181	5226
4653	4682	4711	4740	5045	5137	5182	5227
4654	4683	4712	4741	5046	5138	5183	5228
4655	4684	4713	4742	5047	5139	5184	5229
4656	4685	4714	4743	5048	5140	5185	5230
4657	4686	4715	4744	5049	5141	5186	5231
4658	4687	4716	4745	5050	5142	5187	5232
4659	4688	4717	4746	5051	5143	5188	5233
4660	4689	4718	4747	5052	5144	5189	5234
4661	4690	4719	4748	5053	5145	5190	5235
4662	4691	4720	4749	5101	5146	5191	5236
4663	4692	4721	4750	5102	5147	5192	5237
4664	4693	4722	4751	5103	5148	5193	5238
4665	4694	4723	4752	5104	5149	5194	5239
4666	4695	4724	4753	5105	5150	5195	5240
4667	4696	4725	4754	5106	5151	5196	5241
4668	4697	4726		5107	5152	5197	5242
4669	4698	4727		5108	5153	5198	5243
				5109	5154	5199	5244
				5110	5155	5200	5245
				5111	5156	5201	5246
				5112	5157	5202	5247
				5113	5158	5203	5248
				5114	5159	5204	5249
				5115	5160	5205	5250
				5116	5161	5206	5251

FOUR-CAR NON-CORRIDOR
SUBURBAN UNITS
(4-EPB)

5001	5009	5017	5025	5117	5162	5207	5252
5002	5010	5018	5026	5118	5163	5208	5253
5003	5011	5019	5027	5119	5164	5209	5254
5004	5012	5020	5028	5120	5165	5210	5255
5005	5013	5021	5029	5121	5166	5211	5256
5006	5014	5022	5030	5122	5167	5212	5257
5007	5015	5023	5031	5123	5168	5213	5258
5008	5016	5024	5032	5124	5169	5214	5259

5260	5264	5268	5272
5261	5265	5269	5273
5262	5266	5270	5274
5263	5267	5271	

N.B.—These units are still being delivered.

TWO-CAR NON-CORRIDOR SUBURBAN UNITS

(2-EPB)

5701	5730	5759	5788
5702	5731	5760	5789
5703	5732	5761	5790
5704	5733	5762	5791
5705	5734	5763	5792
5706	5735	5764	5793
5707	5736	5765	5794
5708	5737	5766	5795
5709	5738	5767	5796
5710	5739	5768	5797
5711	5740	5769	5798
5712	5741	5770	5799
5713	5742	5771	5800
5714	5743	5772	5801
5715	5744	5773	5802
5716	5745	5774	5803
5717	5746	5775	5804
5718	5747	5776	5805
5719	5748	5777	5806
5720	5749	5778	5807
5721	5750	5779	5808
5722	5751	5780	5809
5723	5752	5781	5810
5724	5753	5782	5811
5725	5754	5783	5812
5726	5755	5784	5813
5727	5756	5785	5814
5728	5757	5786	5815
5729	5758	5787	5816

N.B.—These units are still being delivered.

FOUR-CAR CORRIDOR BUFFET UNITS

(B.R. Standard design)

7001   7002

FOUR-CAR CORRIDOR UNITS

(4-CEPB)

(B.R. Standard design)

7101   7102   7103   7104

WATERLOO AND CITY LINE MOTOR COACH NOS.

51	54	57	60
52	55	58	61
53	56	59	62

FOUR-CAR SUBURBAN (4-SUB & 4-EPB) UNITS

Make-up, Seating Capacity, etc.

Unit Nos.	Type	Motor Coaches	Trailer Coaches	Seating Capacity
4101–4110	All-Steel Built 1942	9 compt.	1 10 compt. 1 11 compt.	468
4111–4120	All-Steel Built 1946	8 compt.	1 9 compt. 1 10 compt.	420
4121–4129	All-Steel Built 1946	Semi-Saloon	1 Semi-Saloon 1 9 compt.	382
4130	All-Steel Built 1946	Semi-Saloon Lightweight Motors	1 Semi-Saloon 1 9 compt	382
4251	L.B.S C. Stock converted S.R	1 7 compt. 1 8 compt.	2 10 compt.	350
4277–4299	All-Steel Built 1949	Saloon ; Lightweight Motors	1 Saloon 1 10 compt.	386
4300–15/7–9 4321–4325	Augmented W-Section Built 1925	7 compt.	1 9 compt. * 1 All-Steel 10 compt	350
4320	Augmented W-Section Built 1925	7 compt.	1 9 compt. 1 All-Steel 9 compt.	350
4326–4349/ 51–4	Augmented E-Section Built 1925/6	8 compt.	1 9 compt. 1 All-Steel 10 compt.	370
4355–4363	All-Steel Built 1947/8	8 compt.	2 10 compt	432
4364–4376	All-Steel Built 1947/8	8 compt.	1 9 compt. 1 10 compt.	420
4377	All-Steel Built 1947	8 compt.	1 9 compt. 1 Saloon	402
4378–4387	All-Steel Built 1948	Saloon	1 Saloon 1 10 compt.	385
4501/2, 4527–58/ 61/72/9	Augmented L.S.W.R. and L.B.S.C.R. converted S.R.†	1 8 compt. 1 7 compt †	1 10 compt. 1 All Steel 9 compt. or 10 compt.†	353 or 370

* No. 4313 has a 9 compt. all steel trailer.

4601–4607	All-Steel bodies on original underframes Rebuilt 1949/50	Saloon	2	10 compt.	404
4621–4666		Saloon	1 1	Saloon 10 compt.	386
4667–4754	New all-steel bodies (1951 -6) on original underframes.	Saloon	1 1	Saloon 10 compt. '	386
5001–53, 5101–5274		Saloon	1 1	Saloon 10 compt.*	386

* Except Nos. **4688/96, 4723/8/33/9, 5005/20** which have 9 compt. trailers +Except **4501**—1 L.B.S.C. 8-compt. and 1 L.S.W.R. 7-compt. Motor, 1 L.B.S.C. 10-compt. and 1 L.S.W.R. 9-compt. trailer. **4502**—1 L.B.S.C. 8-compt. and 1 7-compt. motors, 2 L.B.S.C. 10-compt. trailers. **4551**—1 L.B.S.C. 7-compt. and 1 8-compt. motor, 1 all-steel 10-compt. and 1 L.S.W.R. 10-compt. trailers.

SOUTHERN RAILWAY LOCOMOTIVE SUPERINTENDENTS AND CHIEF MECHANICAL ENGINEERS OF CONSTITUENT COMPANIES

LONDON & SOUTH WESTERN RAILWAY

J. Woods ...	...	...	1835–1841
J. V. Gooch	...	...	1841–1850
J. Beattie	...	...	1850–1871
W. G. Beattie	...	...	1871–1878
W. Adams ...	...	...	1878–1895
D. Drummond	...	...	1895–1912
R. W. Urie...	...	...	1912–1922

LONDON BRIGHTON AND SOUTH COAST RAILWAY

—. Statham	...	...	? –1845
J. Gray	...	...	1845–1847
S. Kirtley ...	...	...	1847
J. C. Craven	...	...	1847–1869
W. Stroudley	...	...	1870–1889
R. J. Billinton	...	...	1890–1904
D. Earle Marsh	...	...	1905–1911
L. B. Billinton	...	...	1911–1922

SOUTH EASTERN RAILWAY

B. Cubitt ...	...	...	? –1845
J. Cudworth	...	...	1845–1876
A. M. Watkin	...	...	1876
R. Mansell	...	...	1877–1878
J. Stirling ...	...	...	1878–1898

LONDON, CHATHAM AND DOVER RAILWAY

W. Cubitt ...	...	...	? –1860
W. Martley	...	...	1860–1874
W. Kirtley ...	...	...	1874–1898

SOUTH EASTERN AND CHATHAM RAILWAY

H. S. Wainwright ...	...	1899–1913
R. E. L. Maunsell ...	...	1913–1922

SOUTHERN RAILWAY

R. E. L. Maunsell ...	...	1923–1937
O. V. Bulleid ...	...	1937–1949

PULLMAN CARS ALLOCATED
TO THE SOUTHERN REGION

K — Kitchen Car
B — Brake Car

STEAM CARS
First Class

ALICANTE	(K)	MONTANA	(B)
AQUILA	(K)	MYRTLE	(K)
ARGUS	(K)	NEPTUNE	(K)
ARIES	(K)	OCTAVIA	(K)
AURORA	(B)	ONYX	
CAMILLA	(K)	ORION	
CARINA	(K)	ORPHEUS	(K)
CASSANDRA	(K)	PALERMO	(K)
CHLORIA	(K)	PALMYRA	(K)
CLEMENTINA	(K)	PEGASUS	
CORAL	(K)	PENELOPE	(K)
CORUNNA	(K)	PERSEUS	
CYGNUS	(K)	PHILOMEL	(K)
DAPHNE	(K)	PHOENIX	
EMERALD	(K)	PLATO	(K)
FINGALL	(K)	PORTIA	(K)
FLORA	(B)	RAINBOW	(K)
FLORENCE	(K)	REGINA	(K)
GLENCOE		ROSALIND	(K)
GROSVENOR	(K)	ROSAMUND	(K)
HAWTHORN	(K)	ROSEMARY	
HERCULES		RUBY	(K)
HIBERNIA	(K)	SAPPHIRE	(K)
IBIS	(K)	SAPPHO	(K)
ISLE OF THANET	(B)	SAVONA	(K)
JUNO	(B)	SCOTIA	(K)
LATONA	(K)	SEVILLE	(K)
LEGHORN		SORRENTO	(K)
MAID OF KENT	(K)	SUNBEAM	
MALAGA	(K)	THEODORA	(K)
MEDUSA	(K)	TOPAZ	
MIMOSA	(K)	VALENCIA	(K)
MINERVA	(B)	ZENOBIA	(K)
MONACO	(K)		

Second Class

Car No. 5	(B)	Car No. 19	(K)
,, ,, 6	(K)	,, ,, 27	(o)
,, ,, 7	(K)	,, ,, 30	
,, ,, 8	(K)	,, ,, 31	(K)
,, ,, 11	(K)	,, ,, 34	
,, ,, 13 }		,, ,, 36	(B)
,, ,, 14 }	Observation Cars	,, ,, 41	(B)
,, ,, 15	(B)	,, ,, 45	(K)
,, ,, 16	(B)	,, ,, 47	(K)
,, ,, 17	(K)	,, ,, 60	(B)

STEAM CARS—(cont.)

Second Class

Car No	61	(K)		Car No.	166	(K)
,, ,,	94	(K)	,, ,		167	(K)
,, ,,	95	(B)	,, ,,		169	(K)
, ,	96		,, ,		182	(K)
,, ,,	97		,, ,		183	(K)
,, ,,	98		,, ,,		185	(K)
,, ,,	99	(B)	,, ,,		208	(B)
,, ,,	132	(K)	, ,,		249	(K)
,, ,,	133	(K)	,, ,,		294	
,, ,,	135	(K)	,, ,		3u3	(K)
,, ,	137	(K)				

ELECTRIC CARS

First Class

AUDREY	(K)	HAZEL	(K)
DORIS	(K)	MONA	(K)
GWEN	(K)	VERA	(K)

Second Class

Car No.	85			Car No.	90	(B)
,, ,,	86			,, ,,	91	(B)
,, ,,	87			,, ,,	92	(B)
,, ,,	88			,, ,,	93	(B)
,, ,,	89	(B)				
		(B)				

Composite

ALICE	(K)	IRIS	(K)
ANNE	(K)	JOYCE	(K)
BERTHA	(K)	LORNA	(K)
BRENDA	(K)	MAY	(K)
CLARA	(K)	NAOMI	(K)
DAISY	(K)	OLIVE	(K)
ELINOR	(K)	PEGGY	(K)
ENID	(K)	RITA	(K)
ETHEL	(K)	ROSE	(K)
GRACE	(K)	RUTH	(K)
GWLADYS	(K)	VIOLET	(K)
IDA	(K)		

THE abc OF
BRITISH RAILWAYS
LOCOMOTIVES

PART 3—Nos. 40000-59999
and
B.R. STANDARD AND EX-W.D. LOCOMOTIVES
ALSO DIESEL AND ELECTRIC UNITS

WINTER
1956/57
EDITION

LONDON

Ian Allan Ltd

FOREWORD

THIS booklet lists all British Railways locomotives numbered between 40000 and 59999. This series of numbers includes all London Midland Region and Scottish (ex-L.M.S.) Region steam locos. For convenience a complete list of the B.R. standard and Class "WD" locomotives has also been included in this edition, together with Diesel and Electric Units.

1. At the head of each class will be found a list of any important sub-divisions of the class, usually in order of introduction. Each sub-division is given a reference mark, by which its relevant dimensions (if differing from those of other sub-divisions) and the locomotives it comprises (if known) may be identified.

2. The lists of dimensions at the head of each class show locomotives fitted with two inside cylinders unless otherwise stated, e.g. (O)= two outside cylinders.

3. Superheated classes are denoted by the letters " Su " after the boiler pressure. " SS " denotes that some locomotives of the class are superheated.

4. The date on which the first locomotive of a class was built or modified is denoted by " Introduced."

5. S denotes a Service (Departmental) locomotive. This reference letter is introduced only for the reader's guidance and is not borne by the locomotive concerned.

6. The numbers of locomotives in service have been checked to **August 11th, 1956.**

BRITISH RAILWAYS LOCOMOTIVE SHEDS AND SHED CODES

THIS LIST INCLUDES ONLY THOSE DEPOTS WHICH HAVE ENGINES ALLOCATED TO THEM. IT DOES NOT INCLUDE OVERNIGHT STABLING OR SIGNING-ON POINTS.

ALL B.R. LOCOMOTIVES CARRY THE CODE OF THEIR HOME DEPOT ON A SMALL PLATE AFFIXED TO THE SMOKEBOX DOOR.

LONDON MIDLAND REGION

1A	**Willesden**	9A	**Longsight**	18D	Staveley
1B	Camden	9B	Stockport (Edgeley)		Sheepbridge
1C	Watford	9C	Macclesfield		
1D	Devons Road (Bow)	9D	Buxton	19A	**Sheffield**
1E	Bletchley	9E	Trafford Park	19B	Millhouses
	Leighton Buzzard	9F	Heaton Mersey	19C	Canklow
		9G	Northwich		
				*20A	**Leeds (Holbeck)**
2A	**Rugby**	10A	**Springs Branch**		Keighley
	Seaton		(Wigan)	*20B	Stourton
2B	Nuneaton	10B	Preston	*20C	Royston
2C	Warwick	10C	Patricroft	*20D	Normanton
2D	Coventry	10D	Sutton Oak	*20E	Manningham
2E	Northampton				Ilkley
2F	Market	11A	**Carnforth**	20F	Skipton
	Harborough	11B	Barrow	20G	Hellifield
			Coniston		
3A	**Bescot**	11C	Oxenholme	21A	**Saltley**
3B	Bushbury	11D	Tebay	21B	Bournville
3C	Walsall	11E	Lancaster	21C	Bromsgrove
3D	Aston				
3E	Monument Lane	12A	**Carlisle (Upperby)**	22A	**Bristol**
		12B	Penrith	22B	Gloucester
		12C	Workington		Dursley
5A	**Crewe North**				Tewkesbury
	Whitchurch	14A	**Cricklewood**		
5B	Crewe South	14B	Kentish Town	24A	**Accrington**
5C	Stafford	14C	St. Albans	24B	Rose Grove
5D	Stoke			24C	Lostock Hall
5E	Alsager	15A	**Wellingborough**	24D	Lower Darwen
5F	Uttoxeter	15B	Kettering	24E	Blackpool
		15C	Leicester		Blackpool North
		15D	Bedford	24F	Fleetwood
6A	**Chester**				
6B	Mold Junction	16A	**Nottingham**	*25A	**Wakefield**
6C	Birkenhead	16B	Kirkby	*25B	Huddersfield
6D	Chester (Northgate)	16C	Mansfield	*25C	Goole
6E	Wrexham			*25D	Mirfield
6F	Bidston	17A	**Derby**	*25E	Sowerby Bridge
6G	Llandudno Junction	17B	Burton	*25F	Low Moor
6H	Bangor		Horninglow	*25G	Farnley Junction
6J	Holyhead		Overscal		
6K	Rhyl	17C	Coalville	26A	**Newton Heath**
		17D	Rowsley	26B	Agecroft
8A	**Edge Hill**		Cromford	26C	Bolton
8B	Warrington		Middleton	26D	Bury
	Warrington		Sheep Pasture	26E	Lees
	(Arpley)				
8C	Speke Junction	18A	**Toton**	27A	**Bank Hall**
8D	Widnes	18B	Westhouses	27B	Aintree
8E	Brunswick (L'pool)	18C	Hasland	27C	Southport
				27D	Wigan (L. & Y.)
				27E	Walton

* See N.E. Region Codes 53, 55 and 56

EASTERN REGION

30A	**Stratford**	32A	**Norwich**	36A	**Doncaster**	
	Brentwood		Cromer Beach	36B	Mexborough	
	Chelmsford		Swaffham		Wath	
	Enfield Town		Wymondham	36C	Frodingham	
	Epping	32B	Ipswich	36D	Barnsley	
	Ilford		Aldeburgh	36E	Retford	
	Wood St.		Felixstowe Beach		Newark	
	(Walthamstow)		Stowmarket			
30B	Hertford East	32C	Lowestoft	38A	**Colwick**	
	Buntingford	32D	Yarmouth	38B	Annesley	
	Ware		(South Town)	38C	Leicester (G.C.)	
30C	Bishops Stortford	32E	Yarmouth(Vauxhall)	38D	Staveley	
30D	Southend (Victoria)	32F	Yarmouth Beach	38E	Woodford Halse	
	Southminster	32G	Melton Constable			
30E	Colchester		Norwich City			
	Braintree	33A	**Plaistow**	39A	**Gorton**	
	Clacton		Upminster		Dinting	
	Maldon	33B	Tilbury		Hayfield	
	Walton-on-Naze	33C	Shoeburyness			
30F	Parkeston	34A	**Kings Cross**	40A	**Lincoln**	
31A	**Cambridge**	34B	Hornsey		Lincoln	
	Ely	34C	Hatfield		(St. Mark's)	
	Huntingdon East	34D	Hitchin	40B	Immingham	
	Saffron Walden	34E	Neasden		Grimsby	
31B	March		Aylesbury		New Holland	
	Wisbech		Chesham	40C	Louth	
31C	Kings Lynn	35A	**New England**	40D	Tuxford	
	Hunstanton		Spalding	40E	Longwith Junction	
31D	South Lynn		Stamford	40F	Boston	
31E	Bury St. Edmunds	35B	Grantham			
	Sudbury (Suffolk)	35C	Peterborough			
			(Spital)	41A	**Sheffield (Darnall)**	

NORTH EASTERN REGION

50A	**York**	52A	**Gateshead**	54A	**Sunderland**	
50B	Leeds (Neville Hill)		Bowes Bridge		Durham	
50C	Selby	52B	Heaton	54B	Tyne Dock	
50D	Starbeck	52C	Blaydon	54C	Borough Gardens	
50E	Scarborough		Alston	54D	Consett	
50F	Malton		Hexham	*55A	**Leeds (Holbeck)**	
	Pickering	52D	Tweedmouth		Keighley [(20A)	
50G	Whitby		Alnmouth	*55B	Stourton (20B)	
		52E	Percy Main	*55C	Farnley Junction (25G)	
		52E	North Blyth	*55D	Royston (20C)	
51A	**Darlington**		South Blyth	*55E	Normanton (20D)	
51B	Newport (Yorks.)			*55F	Manningham (20E)	
51C	West Hartlepool				Ilkley	
51D	Middlesbrough	53A	**Hull (Dairycoates)**	*55G	Huddersfield (25B)	
51E	Stockton	53B	Hull	*56A	**Wakefield (25A)**	
51F	West Auckland		(Botanic Gardens)	56B	Ardsley	
51G	Haverton Hill	53C	Hull (Springhead)	56C	Copley Hill	
51H	Kirkby Stephen		Alexandra Dock	*56D	Mirfield (25D)	
51J	Northallerton	53D	Bridlington	*56E	Sowerby Bridge (25E)	
51K	Saltburn	*53E	Goole (25C)	*56F	Low Moor (25F)	
				56G	Bradford	

Altered Shed Codes in course of adoption, former code in brackets.

4

SCOTTISH REGION

60A	**Inverness**	63A	**Perth South**	65D	Dawsholm	
	Dingwall		Aberfeldy		Dumbarton	
	Kyle of Lochalsh		Crieff	65E	Kipps	
60B	Aviemore	63B	Stirling South	65F	Grangemouth	
	Boat of Garten		Killin	65G	Yoker	
60C	Helmsdale		Stirling	65H	Helensburgh	
	Dornoch		(Shore Road)	65I	Balloch	
	Tain	63C	Forfar	65J	Fort William	
60D	Wick	63D	Oban		Mallaig	
	Thurso		Ballachulish			
60E	Forres			66A	**Polmadie**	
						(Glasgow)
61A	**Kittybrewster**			66B	Motherwell	
	Ballater	64A	**St. Margarets**	66C	Hamilton	
	Fraserburgh		**(Edinburgh)**	66D	Greenock	
	Inverurie		Dunbar			**(Ladyburn)**
	Peterhead		Galashiels		Greenock	
61B	Aberdeen (Ferryhill)		Longniddry		(Princes Pier)	
61C	Keith		North Berwick			
	Banff	64B	Haymarket	67A	**Corkerhill**	
	Elgin	64C	Dairy Road			**(Glasgow)**
		64D	Carstairs	67B	Hurlford	
		64E	Polmont		Beith	
62A	**Thornton**	64F	Bathgate		Muirkirk	
	Anstruther	64G	Hawick	67C	Ayr	
	Burntisland		Riccarton	67D	Ardrossan	
	Ladybank		St. Boswells	68A	**Carlisle**	
	Methil					**(Kingmoor)**
62B	Dundee (Tay Bridge)			68B	Dumfries	
	Arbroath	65A	**Eastfield**	68C	Stranraer	
	Dundee West		**(Glasgow)**		Newton Stewart	
	Montrose		Arrochar	68D	Beattock	
	St. Andrews	65B	St. Rollox	68E	Carlisle Canal	
62C	Dunfermline	65C	Parkhead			
	Alloa					

SOUTHERN REGION

70A	**Nine Elms**	71I	Southampton Docks	73C	Hither Green
70B	Feltham	71J	Highbridge	73D	Gillingham (Kent)
70C	Guildford			73E	Faversham
70D	Basingstoke	72A	**Exmouth Junction**		
70E	Reading		Bude	74A	**Ashford (Kent)**
70F	Fratton		Exmouth	74B	Ramsgate
70G	Newport (I.O.W.)		Lyme Regis	74C	Dover
70H	Ryde (I.O.W.)		Okehampton		Folkestone
			Seaton	74D	Tonbridge
		72B	Salisbury	74E	St. Leonards
		72C	Yeovil		
71A	**Eastleigh**	72D	Plymouth		
	Andover Junction		Callington	75A	**Brighton**
	Lymington	72E	Barnstaple Junction		Newhaven
	Winchester		Ilfracombe	75B	Redhill
71B	Bournemouth		Torrington	75C	Norwood Junction
	Branksome	72F	Wadebridge	75D	Horsham
71G	Bath (S. & D.)			75E	Three Bridges
	Radstock	73A	**Stewarts Lane**	75F	Tunbridge Wells
71H	Templecombe	73B	Bricklayers Arms		West

BRITISH RAILWAYS LOCOMOTIVES
Nos. 40001-59999

2-6-2T   3

Introduced 1930. Fowler L.M.S. design with parallel boiler.
*Introduced 1930. Condensing locos. for working to Moorgate, London.
Weight: $\begin{cases} 70 \text{ tons } 10 \text{ cwt.} \\ 71 \text{ tons } 16 \text{ cwt.*} \end{cases}$
Pressure: 200 lb. Su.
Cyls : (O) $17\frac{1}{2}'' \times 26''$
Dr. Wheels: 5′ 3″.   T.E.: 21,485 lb.
Walschaerts Valve Gear P.V.

40001	40019	40037*	40054
40002	40020	40038*	40055
40003	40021	40039*	40056
40004	40022*	40040*	40057
40005	40023*	40041	40058
40006	40024*	40042	40059
40007	40025*	40043	40060
40008	40026*	40044	40061
40009	40027*	40045	40062
40010	40028*	40046	40063
40011	40029*	40047	40064
40012	40030*	40048	40065
40013	40031*	40049	40066
40014	40032*	40050	40067
40015	40033*	40051	40068
40016	40034*	40052	40069
40017	40035*	40053	40070
40018	40036*		Total 70

2-6-2T   3

Introduced 1935. Stanier L.M.S. taper boiler development of Fowler design (above).
*Introduced 1941. Rebuilt with larger boiler.
Weight: $\begin{cases} 71 \text{ tons } 5 \text{ cwt.} \\ 72 \text{ tons } 10 \text{ cwt.*} \end{cases}$
Pressure: 200 lb. Su.
Cyls.: (O) $17\frac{1}{2}'' \times 26''$.
Dr. Wheels: 5′ 3″.   T.E.: 21,485 lb.
Walschaerts Valve Gear P.V.

40071	40075	40079	40083
40072	40076	40080	40084
40073	40077	40081	40085
40074	40078	40082	40086

40087	40118	40149	40180
40088	40119	40150	40181
40089	40120	40151	40182
40090	40121	40152	40183
40091	40122	40153	40184
40092	40123	40154	40185
40093	40124	40155	40186
40094	40125	40156	40187
40095	40126	40157	40188
40096	40127	40158	40189
40097	40128	40159	40190
40098	40129	40160	40191
40099	40130	40161	40192
40100	40131	40162	40193
40101	40132	40163*	40194
40102	40133	40164	40195
40103	40134	40165	40196
40104	40135	40166	40197
40105	40136	40167*	40198
40106	40137	40168	40199
40107	40138	40169*	40200
40108	40139	40170	40201
40109	40140	40171	40202
40110	40141	40172	40203*
40111	40142	40173	40204
40112	40143	40174	40205
40113	40144	40175	40206
40114	40145	40176	40207
40115	40146	40177	40208
40116	40147	40178	40209
40117	40148*	40179	

Total 139

4-4-0   2P

Introduced 1912. Fowler rebuild of Johnson locos. with superheater and piston valves.
*Introduced 1914. Locos. built new to superheated design for S. & D.J.R. (taken into L.M.S. stock, 1930).
Weight: Loco. 53 tons 7 cwt.
Pressure: 160 lb. Su.
Cyls.: $20\frac{1}{2}'' \times 26''$.   Dr. Wheels: 7′ 0$\frac{1}{2}$″.
T.E.: 17,585 lb.   P.V.

6

40323*	40420	40485	40525
40332	40421	40486	40531
40337	40426	40487	40534
40356	40433	40489	40536
40362	40434	40491	40537
40396	40439	40493	40538
40402	40443	40495	40540
40404	40447	40501	40541
40407	40450	40502	40542
40409	40452	40504	40543
40411	40453	40509	40548
40412	40454	40511	40550
40413	40458	40513	40552
40414	40461	40518	40553
40416	40464	40519	40557
40418	40482	40520	40559

Total 64

40624	40644	40664	40683
40625	40645	40665	40684
40626	40646	40666	40685
40627	40647	40667	40686
40628	40648	40668	40687
40629	40649	40669	40688
40630	40650	40670	40689
40631	40651	40671	40690
40632	40652	40672	40691
40633*†	40653†	40673	40692
40634*	40654	40674	40693
40635*	40655	40675	40694
40636	40656	40676	40695
40637	40657	40677	40696
40638	40658	40678	40697
40640	40659	40679	40698
40641	40660	40680	40699
40642	40661	40681	40700
40643	40663	40682	

Total 135

4-4-0   2P

Introduced 1928. Post-Grouping development of Midland design, with modified dimensions and reduced boiler mountings.
*Introduced 1928. Locos. built for S. & D.J.R. (taken into L.M.S. stock,1930).
†Fitted experimentally in 1933 with Dabeg feed-water heater
Weight: Loco. 54 tons 1 cwt.
Pressure: 180 lb. Su.
Cyls.: 19″ × 26″.
Dr. Wheels: 6′ 9″   T.E.: 17,730 lb.
P.V.

40563	40578	40594	40609
40564	40579	40595	40610
40565	40580	40596	40611
40566	40581	40597	40612
40567	40582	40598	40613
40568	40583	40599	40614
40569	40584	40600	40615
40570	40585	40601	40616
40571	40586	40602	40617
40572	40587	40603	40618
40573	40588	40604	40619
40574	40589	40605	40620
40575	40590	40606	40621
40576	40592	40607	40622
40577	40593	40608	40623

4-4-0 (3-Cyl. Compd.) 4P

Introduced 1924. Post-Grouping development of Johnson Midland compound with modified dimensions and (with some exceptions) reduced boiler mountings.
Weight: Loco. 61 tons 14 cwt.
Pressure: 200 lb. Su.
Cyls.: L.P. (2) 21″ × 26″.
     H.P. (1) 19″ × 26″.
Dr. Wheels: 6′ 9″.
T.E. (of L.P. cyls. at 80% boiler pressure). 22,650 lb.

P.V. (H.P. cyl. only).

40904	40935	41068	41090
40907	40936	41071	41093
40917	40937	41073	41094
40920	40939	41075	41095
40925	41045	41077	41098
40926	41048	41078	41100
40927	41049	41079	41101
40928	41060	41083	41102
40930	41062	41085	41103
40931	41063	41086	41105
40933	41064	41088	41106
40934	41066	41089	41108

41111–41712

41111	41140	41160	41181
41112	41143	41162	41185
41113	41144	41163	41186
41114	41150	41164	41189
41116	41151	41165	41190
41118	41152	41166	41192
41119	41153	41167	41193
41120	41155	41168	41194
41121	41156	41172	41195
41122	41157	41173	41196
41123	41158	41179	41197
41126	41159	41180	41199
41132			

Total 97

2-6-2T   2

Introduced 1946. Ivatt L.M.S. taper
  boiler design.
Weight: 63 tons 5 cwt.
Pressure: 200 lb. Su.
Cyls.: $\begin{cases} \text{(O) } 16''\times24''. \\ \text{(O) } 16\frac{1}{2}''\times24''. * \end{cases}$
Dr. Wheels: 5' 0''.   T.E.: $\begin{cases} 17,410 \text{ lb.} \\ 18,510 \text{ lb.}* \end{cases}$
Walschaerts Valve Gear. P.V.

41200	41220	41240	41260
41201	41221	41241	41261
41202	41222	41242	41262
41203	41223	41243	41263
41204	41224	41244	41264
41205	41225	41245	41265
41206	41226	41246	41266
41207	41227	41247	41267
41208	41228	41248	41268
41209	41229	41249	41269
41210	41230	41250	41270
41211	41231	41251	41271
41212	41232	41252	41272
41213	41233	41253	41273
41214	41234	41254	41274
41215	41235	41255	41275
41216	41236	41256	41276
41217	41237	41257	41277
41218	41238	41258	41278
41219	41239	41259	41279

41280	41293*	41306*	41318*
41281	41294*	41307*	41319*
41282	41295*	41308*	41320*
41283	41296*	41309*	41321*
41284	41297*	41310*	41322*
41285	41298*	41311*	41323*
41286	41299*	41312*	41324*
41287	41300*	41313*	41325*
41288	41301*	41314*	41326*
41289	41302*	41315*	41327*
41290*	41303*	41316*	41328*
41291*	41304*	41317*	41329*
41292*	41305*		

Total 130

0-4-0ST   0F

Introduced 1897. Johnson Midland
  design.
Weight: 32 tons 3 cwt.
Pressure: 140 lb.
Cyls.: 15'' × 20''.
Dr. Wheels: 3' 10''.
T.E.: 11,640 lb.

41518

Total 1

0-4-0T   0F

Introduced 1907. Deeley Midland
  design.
Weight: 32 tons 16 cwt.
Pressure: 160 lb.
Cyls.: (O) 15''×22''.
Dr. Wheels: 3' 9¾''.   T.E.: 14,635 lb.
Walschaerts Valve Gear.

41528	41531	41534	41536
41529	41532	41535	41537
41530	41533		

Total 10

0-6-0T   1F

Introduced 1878. Johnson Midland
  design.
*Rebuilt with Belpaire firebox.
Weight: 39 tons 11 cwt.
Pressure: $\begin{cases} 150 \text{ lb.} \\ 140 \text{ lb.}* \end{cases}$
Cyls.: 17''×24''.
Dr. Wheels: 4' 7''.
T.E.: $\begin{cases} 16,080 \text{ lb.} \\ 15,005 \text{ lb.}* \end{cases}$

41661*	41699*	41706*	41710*
41686*	41702*	41708*	41712*

8

41720*	41753*	41797*	41857*
41724*	41754*	41803*	41860*
41726*	41763*	41804*	41875*
41734*	41769*	41835	41878*
41739*	41773*	41844*	41879*
41748*	41779	41847*	41885*
41752*	41795*	41855*	

Total 35

0-4-4T   2P

Introduced 1932. Stanier L.M.S. design. Push-and-pull fitted.
Weight: 58 tons 1 cwt.
Pressure: 160 lb.
Cyls.: 18″ × 26″.
Dr. Wheels: 5′ 7″.   T.E.: 17,100 lb.

41900	41903	41906	41908
41901	41904	41907	41909
41902	41905		

Total 10

4-4-2T   3P

Introduced 1923. Midland and L.M.S. development of Whitelegg L.T. & S. " 79 " Class.
Weight: 71 tons 10 cwt
Pressure: 170 lb.
Cyls.: 19″ × 26″
Dr. Wheels: 6′ 6″   T.E.: 17,390 lb.

41928	41944	41949	41970
41936	41945	41950	41975
41939	41946	41951	41976
41941	41947	41952	41977
41942	41948	41969	41978

Total 20

0-6-2T   3F

Introduced 1903. Whitelegg L.T. & S. " 69 " Class (Nos. 41990-3 built 1912 taken directly into M.R. stock).
Weight: 64 tons 13 cwt.
Pressure: 170 lb.
Cyls.: 18″ × 26″.
Dr. Wheels: 5′ 3″.   T.E.: 19,320 lb.

41980	41984	41988	41991
41981	41985	41989	41992
41982	41986	41990	41993
41983	41987		

Total 14

2-6-4T   4

*Introduced 1927. Fowler L.M.S. parallel boiler design.
†Introduced 1933. As earlier engines, but with side-window cab and doors.
‡Introduced 1934. Stanier taper-boiler 3-cylinder design for L.T. & S.
§Introduced 1935. Stanier taper boiler 2-cylinder design.
¶Introduced 1945. Fairburn development of Stanier design with shorter wheelbase and detail alterations.
Weight: 86 tons 5 cwt.*† / 92 tons 5 cwt.‡ / 87 tons 17 cwt.§ / 85 tons 5 cwt.¶
Pressure (all types): 200 lb Su.
Cyls.: (O) 19″ × 26″*† / (3) 16″ × 26″‡ / (O) 19½″ × 26″§¶
Dr. Wheels (all types): 5′ 9″.
T.E.: 23,125 lb.*† / 24,600 lb.‡ / 24,670 lb.§¶
Walschaerts valve gear. P.V.

¶FAIRBURN LOCOS.

42050	42074	42098	42122
42051	42075	42099	42123
42052	42076	42100	42124
42053	42077	42101	42125
42054	42078	42102	42126
42055	42079	42103	42127
42056	42080	42104	42128
42057	42081	42105	42129
42058	42082	42106	42130
42059	42083	42107	42131
42060	42084	42108	42132
42061	42085	42109	42133
42062	42086	42110	42134
42063	42087	42111	42135
42064	42088	42112	42136
42065	42089	42113	42137
42066	42090	42114	42138
42067	42091	42115	42139
42068	42092	42116	42140
42069	42093	42117	42141
42070	42094	42118	42142
42071	42095	42119	42143
42072	42096	42120	42144
42073	42097	42121	42145

42146–42484

42146	42185	42224	42263
42147	42186	42225	42264
42148	42187	42226	42265
42149	42188	42227	42266
42150	42189	42228	42267
42151	42190	42229	42268
42152	42191	42230	42269
42153	42192	42231	42270
42154	42193	42232	42271
42155	42194	42233	42272
42156	42195	42234	42273
42157	42196	42235	42274
42158	42197	42236	42275
42159	42198	42237	42276
42160	42199	42238	42277
42161	42200	42239	42278
42162	42201	42240	42279
42163	42202	42241	42280
42164	42203	42242	42281
42165	42204	42243	42282
42166	42205	42244	42283
42167	42206	42245	42284
42168	42207	42246	42285
42169	42208	42247	42286
42170	42209	42248	42287
42171	42210	42249	42288
42172	42211	42250	42289
42173	42212	42251	42290
42174	42213	42252	42291
42175	42214	42253	42292
42176	42215	42254	42293
42177	42216	42255	42294
42178	42217	42256	42295
42179	42218	42257	42296
42180	42219	42258	42297
42181	42220	42259	42298
42182	42221	42260	42299
42183	42222	42261	
42184	42223	42262	

*FOWLER LOCOS.

42300	42305	42310	42315
42301	42306	42311	42316
42302	42307	42312	42317
42303	42308	42313	42318
42304	42309	42314	42319

42320	42339	42358	42377
42321	42340	42359	42378
42322	42341	42360	42379
42323	42342	42361	42380
42324	42343	42362	42381
42325	42344	42363	42382
42326	42345	42364	42383
42327	42346	42365	42384
42328	42347	42366	42385
42329	42348	42367	42386
42330	42349	42368	42387
42331	42350	42369	42388
42332	42351	42370	42389
42333	42352	42371	42390
42334	42353	42372	42391
42335	42354	42373	42392
42336	42355	42374	42393
42337	42356	42375	42394
42338	42357	42376	

†FOWLER LOCOS. WITH SIDE-WINDOW CAB.

42395	42403	42411	42418
42396	42404	42412	42419
42397	42405	42413	42420
42398	42406	42414	42421
42399	42407	42415	42422
42400	42408	42416	42423
42401	42409	42417	42424
42402	42410		

§STANIER 2-CYL. LOCOS.

42425	42440	42455	42470
42426	42441	42456	42471
42427	42442	42457	42472
42428	42443	42458	42473
42429	42444	42459	42474
42430	42445	42460	42475
42431	42446	42461	42476
42432	42447	42462	42477
42433	42448	42463	42478
42434	42449	42464	42479
42435	42450	42465	42480
42436	42451	42466	42481
42437	42452	42467	42482
42438	42453	42468	42483
42439	42454	42469	42484

42485	42488	42491	42493
42486	42489	42492	42494
42487	42490		

‡STANIER 3-CYL. LOCOS.

42500	42510	42519	42528
42501	42511	42520	42529
42502	42512	42521	42530
42503	42513	42522	42531
42504	42514	42523	42532
42505	42515	42524	42533
42506	42516	42525	42534
42507	42517	42526	42535
42508	42518	42527	42536
42509			

§STANIER 2-CYL. LOCOS.

42537	42566	42595	42624
42538	42567	42596	42625
42539	42568	42597	42626
42540	42569	42598	42627
42541	42570	42599	42628
42542	42571	42600	42629
42543	42572	42601	42630
42544	42573	42602	42631
42545	42574	42603	42632
42546	42575	42604	42633
42547	42576	42605	42634
42548	42577	42606	42635
42549	42578	42607	42636
42550	42579	42608	42637
42551	42580	42609	42638
42552	42581	42610	42639
42553	42582	42611	42640
42554	42583	42612	42641
42555	42584	42613	42642
42556	42585	42614	42643
42557	42586	42615	42644
42558	42587	42616	42645
42559	42588	42617	42646
42560	42589	42618	42647
42561	42590	42619	42648
42562	42591	42620	42649
42563	42592	42621	42650
42564	42593	42622	42651
42565	42594	42623	42652

42653	42658	42663	42668
42654	42659	42664	42669
42655	42660	42665	42670
42656	42661	42666	42671
42657	42662	42667	42672

¶FAIRBURN LOCOS

42673	42680	42687	42694
42674	42681	42688	42695
42675	42682	42689	42696
42676	42683	42690	42697
42677	42684	42691	42698
42678	42685	42692	42699
42679	42686	42693	

Total 645

2-6-0   6P5F

Introduced 1926. Hugees L.M.S. design built under Fowler's direction Walschaerts Valve Gear. P.V.
*Introduced 1953. Locos. rebuilt experimentally with Lentz R.C. poppet valves in 1931; rebuilt with Reidinger rotary poppet valve gear in 1953.
Weight: Loco. 66 tons 0 cwt.
Pressure: 180 lb. Su.
Cyls.: (O) 21″ × 26″.
Dr. Wheels: 5′ 6″.   T.E.: 26,580 lb.

42700	42717	42734	42751
42701	42718	42735	42752
42702	42719	42736	42753
42703	42720	42737	42754
42704	42721	42738	42755
42705	42722	42739	42756
42706	42723	42740	42757
42707	42724	42741	42758
42708	42725	42742	42759
42709	42726	42743	42760
42710	42727	42744	42761
42711	42728	42745	42762
42712	42729	42746	42763
42713	42730	42747	42764
42714	42731	42748	42765
42715	42732	42749	42766
42716	42733	42750	42767

42768	42813	42857	42901
42769	42814	42858	42902
42770	42815	42859	42903
42771	42816	42860	42904
42772	42817	42861	42905
42773	42818*	42862	42906
42774	42819	42863	42907
42775	42820	42864	42908
42776	42821	42865	42909
42777	42822*	42866	42910
42778	42823	42867	42911
42779	42824*	42868	42912
42780	42825*	42869	42913
42781	42826	42870	42914
42782	42827	42871	42915
42783	42828	42872	42916
42784	42829*	42873	42917
42785	42830	42874	42918
42786	42831	42875	42919
42787	42832	42876	42920
42788	42833	42877	42921
42789	42834	42878	42922
42790	42835	42879	42923
42791	42836	42880	42924
42792	42837	42881	42925
42793	42838	42882	42926
42794	42839	42883	42927
42795	42840	42884	42928
42796	42841	42885	42929
42797	42842	42886	42930
42798	42843	42887	42931
42799	42844	42888	42932
42800	42845	42889	42933
42801	42846	42890	42934
42802	42847	42891	42935
42803	42848	42892	42936
42804	42849	42893	42937
42805	42850	42894	42938
42806	42851	42895	42939
42807	42852	42896	42940
42808	42853	42897	42941
42809	42854	42898	42942
42810	42855	42899	42943
42811	42856	42900	42944
42812			

Total 245

2-6-0   6P5F

Introduced 1933. Stanier L.M.S. taper
boiler design, some with safety valves
mounted on the top feed.
Weight: Loco. 69 tons 2 cwt.
Pressure: 225 lb. Su.
Cyls.: (O) 18″ x 28″.
Dr. Wheels: 5′ 6″.   T.E.: 26,290 lb.
Walschaerts Valve Gear.   P.V.

42945	42955	42965	42975
42946	42956	42966	42976
42947	42957	42967	42977
42948	42958	42968	42978
42949	42959	42969	42979
42950	42960	42970	42980
42951	42961	42971	42981
42952	42962	42972	42982
42953	42963	42973	42983
42954	42964	42974	42984

Total 40

2-6-0   4

Introduced 1947. Ivatt L.M.S. taper
boiler design with double chimney.
Later engines introduced with single
chimney, with which earlier engines
are being rebuilt.
Weight: Loco. 59 tons 2 cwt.
Pressure: 225 lb. Su.
Cyls.: (O) 17½″ x 26″.
Dr. Wheels: 5′ 3″.   T.E.: 24,170 lb.
Walschaerts Valve Gear.   P.V.

43000	43018	43036	43054
43001	43019	43037	43055
43002	43020	43038	43056
43003	43021	43039	43057
43004	43022	43040	43058
43005	43023	43041	43059
43006	43024	43042	43060
43007	43025	43043	43061
43008	43026	43044	43062
43009	43027	43045	43063
43010	43028	43046	43064
43011	43029	43047	43065
43012	43030	43048	43066
43013	43031	43049	43067
43014	43032	43050	43068
43015	43033	43051	43069
43016	43034	43052	43070
43017	43035	43053	43071

43072	43095	43118	43140
43073	43096	43119	43141
43074	43097	43120	43142
43075	43098	43121	43143
43076	43099	43122	43144
43077	43100	43123	43145
43078	43101	43124	43146
43079	43102	43125	43147
43080	43103	43126	43148
43081	43104	43127	43149
43082	43105	43128	43150
43083	43106	43129	43151
43084	43107	43130	43152
43085	43108	43131	43153
43086	43109	43132	43154
43087	43110	43133	43155
43088	43111	43134	43156
43089	43112	43135	43157
43090	43113	43136	43158
43091	43114	43137	43159
43092	43115	43138	43160
43093	43116	43139	43161
43094	43117		

Total 162

43222	43294	43387	43502
43223	43295	43388	43506
43224	43300	43389	43507
43225	43301	43392	43509
43226	43305	43394	43510
43231	43306	43395	43514
43232	43307	43396	43515
43233	43308	43398	43520
43234	43309	43399	43521
43235	43312	43400	43522
43237	43314	43401	43523
43239	43315	43402	43529
43240	43318	43405	43531
43241	43321	43406	43538
43242	43323	43410	43546
43243	43324	43411	43548
43244	43325	43419	43550
43245	43326	43427	43553
43246	43327	43428	43558
43247	43329	43429	43562
43248†	43330	43431	43565
43249	43332	43433	43570
43250	43333	43435	43572
43251	43335	43436	43574
43253	43337	43440	43575
43254	43339	43441	43578
43256	43340	43443	43579
43257	43341	43444	43580
43258	43342	43446	43583
43259	43344	43449	43584
43261	43355	43453	43585
43263	43356	43456	43586
43266	43357	43457	43587
43267	43359	43459	43593
43268	43361	43463	43594
43271	43367	43464	43595
43274	43368	43468	43596
43277	43369	43469	43598
43278	43370	43474	43599
43281	43371	43476	43605
43282	43373	43482	43608
43284	43374	43484	43612
43286	43378	43490	43615
43287	43379	43491	43618
43290	43381	43496	43619
43292	43386	43499	43620

0-6-0   3F

Introduced 1885. Johnson Midland locos., rebuilt from 1916 by Fowler with Belpaire firebox.

*Introduced 1885. Johnson Midland locos.. rebuilt from 1920 by Fowler with Belpaire firebox.

†Introduced 1896. Locos. built for S. & D.J. (taken into L.M.S. stock 1930).

Weight: Loco. 43 tons 17 cwt.

Pressure: 175 lb.

Cyls.: 18″ × 26″.

Dr. Wheels: $\begin{cases} 5'\ 3'' \\ 4'\ 11''.* \end{cases}$ T.E.: $\begin{cases} 19,890\ \text{lb.} \\ 21,240\ \text{lb.*} \end{cases}$

43174*	43187*	43201†	43211†
43178*	43188*	43203	43212
43180*	43189*	43204†	43213
43181*	43192	43205	43214
43183*	43193	43207	43216†
43185*	43194†	43208	43218†
43186*	43200	43210	43219

43621	43657	43693	43742
43622	43658	43698	43745
43623	43660	43705	43748
43624	43664	43709	43749
43627	43665	43710	43750*
43629	43668	43711	43751
43630	43669	43712	43753
43631	43673	43714	43754
43634	43674	43715	43756
43637	43675	43717	43757
43638	43678	43721	43759
43639	43679	43727	43760
43644	43680	43728	43762
43645	43681	43729	43763
43650	43682	43731	43766
43651	43684	43734	43771
43652	43687	43735	43773
43656	43690	43737	

Total 283

0-6-0   3F

Introduced 1906. Deeley Midland design. Rebuilt by Fowler with Belpaire firebox.

Weight: Loco. 46 tons 3 cwt.

Pressure: 175 lb.

Cyls.: 18½″ × 26″.

Dr. Wheels: 5′ 3″   T.E.: 21,010 lb.

43776	43793	43808	43823
43778	43795	43809	43825
43784	43798	43812	43826
43785	43799	43814	43828
43786	43800	43815	43829
43787	43806	43822	43832
43789			

Total 25

0-6-0   4F

Introduced 1911. Fowler superheated Midland design.

Weight: Loco. 48 tons 15 cwt.

Pressure: 175 lb. Su.

Cyls.: 20″ × 26″.

Dr. Wheels: 5′ 3″.   T.E.: 24,555 lb.

P.V.

43836	43877	43916	43953
43837	43878	43917	43954
43839	43879	43918	43955
43840	43880	43919	43957
43841	43881	43920	43958
43842	43882	43921	43959
43843	43883	43922	43960
43844	43884	43923	43961
43845	43885	43924	43962
43846	43886	43925	43963
43847	43887	43926	43964
43848	43888	43927	43965
43849	43889	43928	43966
43850	43890	43929	43967
43851	43891	43930	43968
43852	43892	43931	43969
43853	43893	43932	43970
43854	43896	43933	43971
43855	43897	43934	43972
43856	43898	43935	43973
43857	43899	43937	43975
43858	43900	43938	43976
43859	43901	43939	43977
43860	43902	43940	43978
43861	43903	43941	43979
43863	43904	43942	43980
43864	43905	43943	43981
43865	43906	43944	43982
43866	43907	43945	43983
43868	43908	43946	43984
43869	43910	43947	43985
43870	43911	43948	43986
43871	43912	43949	43987
43872	43913	43950	43988
43873	43914	43951	43989
43876	43915	43952	43990

43991	44000	44010	44019
43992	44001	44011	44020
43993	44002	44012	44021
43994	44003	44013	44022
43995	44004	44014	44023
43996	44005	44015	44024
43997	44007	44016	44025
43998	44008	44017	44026
43999	44009	44018	

Total 179

0-6-0   4F

Introduced 1924. Post-grouping development of Midland design with reduced boiler mountings.

*Introduced 1922. Locos. built for S. & D.J.R. to M.R. design taken into L.M.S. stock 1930).
Weight: Loco. 48 tons 15 cwt.
Pressure: 175 lb. Su.
Cyls.: 20″×26″.
Dr. Wheels: 5′ 3″.   T.E.: 24,555 lb.
P.V.

44027	44039	44051	44063
44028	44040	44052	44064
44029	44041	44053	44065
44030	44042	44054	44066
44031	44043	44055	44067
44032	44044	44056	44068
44033	44045	44057	44069
44034	44046	44058	44070
44035	44047	44059	44071
44036	44048	44060	44072
44037	44049	44061	44073
44038	44050	44062	44074

44075	44121	44167	44213
44076	44122	44168	44214
44077	44123	44169	44215
44078	44124	44170	44216
44079	44125	44171	44217
44080	44126	44172	44218
44081	44127	44173	44219
44082	44128	44174	44220
44083	44129	44175	44221
44084	44130	44176	44222
44085	44131	44177	44223
44086	44132	44178	44224
44087	44133	44179	44225
44088	44134	44180	44226
44089	44135	44181	44227
44090	44136	44182	44228
44091	44137	44183	44229
44092	44138	44184	44230
44093	44139	44185	44231
44094	44140	44186	44232
44095	44141	44187	44233
44096	44142	44188	44234
44097	44143	44189	44235
44098	44144	44190	44236
44099	44145	44191	44237
44100	44146	44192	44238
44101	44147	44193	44239
44102	44148	44194	44240
44103	44149	44195	44241
44104	44150	44196	44242
44105	44151	44197	44243
44106	44152	44198	44244
44107	44153	44199	44245
44108	44154	44200	44246
44109	44155	44201	44247
44110	44156	44202	44248
44111	44157	44203	44249
44112	44158	44204	44250
44113	44159	44205	44251
44114	44160	44206	44252
44115	44161	44207	44253
44116	44162	44208	44254
44117	44163	44209	44255
44118	44164	44210	44256
44119	44165	44211	44257
44120	44166	44212	44258

44259	44305	44351	44397	44443	44484	44525	44566
44260	44306	44352	44398	44444	44485	44526	44567
44261	44307	44353	44399	44445	44486	44527	44568
44262	44308	44354	44400	44446	44487	44528	44569
44263	44309	44355	44401	44447	44488	44529	44570
44264	44310	44356	44402	44448	44489	44530	44571
44265	44311	44357	44403	44449	44490	44531	44572
44266	44312	44358	44404	44450	44491	44532	44573
44267	44313	44359	44405	44451	44492	44533	44574
44268	44314	44360	44406	44452	44493	44534	44575
44269	44315	44361	44407	44453	44494	44535	44576
44270	44316	44362	44408	44454	44495	44536	44577
44271	44317	44363	44409	44455	44496	44537	44578
44272	44318	44364	44410	44456	44497	44538	44579
44273	44319	44365	44411	44457	44498	44539	44580
44274	44320	44366	44412	44458	44499	44540	44581
44275	44321	44367	44413	44459	44500	44541	44582
44276	44322	44368	44414	44460	44501	44542	44583
44277	44323	44369	44415	44461	44502	44543	44584
44278	44324	44370	44416	44462	44503	44544	44585
44279	44325	44371	44417	44463	44504	44545	44586
44280	44326	44372	44418	44464	44505	44546	44587
44281	44327	44373	44419	44465	44506	44547	44588
44282	44328	44374	44420	44466	44507	44548	44589
44283	44329	44375	44421	44467	44508	44549	44590
44284	44330	44376	44422	44468	44509	44550	44591
44285	44331	44377	44423	44469	44510	44551	44592
44286	44332	44378	44424	44470	44511	44552	44593
44287	44333	44379	44425	44471	44512	44553	44594
44288	44334	44380	44426	44472	44513	44554	44595
44289	44335	44381	44427	44473	44514	44555	44596
44290	44336	44382	44428	44474	44515	44556	44597
44291	44337	44383	44429	44475	44516	44557*	44598
44292	44338	44384	44430	44476	44517	44558*	44599
44293	44339	44385	44431	44477	44518	44559*	44600
44294	44340	44386	44432	44478	44519	44560*	44601
44295	44341	44387	44433	44479	44520	44561*	44602
44296	44342	44388	44434	44480	44521	44562	44603
44297	44343	44389	44435	44481	44522	44563	44604
44298	44344	44390	44436	44482	44523	44564	44605
44299	44345	44391	44437	44483	44524	44565	44606
44300	44346	44392	44438				
44301	44347	44393	44439			**Total 580**	
44302	44348	44394	44440				
44303	44349	44395	44441				
44304	44350	44396	44442				

Class 2P (Midland) 4-4-0 No. 40461   [K. R. Pirt

Class 2P (L.M.S.) 4-4-0 No. 40700   [W. Vaughan-Jenkins

Class 4P 4-4-0 No. 40907   [Brian E. Morrison

Class 3 (Fowler) 2-6-2T No. 40058   [Brian E. Morrison

Class 3 (Stanier) 2-6-2T No. 40168   [Brian E. Morrison

Class 4 (Fowler) 2-6-4T No. 42400 (with side-window cab)   [R. J. Buckley

Class 4 (Stanier 2-cylinder) 2-6-4T No. 42557   [*Brian E. Morrison*

Class 4 (Stanier 3-cylinder) 2-6-4T No. 42517   [*T. K. Widd*

Class 4 (Riddles) 2-6-4T No. 80027   [*W. A. C. Smith*

Class 2 (Ivatt) 2-6-2T No. 41249

[W. Vaughan-Jenkins

Class 2 (Riddles) 2-6-2T No. 84012

[Brian E. Morrison

Class 3 (Riddles) 2-6-2T No. 82016

[P. Ransome-Wallis

Class 6P5F (Stanier) 2-6-0 No. 42970   [Brian E. Morrison

Class 6P5F (Hughes-Fowler) 2-6-0 No. 42854   [D. Penney

Class 6P5F (Hughes-Fowler) 2-6-0 No. 42829 (with Reidinger rotary poppet valve gear)
[K. R. Pirt

Class 4 2-6-0 No. 76003   [P. J. Lynch

Class 4 4-6-0 No. 75070   [C. P. Boocock

Class 6P5F 4-6-2 No. 72004 *Clan Macdonald*   [P. Ransome-Wallis

Class 5 4-6-0 No. 44740 (with Caprotti valve gear)
[T. K. Widd

Class 5 4-6-0 No. 44687 (with Caprotti valve gear and double chimney)
[T. K. Widd

Class 5 (Riddles) 4-6-0 No. 73125 (with Caprotti valve gear)
[E. Gamblin

Class 6P5F 4-6-0 No. 45623 *Palestine*   [*Eric Treacy*

Class 6P5F 4-6-0 No. 45518 *Bradshaw*   [*Brian E. Morrison*

Class 8P 4-6-2 No. 46205 *Princess Victoria* (with inside valve gear operated by rocking shafts)   [*T. K. Widd*

4-6-0   5

Introduced 1934. Stanier L.M.S. taper boiler design.

Experimental locomotives:—
1. Introduced 1947. Stephenson link motion (outside), Timken roller bearings.
2. Introduced 1948. Caprotti Valve Gear.
3. Introduced 1948. Caprotti Valve Gear, Timken roller bearings
4. Introduced 1948. Caprotti Valve Gear, Timken roller bearings, double chimney.
5. Introduced 1947. Timken roller bearings.
6. Introduced 1947. Timken roller bearings, double chimney.
7. Introduced 1949. Fitted with steel firebox.
8. Introduced 1950. Skefko roller bearings.
9. Introduced 1950. Timken roller bearings on driving coupled axle only
10. Introduced 1950. Skefko roller bearings on driving coupled axle only.
11. Introduced 1951 Caprotti valve gear, Skefko roller bearings.

Weight: Loco. $\begin{cases} 72 \text{ tons 2 cwt.} \\ 75 \text{ tons 6 cwt. (1, 5, 6,} \\ \quad 8, 9, 10). \\ 74 \text{ tons 0 cwt. (2, 3, 4} \\ \quad 11). \\ 72 \text{ tons 2 cwt. (7).} \end{cases}$

Pressure: 225 lb. Su.
Cyls.: (O) 18½" × 28"
Dr. Wheels: 6' 0".   T.E.: 25,455 lb.
Walschaerts Valve Gear, and P.V. except where otherwise shown.

44658	44671[10]	44684[8]	44697[9]
44659	44672[10]	44685[8]	44698
44660	44673[10]	44686[11]	44699
44661	44674[10]	44687[11]	44700
44662	44675[10]	44688[9]	44701
44663	44676[10]	44689[9]	44702
44664	44677[10]	44690[9]	44703
44665	44678[8]	44691[9]	44704
44666	44679[8]	44692[9]	44705
44667	44680[8]	44693[9]	44706
44668[10]	44681[8]	44694[9]	44707
44669[10]	44682[8]	44695[9]	44708
44670[10]	44683[8]	44696[9]	44709

44710	44756[4]	44802	44848
44711	44757[4]	44803	44849
44712	44758[5]	44804	44850
44713	44759[5]	44805	44851
44714	44760[5]	44806	44852
44715	44761[5]	44807	44853
44716	44762[5]	44808	44854
44717	44763[5]	44809	44855
44718[7]	44764[5]	44810	44856
44719[7]	44765[6]	44811	44857
44720[7]	44766[6]	44812	44858
44721[7]	44767[1]	44813	44859
44722[7]	44768	44814	44860
44723[7]	44769	44815	44861
44724[7]	44770	44816	44862
44725[7]	44771	44817	44863
44726[7]	44772	44818	44864
44727[7]	44773	44819	44865
44728	44774	44820	44866
44729	44775	44821	44867
44730	44776	44822	44868
44731	44777	44823	44869
44732	44778	44824	44870
44733	44779	44825	44871
44734	44780	44826	44872
44735	44781	44827	44873
44736	44782	44828	44874
44737	44783	44829	44875
44738[2]	44784	44830	44876
44739[2]	44785	44831	44877
44740[2]	44786	44832	44878
44741[2]	44787	44833	44879
44742[2]	44788	44834	44880
44743[2]	44789	44835	44881
44744[2]	44790	44836	44882
44745[2]	44791	44837	44883
44746[2]	44792	44838	44884
44747[2]	44793	44839	44885
44748[3]	44794	44840	44886
44749[3]	44795	44841	44887
44750[3]	44796	44842	44888
44751[3]	44797	44843	44889
44752[3]	44798	44844	44890
44753[3]	44799	44845	44891
44754[3]	44800	44846	44892
44755[4]	44801	44847	44893

44894	44934	44974	45014	45054	45095	45136	45177
44895	44935	44975	45015	45055	45096	45137	45178
44896	44936	44976	45016	45056	45097	45138	45179
44897	44937	44977	45017	45057	45098	45139	45180
44898	44938	44978	45018	45058	45099	45140	45181
44899	44939	44979	45019	45059	45100	45141	45182
44900	44940	44980	45020	45060	45101	45142	45183
44901	44941	44981	45021	45061	45102	45143	45184
44902	44942	44982	45022	45062	45103	45144	45185
44903	44943	44983	45023	45063	45104	45145	45186
44904	44944	44984	45024	45064	45105	45146	45187
44905	44945	44985	45025	45065	45106	45147	45188
44906	44946	44986	45026	45066	45107	45148	45189
44907	44947	44987	45027	45067	45108	45149	45190
44908	44948	44988	45028	45068	45109	45150	45191
44909	44949	44989	45029	45069	45110	45151	45192
44910	44950	44990	45030	45070	45111	45152	45193
44911	44951	44991	45031	45071	45112	45153	45194
44912	44952	44992	45032	45072	45113	45154*	45195
44913	44953	44993	45033	45073	45114	45155	45196
44914	44954	44994	45034	45074	45115	45156*	45197
44915	44955	44995	45035	45075	45116	45157*	45198
44916	44956	44996	45036	45076	45117	45158*	45199
44917	44957	44997	45037	45077	45118	45159	45200
44918	44958	44998	45038	45078	45119	45160	45201
44919	44959	44999	45039	45079	45120	45161	45202
44920	44960	45000	45040	45080	45121	45162	45203
44921	44961	45001	45041	45081	45122	45163	45204
44922	44962	45002	45042	45082	45123	45164	45205
44923	44963	45003	45043	45083	45124	45165	45206
44924	44964	45004	45044	45084	45125	45166	45207
44925	44965	45005	45045	45085	45126	45167	45208
44926	44966	45006	45046	45086	45127	45168	45209
44927	44967	45007	45047	45087	45128	45169	45210
44928	44968	45008	45048	45088	45129	45170	45211
44929	44969	45009	45049	45089	45130	45171	45212
44930	44970	45010	45050	45090	45131	45172	45213
44931	44971	45011	45051	45091	45132	45173	45214
44932	44972	45012	45052	45092	45133	45174	45215
44933	44973	45013	45053	45093	45134	45175	45216
				45094	45135	45176	45217

NOTE

To understand the system of reference marks used in this book it is essential to read the notes on page 2.

* NAMES:

45154 Lanarkshire Yeomanry.
45156 Ayrshire Yeomanry.
45157 The Glasgow Highlander.
45158 Glasgow Yeomanry.

45218	45264	45310	45356	45402	45427	45452	45476
45219	45265	45311	45357	45403	45428	45453	45477
45220	45266	45312	45358	45404	45429	45454	45478
45221	45267	45313	45359	45405	45430	45455	45479
45222	45268	45314	45360	45406	45431	45456	45480
45223	45269	45315	45361	45407	45432	45457	45481
45224	45270	45316	45362	45408	45433	45458	45482
45225	45271	45317	45363	45409	45434	45459	45483
45226	45272	45318	45364	45410	45435	45460	45484
45227	45273	45319	45365	45411	45436	45461	45485
45228	45274	45320	45366	45412	45437	45462	45486
45229	45275	45321	45367	45413	45438	45463	45487
45230	45276	45322	45368	45414	45439	45464	45488
45231	45277	45323	45369	45415	45440	45465	45489
45232	45278	45324	45370	45416	45441	45466	45490
45233	45279	45325	45371	45417	45442	45467	45491
45234	45280	45326	45372	45418	45443	45468	45492
45235	45281	45327	45373	45419	45444	45469	45493
45236	45282	45328	45374	45420	45445	45470	45494
45237	45283	45329	45375	45421	45446	45471	45495
45238	45284	45330	45376	45422	45447	45472	45496
45239	45285	45331	45377	45423	45448	45473	45497
45240	45286	45332	45378	45424	45449	45474	45498
45241	45287	45333	45379	45425	45450	45475	45499
45242	45288	45334	45380	45426	45451		
45243	45289	45335	45381				
45244	45290	45336	45382				
45245	45291	45337	45383				
45246	45292	45338	45384				
45247	45293	45339	45385				
45248	45294	45340	45386				
45249	45295	45341	45387				
45250	45296	45342	45388				
45251	45297	45343	45389				
45252	45298	45344	45390				
45253	45299	45345	45391				
45254	45300	45346	45392				
45255	45301	45347	45393				
45256	45302	45348	45394				
45257	45303	45349	45395				
45258	45304	45350	45396				
45259	45305	45351	45397				
45260	45306	45352	45398				
45261	45307	45353	45399				
45262	45308	45354	45400				
45263	45309	45355	45401				

Total 842

"Patriot" Class

4-6-0   6P5F & 7P

*6P5F Introduced 1930. Fowler 3-cyl. rebuild of L.N.W. "Claughton" Class (introduced 1912), retaining original wheels and other details.

Remainder. Introduced 1933. New locos. to Fowler design (45502–41 were officially considered as rebuilds).

†7P Introduced 1946. Ivatt rebuild of Fowler locos. with large taper boiler, new cylinders and double chimney.

Weight: Loco. $\begin{cases} 80 \text{ tons } 15 \text{ cwt.} \\ 82 \text{ tons } 0 \text{ cwt.†} \end{cases}$

Pressure: $\begin{cases} 200 \text{ lb. Su.} \\ 250 \text{ lb. Su.†} \end{cases}$

Cyls.: $\begin{cases} (3) \ 18'' \times 26''. \\ (3) \ 17'' \times 26''.† \end{cases}$

Dr. Wheels: 6' 9".

T.E.: $\begin{cases} 26,520 \text{ lb.} \\ 29,570 \text{ lb.†} \end{cases}$

Walschaerts Valve Gear. P.V.

45500*Patriot
45501*St. Dunstan's
45502 Royal Naval Division
45503 The Royal Leicestershire
       Regiment
45504 Royal Signals
45505 The Royal Army
       Ordnance Corps
45506 The Royal Pioneer Corps
45507 Royal Tank Corps
45508
45509 The Derbyshire
       Yeomanry
45510
45511 Isle of Man
45512†Bunsen
45513
45514†Holyhead
45515 Caernarvon
45516 The Bedfordshire and
       Hertfordshire Regiment
45517
45518 Bradshaw
45519 Lady Godiva
45520 Llandudno
45521†Rhyl
45522†Prestatyn
45523†Bangor
45524 Blackpool
45525†Colwyn Bay
45526†Morecambe and Heysham
45527†Southport
45528†
45529†Stephenson
45530†Sir Frank Ree
45531†Sir Frederick Harrison
45532†Illustrious
45533 Lord Rathmore
45534†E. Tootal Broadhurst
45535†Sir Herbert Walker,
       K.C.B.
45536†Private W. Wood, V.C.
45537 Private E. Sykes, V.C.
45538 Giggleswick
45539 E. C. Trench
45540†Sir Robert Turnbull

45541 Duke of Sutherland
45542
45543 Home Guard
45544
45545†Planet
45546 Fleetwood
45547
45548 Lytham St. Annes
45549
45550
45551

Total 52

"Jubilee" Class

4-6-0   6P5F & 7P

6P5F Introduced 1934. Stanier L.M.S. taper boiler development of the "Patriot" class.
*7P Introduced 1942. Rebuilt with larger boiler and double chimney.

Weight: Loco. $\begin{cases} 79 \text{ tons } 11 \text{ cwt.} \\ 82 \text{ tons } 0 \text{ cwt.}^* \end{cases}$

Pressure: $\begin{cases} 225 \text{ lb. Su.} \\ 250 \text{ lb. Su.}^* \end{cases}$

Cyls.: (3) 17" × 26".
Dr. Wheels: 6' 9".

T.E.: $\begin{cases} 26,610 \text{ lb.} \\ 29,570 \text{ lb.}^* \end{cases}$

Walschaerts Valve Gear. P.V.

45552 Silver Jubilee
45553 Canada
45554 Ontario
45555 Quebec
45556 Nova Scotia
45557 New Brunswick
45558 Manitoba
45559 British Columbia
45560 Prince Edward Island
45561 Saskatchewan
45562 Alberta
45563 Australia
45564 New South Wales
45565 Victoria

45566	Queensland	45612	Jamaica
45567	South Australia	45613	Kenya
45568	Western Australia	45614	Leeward Islands
45569	Tasmania	45615	Malay States
45570	New Zealand	45616	Malta G.C.
45571	South Africa	45617	Mauritius
45572	Eire	45618	New Hebrides
45573	Newfoundland	45619	Nigeria
45574	India	45620	North Borneo
45575	Madras	45621	Northern Rhodesia
45576	Bombay	45622	Nyasaland
45577	Bengal	45623	Palestine
45578	United Provinces	45624	St. Helena
45579	Punjab	45625	Sarawak
45580	Burma	45626	Seychelles
45581	Bihar and Orissa	45627	Sierra Leone
45582	Central Provinces	45628	Somaliland
45583	Assam	45629	Straits Settlements
45584	North West Frontier	45630	Swaziland
45585	Hyderabad	45631	Tanganyika
45586	Mysore	45632	Tonga
45587	Baroda	45633	Aden
45588	Kashmir	45634	Trinidad
45589	Gwalior	45635	Tobago
45590	Travancore	45636	Uganda
45591	Udaipur	45638	Zanzibar
45592	Indore	45639	Raleigh
45593	Kolhapur	45640	Frobisher
45594	Bhopal	45641	Sandwich
45595	Southern Rhodesia	45642	Boscawen
45596	Bahamas	45643	Rodney
45597	Barbados	45644	Howe
45598	Basutoland	45645	Collingwood
45599	Bechuanaland	45646	Napier
45600	Bermuda	45647	Sturdee
45601	British Guiana	45648	Wemyss
45602	British Honduras	45649	Hawkins
45603	Solomon Islands	45650	Blake
45604	Ceylon	45651	Shovell
45605	Cyprus	45652	Hawke
45606	Falkland Islands	45653	Barham
45607	Fiji	45654	Hood
45608	Gibraltar	45655	Keith
45609	Gilbert and Ellice Islands	45656	Cochrane
45610	Gold Coast	45657	Tyrwhitt
45611	Hong Kong	45658	Keyes

45659 Drake	45704 Leviathan
45660 Rooke	45705 Seahorse
45661 Vernon	45706 Express
45662 Kempenfelt	45707 Valiant
45663 Jervis	45708 Resolution
45664 Nelson	45709 Implacable
45665 Lord Rutherford of Nelson	45710 Irresistible
45666 Cornwallis	45711 Courageous
45667 Jellicoe	45712 Victory
45668 Madden	45713 Renown
45669 Fisher	45714 Revenge
45670 Howard of Effingham	45715 Invincible
45671 Prince Rupert	45716 Swiftsure
45672 Anson	45717 Dauntless
45673 Keppel	45718 Dreadnought
45674 Duncan	45719 Glorious
45675 Hardy	45720 Indomitable
45676 Codrington	45721 Impregnable
45677 Beatty	45722 Defence
45678 De Robeck	45723 Fearless
45679 Armada	45724 Warspite
45680 Camperdown	45725 Repulse
45681 Aboukir	45726 Vindictive
45682 Trafalgar	45727 Inflexible
45683 Hogue	45728 Defiance
45684 Jutland	45729 Furious
45685 Barfleur	45730 Ocean
45686 St. Vincent	45731 Perseverance
45687 Neptune	45732 Sanspareil
45688 Polyphemus	45733 Novelty
45689 Ajax	45734 Meteor
45690 Leander	45735*Comet
45691 Orion	45736*Phoenix
45692 Cyclops	45737 Atlas
45693 Agamemnon	45738 Samson
45694 Bellerophon	45739 Ulster
45695 Minotaur	45740 Munster
45696 Arethusa	45741 Leinster
45697 Achilles	45742 Connaught
45698 Mars	
45699 Galatea	**Total 190**
45700 Amethyst	
45701 Conqueror	
45702 Colossus	
45703 Thunderer	

"Royal Scot" Class

4-6-0   **7P**

Introduced 1943. Stanier rebuild of Fowler locos. (Introduced 1927) with taper boiler, new cylinders and double chimney.

•Introduced 1935. Stanier taper boiler rebuild with simple cyls. of experimental high pressure compound loco. No. 6399 *Fury*. (Introduced 1929.)

Weight: Loco. $\begin{cases} 83 \text{ tons} \\ 84 \text{ tons 1 cwt.}^\bullet \end{cases}$

Pressure: 250 lb. Su.

Cyls.: (3) 18″ × 26″.

Dr. Wheels: 6′ 9″.   T.E.: 33,150 lb.

Walschaerts Valve Gear.   P.V.

46100 Royal Scot
46101 Royal Scots Grey
46102 Black Watch
46103 Royal Scots Fusilier
46104 Scottish Borderer
46105 Cameron Highlander
46106 Gordon Highlander
46107 Argyll and Sutherland Highlander
46108 Seaforth Highlander
46109 Royal Engineer
46110 Grenadier Guardsman
46111 Royal Fusilier
46112 Sherwood Forester
46113 Cameronian
46114 Coldstream Guardsman
46115 Scots Guardsman
46116 Irish Guardsman
46117 Welsh Guardsman
46118 Royal Welch Fusilier
46119 Lancashire Fusilier
46120 Royal Inniskilling Fusilier
46121 Highland Light Infantry, City of Glasgow Regiment
46122 Royal Ulster Rifleman
46123 Royal Irish Fusilier
46124 London Scottish
46125 3rd Carabinier
46126 Royal Army Service Corps
46127 Old Contemptibles
46128 The Lovat Scouts
46129 The Scottish Horse
46130 The West Yorkshire Regiment
46131 The Royal Warwickshire Regiment
46132 The King's Regiment Liverpool
46133 The Green Howards
46134 The Cheshire Regiment
46135 The East Lancashire Regiment
46136 The Border Regiment
46137 The Prince of Wales's Volunteers (South Lancashire)
46138 The London Irish Rifleman
46139 The Welch Regiment
46140 The King's Royal Rifle Corps
46141 The North Staffordshire Regiment
46142 The York & Lancaster Regiment
46143 The South Staffordshire Regiment
46144 Honourable Artillery Company
46145 The Duke of Wellington's Regt. (West Riding)
46146 The Rifle Brigade
46147 The Northamptonshire Regiment
46148 The Manchester Regiment
46149 The Middlesex Regiment
46150 The Life Guardsman
46151 The Royal Horse Guardsman
46152 The King's Dragoon Guardsman

46153 The Royal Dragoon
46154 The Hussar
46155 The Lancer
46156 The South Wales Borderer
46157 The Royal Artilleryman
46158 The Loyal Regiment
46159 The Royal Air Force
46160 Queen Victoria's Rifleman
46161 King's Own
46162 Queen's Westminster Rifleman
46163 Civil Service Rifleman
46164 The Artists' Rifleman
46165 The Ranger (12th London Regt.)
46166 London Rifle Brigade
46167 The Hertfordshire Regiment
46168 The Girl Guide
46169 The Boy Scout
46170*British Legion

Total 71

"Princess Royal" Class

4-6-2   8P

*Introduced 1933. Stanier L.M.S. taper boiler design.

Remainder. Introduced 1935. Development of original design with alterations to valve gear, boiler and other details.

Weight : Loco. 104 tons 10 cwt.

Pressure: 250 lb. Su.

Cyls.: (4)   16¼"×28"

Dr. Wheels: 6' 6".   T.E.: 40,285 lb.

Walschaerts Valve Gear (inside valves operated by rocking shafts on No. 46205 ; remainder have four sets of valve gear). P.V

46200*The Princess Royal
46201*Princess Elizabeth
46203 Princess Margaret Rose
46204 Princess Louise
46205 Princess Victoria
46206 Princess Marie Louise
46207 Princess Arthur of Connaught
46208 Princess Helena Victoria
46209 Princess Beatrice
46210 Lady Patricia
46211 Queen Maud
46212 Duchess of Kent

Total 12

"Princess Coronation" Class

4-6-2   8P

Introduced 1937. Stanier L.M.S. enlargement of "Princess Royal" class. All except Nos. 46230-4/49-55 originally streamlined. (Streamlining removed from 1946).

*Introduced 1947. Ivatt development with roller bearings and details alterations.

Weight: Loco. { 105 tons 5 cwt.
                106 tons 8 cwt.*

Pressure: 250 lb. Su.

Cyls.: (4) 16¼"×28"

Dr. Wheels: 6' 9".   T.E. 40,000 lb.

Walschaerts Valve Gear and rocking shafts. P.V.

46220 Coronation
46221 Queen Elizabeth
46222 Queen Mary
46223 Princess Alice
46224 Princess Alexandra
46225 Duchess of Gloucester
46226 Duchess of Norfolk
46227 Duchess of Devonshire
46228 Duchess of Rutland
46229 Duchess of Hamilton
46230 Duchess of Buccleuch

46231 Duchess of Atholl	
46232 Duchess of Montrose	
46233 Duchess of Sutherland	
46234 Duchess of Abercorn	
46235 City of Birmingham	
46236 City of Bradford	
46237 City of Bristol	
46238 City of Carlisle	
46239 City of Chester	
46240 City of Coventry	
46241 City of Edinburgh	
46242 City of Glasgow	
46243 City of Lancaster	
46244 King George VI	
46245 City of London	
46246 City of Manchester	
46247 City of Liverpool	
46248 City of Leeds	
46249 City of Sheffield	
46250 City of Lichfield	
46251 City of Nottingham	
46252 City of Leicester	
46253 City of St. Albans	
46254 City of Stoke-on-Trent	
46255 City of Hereford	
46256*Sir William A. Stanier, F.R.S.	
46257*City of Salford	

Total 38

46420	46447	46474*	46501*
46421	46448	46475*	46502*
46422	46449	46476*	46503*
46423	46450	46477*	46504*
46424	46451	46478*	46505*
46425	46452	46479*	46506*
46426	46453	46480*	46507*
46427	46454	46481*	46508*
46428	46455	46482*	46509*
46429	46456	46483*	46510*
46430	46457	46484*	46511*
46431	46458	46485*	46512*
46432	46459	46486*	46513*
46433	46460	46487*	46514*
46434	46461	46488*	46515*
46435	46462	46489*	46516*
46436	46463	46490*	46517*
46437	46464	46491*	46518*
46438	46465*	46492*	46519*
46439	46466*	46493*	46520*
46440	46467*	46494*	46521*
46441	46468*	46495*	46522*
46442	46469*	46496*	46523*
46443	46470*	46497*	46524*
46444	46471*	46498*	46525*
46445	46472*	46499*	46526*
46446	46473*	46500*	46527*

Total 128

2-6-0   2

Introduced 1946. Ivatt L.M.S taper boiler design.
Weight: Loco. 47 ton; 2 cwt.
Pressure: 200 lb. Su.
Cyls.: (O) 16" × 24".
       (O) 16¼" × 24".•
Dr Wheels: 5' 0"   T.E.: 17,410 lb.
                        18.510 lb •
Walschaerts Valve Gear. P.V.

46400	46405	46410	46415
46401	46406	46411	46416
46402	46407	46412	46417
46403	46408	46413	46418
46404	46409	46414	46419

0-4-0ST   0F

Introduced 1932. Kitson design prepared to Stanier's requirements for L.M.S.
*Introduced 1953 Extended saddle tanks and coal space.
Weight: 33 tons 0 cwt.
        34 tons 0 cwt.•
Pressure: 160 lb.
Cyls. :(O) 15½" × 30".
Dr. Wheels: 3' 10".   T.E.: 14,205 lb.

47000	47003	47006*	47008*
47001	47004	47007*	47009*
47002	47005*		

Total 10

0-6-0T   2F

Introduced 1928. Fowler L.M.S. short-wheelbase dock tanks.
Weight: 43 tons 12 cwt.
Pressure: 160 lb.
Cyls.: (O) 17″×22″.
Dr. Wheels: 3′ 11″.   T.E.: 18,400 lb.
Walschaerts Valve Gear.

47160	47163	47166	47168
47161	47164	47167	47169
47162	47165		

Total 10

0-4-0T   Sentinel

Geared Sentinel locos.
*Introduced 1929. Single-speed locos. for S. & D.J. (taken into L.M.S. stock 1930).
†Introduced 1930. Two-speed loco. for L.M.S.
Weight: { 27 tons 15 cwt.* 20 tons 17 cwt.†
Pressure: 275 lb Su.
Cyls.: { (4) 6¾″×9″.* 6¾″×9″.†
Dr. Wheels: { 3′ 1½″.* 2′ 6″.†
T.E.: { 15,500 lb.* 11,800 lb.†
Foppet Valves.

47181†   47190*   47191*

Total 3

NOTE
To understand the system of reference marks used in this book it is essential to read the notes on page 2.

0-6-0T   3F

Introduced 1899. Johnson large Midland design, rebuilt with Belpaire firebox from 1919; fitted with condensers for London area.
*Introduced 1899. Non-Condensing locos.
Weight: 48 tons 15 cwt.
Pressure: 160 lb.
Cyls.: 18″×26″
Dr. Wheels: 4′ 7″   T.E.: 20,835 lb.

47200	47213	47228	47243
47201*	47214	47229	47246*
47202	47216	47230*	47247
47203	47217	47231*	47248*
47204	47218	47233*	47249
47205	47219	47234*	47250*
47206	47221	47235*	47251
47207	47222	47236*	47254*
47208	47223	47238*	47255*
47209	47224	47239*	47256*
47210	47225	47240	47257*
47211	47226	47241	47258*
47212	47227	47242	47259*

Total 52

0-6-0T   3F

Introduced 1924. Post-grouping development of Midland design with detail alterations.
*Introduced 1929. Locos. built for S. & D.J. (taken into L.M.S. stock 1930).
†Push-and-pull fitted.
Weight: 49 tons 10 cwt.
Pressure: 160 lb.
Cyls.: 18″×26″.
Dr. Wheels: 4′ 7″   T.E.: 20,835 lb.

47260	47270	47280	47290
47261	47271	47281	47291
47262	47272	47282	47292
47263	47273	47283	47293
47264	47274	47284	47294
47265	47275	47285	47295
47266	47276	47286	47296
47267	47277	47287	47297
47268	47278	47288	47298
47269	47279	47289	47299

47300	47346	47392	47438	47485	47531	47578	47626
47301	47347	47393	47439	47486	47532	47579	47627
47302	47348	47394	47440	47487	47533	47580	47628
47303	47349	47395	47441	47488	47534	47581	47629
47304	47350	47396	47442	47489	47535	47582	47630
47305	47351	47397	47443	47490	47536	47583	47631
47306	47352	47398	47444	47491	47537	47584	47632
47307	47353	47399	47445	47492	47538	47585	47633
47308	47354	47400	47446	47493	47539	47586	47634
47309	47355	47401	47447	47494	47540	47587	47635
47310*	47356	47402	47448	47495	47541	47588	47636
47311*	47357	47403	47449	47496	47542	47589	47637
47312*	47358	47404	47450	47497	47543	47590	47638
47313*	47359	47405	47451	47498	47544	47591	47639
47314*	47360	47406	47452	47499	47545	47592S	47640
47315*	47361	47407	47453	47500	47546	47593	47641
47316*	47362	47408	47454	47501	47547	47594	47642
47317	47363	47409	47455	47502	47548	47595	47643
47318	47364	47410	47457	47503	47549	47596	47644
47319	47365	47411	47458	47504	47550	47597	47645
47320	47366	47412	47459	47505	47551	47598	47646
47321	47367	47413	47460	47506	47552	47599	47647
47322	47368	47414	47461	47507	47554	47600	47648
47323	47369	47415	47462	47508	47555	47601	47649
47324	47370	47416	47463	47509	47556	47602	47650
47325	47371	47417	47464	47510	47557	47603	47651
47326	47372	47418	47465	47511	47558	47604	47652
47327	47373	47419	47466	47512	47559	47605	47653
47328	47374	47420	47467	47513	47560	47606	47654
47329	47375	47421	47468	47514	47561	47607	47655†
47330	47376	47422	47469	47515	47562	47608	47656
47331	47377	47423	47470	47516	47563	47609	47657
47332	47378	47424	47471	47517	47564	47610	47658
47333	47379	47425	47472	47518	47565	47611	47659
47334	47380	47426	47473	47519	47566	47612	47660
47335	47381	47427	47474	47520	47567	47614	47661
47336	47382	47428	47475	47521	47568	47615	47662
47337	47383	47429	47476	47522	47569	47616	47664
47338	47384	47430	47477†	47523	47570	47618	47665
47339	47385	47431	47478†	47524	47571	47619	47666
47340	47386	47432	47479†	47525	47572	47620	47667
47341	47387	47433	47480†	47526	47573	47621	47668
47342	47388	47434	47481†	47527	47574	47622	47669
47343	47389	47435	47482	47528	47575	47623	47670
47344	47390	47436	47483	47529	47576	47624	47671
47345	47391	47437	47484	47530	47577	47625	47672

47673	47676	47678	47680
47674	47677	47679	47681†
47675			**Total 417**

0-4-2ST   1F

Introduced 1896. Webb L.N.W.
  Bissel truck design.
Weight: 34 tons 17 cwt.
Pressure: 150 lb.
Cyls.: 17″×24″.
Dr. Wheels: 4′ 5½″.   T.E.: 16,530 lb.

47862S		**Total 1**

2-6-6-2T   Beyer-Garratt

*Introduced 1927. Fowler & Beyer-
  Peacock, L.M.S. design with fixed
  coal bunker.
Remainder. Introduced 1930. Develop-
  ment with detail alterations, later
  fitted with revolving coal bunkers.
Weight: { 148 tons 15 cwt.*
         { 155 tons 10 cwt.
Pressure: 190 lb. Su.
Cyls. (4) 18½″×26″.
Dr. Wheels: 5′ 3″.   T.E.: 45,620 lb.
Walschaerts Valve Gear. P.V.

47967	47973	47981	47988
47968	47978	47982	47994
47969	47979	47986	47995
47971	47980	47987	47998*
47972			

			Total 17

2-8-0   8F

Introduced 1935. Stanier L.M.S. taper
boiler design.
Weight: Loco. 72 tons 2 cwt.
Pressure: 225 lb. Su.
Cyls.: (O) 18½″ × 28″
Dr. Wheels: 4′ 8½″.   T.E.: 32,440 lb
Walschaerts Valve gear. P.V.

48000	48001	48002	48003

48004	48080	48129	48175
48005	48081	48130	48176
48006	48082	48131	48177
48007	48083	48132	48178
48008	48084	48133	48179
48009	48085	48134	48180
48010	48088	48135	48181
48011	48089	48136	48182
48012	48090	48137	48183
48016	48092	48138	48184
48017	48093	48139	48185
48018	48094	48140	48186
48020	48095	48141	48187
48024	48096	48142	48188
48026	48097	48143	48189
48027	48098	48144	48190
48029	48099	48145	48191
48033	48100	48146	48192
48035	48101	48147	48193
48036	48102	48148	48194
48037	48103	48149	48195
48039	48104	48150	48196
48045	48105	48151	48197
48046	48106	48152	48198
48050	48107	48153	48199
48053	48108	48154	48200
48054	48109	48155	48201
48055	48110	48156	48202
48056	48111	48157	48203
48057	48112	48158	48204
48060	48113	48159	48205
48061	48114	48160	48206
48062	48115	48161	48207
48063	48116	48162	48208
48064	48117	48163	48209
48065	48118	48164	48210
48067	48119	48165	48211
48069	48120	48166	48212
48070	48121	48167	48213
48073	48122	48168	48214
48074	48123	48169	48215
48075	48124	48170	48216
48076	48125	48171	48217
48077	48126	48172	48218
48078	48127	48173	48219
48079	48128	48174	48220

48221	48287	48336	48382	48428	48474	48534	48620
48222	48288	48337	48383	48429	48475	48535	48621
48223	48289	48338	48384	48430	48476	48536	48622
48224	48290	48339	48385	48431	48477	48537	48623
48225	48291	48340	48386	48432	48478	48538	48624
48246	48292	48341	48387	48433	48479	48539	48625
48247	48293	48342	48388	48434	48490	48540	48626
48248	48294	48343	48389	48435	48491	48541	48627
48249	48295	48344	48390	48436	48492	48542	48628
48250	48296	48345	48391	48437	48493	48543	48629
48251	48297	48346	48392	48438	48494	48544	48630
48252	48301	48347	48393	48439	48495	48545	48631
48253	48302	48348	48394	48440	48500	48546	48632
48254	48303	48349	48395	48441	48501	48547	48633
48255	48304	48350	48396	48442	48502	48548	48634
48256	48305	48351	48397	48443	48503	48549	48635
48257	48306	48352	48398	48444	48504	48550	48636
48258	48307	48353	48399	48445	48505	48551	48637
48259	48308	48354	48400	48446	48506	48552	48638
48260	48309	48355	48401	48447	48507	48553	48639
48261	48310	48356	48402	48448	48508	48554	48640
48262	48311	48357	48403	48449	48509	48555	48641
48263	48312	48358	48404	48450	48510	48556	48642
48264	48313	48359	48405	48451	48511	48557	48643
48265	48314	48360	48406	48452	48512	48558	48644
48266	48315	48361	48407	48453	48513	48559	48645
48267	48316	48362	48408	48454	48514	48600	48646
48268	48317	48363	48409	48455	48515	48601	48647
48269	48318	48364	48410	48456	48516	48602	48648
48270	48319	48365	48411	48457	48517	48603	48649
48271	48320	48366	48412	48458	48518	48604	48650
48272	48321	48367	48413	48459	48519	48605	48651
48273	48322	48368	48414	48460	48520	48606	48652
48274	48323	48369	48415	48461	48521	48607	48653
48275	48324	48370	48416	48462	48522	48608	48654
48276	48325	48371	48417	48463	48523	48609	48655
48277	48326	48372	48418	48464	48524	48610	48656
48278	48327	48373	48419	48465	48525	48611	48657
48279	48328	48374	48420	48466	48526	48612	48658
48280	48329	48375	48421	48467	48527	48613	48659
48281	48330	48376	48422	48468	48528	48614	48660
48282	48331	48377	48423	48469	48529	48615	48661
48283	48332	48378	48424	48470	48530	48616	48662
48284	48333	48379	48425	48471	48531	48617	48663
48285	48334	48380	48426	48472	48532	48618	48664
48286	48335	48381	48427	48473	48533	48619	48665

48666	48693	48720	48747	49010	49116	49200	49311
48667	48694	48721	48748	49018	49117	49202	49313
48668	48695	48722	48749	49020	49119	49203	49314
48669	48696	48723	48750	49021	49120	49209	49315
48670	48697	48724	48751	49023	49121	49210	49316
48671	48698	48725	48752	49024	49122	49214	49318
48672	48699	48726	48753	49025	49125	49216	49321
48673	48700	48727	48754	49027	49126	49223	49323
48674	48701	48728	48755	49033	49129	49224	49327
48675	48702	48729	48756	49034	49130	49226	49328
48676	48703	48730	48757	49035	49132	49228	49330
48677	48704	48731	48758	49037	49134	49229	49335
48678	48705	48732	48759	49044	49137	49230	49340
48679	48706	48733	48760	49045	49139	49234	49341
48680	48707	48734	48761	49046	49141	49239	49342
48681	48708	48735	48762	49047	49142	49240	49343
48682	48709	48736	48763	49048	49143	49243	49344
48683	48710	48737	48764	49049	49144	49245	49345
48684	48711	48738	48765	49051	49145	49246	49348
48685	48712	48739	48766	49057	49146	49247	49350
48686	48713	48740	48767	49061	49147	49249	49352
48687	48714	48741	48768	49063	49148	49252	49355
48688	48715	48742	48769	49064	49149	49254	49357
48689	48716	48743	48770	49066	49150	49260	49358
48690	48717	48744	48771	49068	49153	49262	49361
48591	48718	48745	48772	49070	49154	49266	49366
48692	48719	48746		49073	49155	49267	49367

Total 663

0 8-0   7F

Introduced 1936. L.N.W. G2a Class.
Bowen-Cooke G1 superheated design
of 1912, rebuilt with G2 boiler and
Belpaire firebox.
Weight: Loco. 62 tons 0 cwt.
Pressure: 175 lb. Su.
Cyls.: 20½" × 24".
Dr. Wheels: 4' 5½".
T.E.: 28,045 lb.
Joy Valve Gear.   P.V.

				49077	49157	49268	49368
				49078	49158	49270	49373
				49079	49160	49271	49375
				49081	49161	49275	49376
				49082	49164	49276	49377
				49087	49167	49277	49378
				49088	49168	49278	49381
				49093	49172	49281	49382
				49094	49173	49287	49385
				49099	49174	49288	49386
				49104	49177	49289	49387
				49105	49180	49293	49390
48895	48921	48942	48953	49106	49181	49301	49391
48898	48922	48943	48964	49108	49186	49304	49392
48905	48926	48944	49002	49109	49189	49306	49393
48907	48927	48945	49005	49112	49191	49308	49394
48914	48930	48950	49007	49113	49196	49310	
48915	48932	48951	49008	49114	49198		
48917	48940	48952	49009	49115	49199		

Total 207

49395 51413

0-8-0   7F

Introduced 1921. Development of L.N.W. G2 Class. Bowen-Cooke G1 superheated design of 1912 with higher pressure boiler. Many later rebuilt with Belpaire firebox.
Weight: Loco. 62 tons 0 cwt.
Pressure: 175 lb. Su.
Cyls.: 20½" × 24".
Dr. Wheels: 4' 5½".
T.E.: 28,045 lb.
Joy Valve Gear. P.V.

49395	49410	49425	49440
49396	49411	49426	49441
49397	49412	49427	49442
49398	49413	49428	49443
49399	49414	49429	49444
49400	49415	49430	49445
49401	49416	49431	49446
49402	49417	49432	49447
49403	49418	49433	49448
49404	49419	49434	49449
49405	49420	49435	49450
49406	49421	49436	49451
49407	49422	49437	49452
49408	49423	49438	49453
49409	49424	49439	49454

Total 60

0-8-0   7F

Introduced 1929. Fowler L.M.S. design, developed from L.N.W. G2.
Weight: Loco. 60 tons 15 cwt.
Pressure: 200 lb. Su.
Cyls.: 19½" × 26".
Dr. Wheels: 4' 8½".   T.E.: 29,745 lb.
Walschaerts Valve Gear. P.V.

49505	49547	49592	49657
49508	49552	49593	49659
49509	49555	49618	49662
49511	49560	49624	49664
49515	49566	49627	49667
49536	49578	49637	49668
49538	49582	49640	49672
49544	49586	49648	49674
49545			

Total 33

2-4-2T   2P

Introduced 1889.   Aspinall L. & Y. Class 5 with 2 tons coal capacity.

*Introduced 1890. Locos. built or rebuilt with smaller cylinders.
†Introduced 1893. Locos. with longer tanks and 4 tons coal capacity.
‡Introduced 1905. Hughes loco. built with Belpaire firebox and extended smokebox.
¶ ntroduced 1910. Locos. rebuilt with Belpaire firebox and extended smokebox.
Weight: { 55 tons 19 cwt. / 55 tons 19 cwt.* / 59 tons 3 cwt.†‡¶
Pressure: 180 lb.
Cyls.: { 17½"×26".* / 18"×26".   T.E.: { 18,360 lb.* / 18,955 lb.
Dr Wheels: 5' 8.   Joy Valve Gear.

50636	50660	50752*	50829†¶
50643*	50705	50757	50831†
50644	50712	50777	50850†¶
50646	50721	50781	50855*†
50647	50725	50795*	50865*†
50650¶	50746	50818	50887‡†
50652*¶			

Total 25

0-4-0ST   0F

Introduced 1891.   Aspinall L. & Y. Class 21.
Weight: 21 tons 5 cwt.
Pressure: 160 lb.
Cyls.: (O) 13"×18".
Dr. Wheels: 3' 0⅜".   T.E.: 11,335 lb.

51202	51217	51230	51240
51204	51218	51231	51241
51206	51221	51232	51244
51207	51222	51234	51246
51212	51227	51235	51253
51216	51229	51237	

Total 23

0-6-0ST   2F

Introduced 1891. Aspinall rebuild of L. & Y. Barton Wright Class 23 0-6-0. Originally introduced 1877.
Weight: 43 tons 17 cwt.
Pressure: 140 lb.   Cyls.: 17½"×26".
Dr Wheels: 4' 6".   T.E.: 17,545 lb.

51304S	51321	51353	51394S
51305S	51324S	51358	51397
51307	51336	51361	51404
51313	51338	51368S	51408
51316	51343	51371	51412S
51319	51345	51381	51413

39

51415	51446S	51481	51500
51419	51447	51484	51503
51423	51453	51486	51506
51424	51457	51491	51512
51429S	51458	51496	51516
51432	51462	51497	51521
51441	51464	51498	51524
51444S	51474	51499	51526
51445	51479		

Total 58

Dr. Wheels: $\begin{cases} 5' \ 1". \\ 5' \ 1".• \\ 4' \ 7\frac{1}{2}".† \end{cases}$

T.E.: $\begin{cases} 21,130 \ \text{lb.} \\ 21,130 \ \text{lb.}* \\ 23,225 \ \text{lb.}† \end{cases}$

Joy Valve Gear

0-6-0T 1F

Introduced 1897. Aspinall L. & Y.
Class 24 dock tanks.
Weight: 50 tons 0 cwt.
Pressure: 140 lb.
Cyls.: (O) 17"×24"
Dr. Wheels: 4' 0".   T.E.: 15,285 lb.
Allan straight link gear.

51535	51537	51544	51546

Total 4

0-6-0 2F

Introduced 1887. Barton Wright
L. & Y. Class 25.
Weight: Loco. 39 tons 1 cwt.
Pressure: 140 lb.
Cyls.: 17½"×26".
Dr. Wheels: 4' 6".   T.E.: 17,545 lb.

52016	52044

Total 2

0-6-0 3F

Introduced 1889. Aspinall L. & Y. Class 27. Nos. 52515-29 built superheated with roundtop firebox and extended smokebox, later rebuilt with saturated boiler and short smokebox.
*Introduced 1911. Rebuilt with Belpaire firebox and extended smokebox.
†Furness 0-6-0s rebuilt with ex-L. & Y. boiler.

Weight: Loco. $\begin{cases} 42 \text{ tons } 3 \text{ cwt.} \\ 43 \text{ tons } 11 \text{ cwt.}* \\ 42 \text{ tons } 3 \text{ cwt.}† \end{cases}$

Pressure: 180 lb.
Cyls.: 18"×26".

52089	52183	52311	52415
52093S	52186	52312*S	52418
52094*	52196	52319*	52427
52095	52197*	52322	52429
52108	52201*	52328	52431*
52119	52203	52336	52432
52120	52207S	52338	52438*
52121	52212S	52341	52441S
52123	52216	52345S	52443
52125	52217	52348	52445*
52129	52218S	52350	52449
52132*	52225	52351	52452
52133	52230	52355	52455
52135*	52232	52356	52456
52136	52235	52358	52458
52139	52236	52360	52459S
52140*	52237	52366	52461
52141	52240	52368	52464S
52143	52244	52376	52466
52154*	52248	52378	52499†
52159	52252	52379*	52501†
52160	52260	52387	52509†
52161*	52268	52388	52510†
52162*	52269	52389	52515
52165	52270	52390	52517S
52166	52271	52393	52521
52171	52273*	52399	52523
52172	52275	52400*	52526
52175	52289	52405	52527
52177	52290	52410	52529
52179	52293	52411	
52182	52305	52412	
		52413*	

Total: L. & Y. 125, F.R. 4

Class 7P 4-6-0 No. 46110 *Grenadier Guardsman* [Brian E. Morrison

Class 7P 4-6-0 No. 46170 *British Legion* (rebuilt in 1935 from experimental compound loco. No. 6399) [G. Wheeler

Class 8P 4-6-2 No. 46222 *Queen Mary* [P. H. Groom

Class 2P 0-4-4T No. 41908   [J. R. Paterson

Class 0F 0-4-0ST No. 47006   [P. R. Gooalad

Class 1P 0-4-4T No. 58051   [D. Penney

Right: Class 2F 0-6-0T
No. 47166
    [*R. J. Buckley*

Below: Class 1F 0-6-0T
No. 41726
    [*Brian E. Morrison*

Right: Class 2F 0-6-0T
No. 58857
    [*R. E. Vincent*

Class 2F 0-6-0 No. 58170 [D. Penney

Class 3F 0-6-0 No. 43436 [W. Vaughan-Jenkins

Beyer-Garratt 2-6-6-2T No. 47987 [J. Davenport

Above: Class 2F 0-6-0ST
No. 51425 (now with-
drawn)
[*Brian E. Morrison*

Right: Class 1F 0-6-0T
No. 51535

Below: Class 2P 2-4-2T
No. 50757
[*D. Penney*

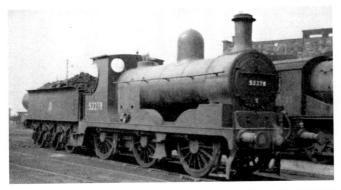

Above: Class 3F (L & Y)
0-6-0 No. 52278
[*T. K. Widd*

Left: Class 3F (L & Y)
0-6-0 No. 52135 (with
Belpaire firebox and
extended smokebox)
[*R. K. Evans*

Below: Class 3F (Furness) 0-6-0 No. 52501
(rebuilt with ex-L & Y
boiler)
[*D. Marriott*

Class 2F (Drummond) 0-5-0 No. 57354   [D. Marriott

Class 3F (McIntosh) 0-6-0 No. 57589   [M. J. Ecclestone

Class 3F (Pickersgill) 0-6-0 No. 57661   [R. K. Evans

Class OF 0-4-0ST No. 56011 (*left*) and Class IP 0-4-4T No. 55053 (the last ex-Highland engine in service)

[K. R. Pirt

Class 2P (McIntosh) 0-4-4T No. 55203

[J. Robertson

Class 2F (McIntosh) 0-6-0T No. 56170

[L. Marshall

0-6-0   3F

Introduced 1912. Huges L. & Y.
Class 28, superheated development
of Class 27.
*Introduced 1913. Rebuild of Class 27.
Weight: Loco. 46 tons 10 cwt.
Pressure: 180 lb. Su.
Cyls.: 20½″×26″
Dr. Wheels: 5′ 1″.   T.E.: 27,405 lb.
Joy Valve gear. P.V.

52551   52576*

Total 2

2-8-0   7F

Introduced 1914. Fowler design for
S. & D.J.
(All taken into L.M.S. stock, 1930.)
Weight: Loco. 64 tons 15 cwt.
Pressure: 190 lb. Su.
Cyls.: (O) 21″×28″.
Dr. Wheels: 4′ 8½″.   T.E.: 35,295 lb.
Walschaerts Valve Gear. P.V.

53800	53803	53806	53809
53801	53804	53807	53810
53802	53805	53808	

Total 11

4-4-0   3P

Introduced 1910. McIntosh Caledonian
" Dunalastair IV Superheater " or
" 139 " class.
*Introduced 1915. Superheated rebuild of McIntosh Caledonian " Dunalastair IV " or " 140 " class (originally introduced 1904).
Weight: Loco. 61 tons 5 cwt.
Pressure: 180 lb. Su.
Cyls.: 20½″×26″.
Dr. Wheels: 6′ 6″.   T.E.: 20,915 lb.
P.V.

54439*	54441	54453	54458
54440	54452	54456	

Total 7

4-4-0   3P

Introduced 1916. Pickersgill Caledonian " 113 " and " 928 " classes.
Weight: Loco. 61 tons 5 cwt.
Pressure: 180 lb. Su.   Cyls.: 20″×26″.
Dr. Wheels: 6′ 6″. T.E.: 20,400 lb. P.V.

54461	54465	54469	54473
54462	54466	54470	54474
54463	54467	54471	54475
54464	54468	54472	54476

Total 16

4-4-0   3P

Introduced 1920. Pickersgill Caledonian " 72 " class.
Weight: Loco. 61 tons 5 cwt.
Pressure: 180 lb. Su. Cyls.: 20½″×26″.
Dr. Wheels: 6′ 6″. T.E.: 21,435 lb. P.V.

54477	54486	54494	54502
54478	54487	54495	54503
54479	54488	54496	54504
54480	54489	54497	54505
54482	54490	54498	54506
54483	54491	54499	54507
54484	54492	54500	54508
54485	54493	54501	

Total 31

0-4-4T   1P

Introduced 1905. Drummond Highland
design.
Weight: 35 tons 15 cwt.
Pressure: 150 lb.   Cyls.: 14″×20″.
Dr. Wheels: 4′ 6″   T.E.: 9,255 lb.

55053   **Total 1**

0-4-4T   2P

*Introduced 1895. McIntosh Caledonian " 19 " class, with railed coal
bunker.
Remainder. Introduced 1897. McIntosh
" 92 " class, developed from " 29 "
class with larger tanks and highsided
coal bunker (both classes originally
fitted for condensing on Glasgow
Central Low Level lines).
Weight: { 53 tons 16 cwt.*
         { 53 tons 19 cwt.
Pressure: 180 lb.   Cyls.: 18″×26″.
Dr. Wheels: 5′ 9″.   T.E.: 18,680 lb.
55124*   55125   55126   55141

Total 4

49

0-4-4T   2P

Introduced 1900. McIntosh Caledonian " 439 " or " Standard Passenger " class.
*Introduced 1915. Pickersgill locos. with detail alterations.
Weight: {53 tons 19 cwt.
        {57 tons 12 cwt.*
Pressure: 180 lb.
Cyls.: 18″×26″.
Dr. Wheels: 5′ 9″.   T.E.: 18,680 lb.

55160	55198	55212	55225
55164	55199	55213	55226
55165	55200	55214	55227*
55167	55201	55215	55228*
55168	55202	55216	55229*
55169	55203	55217	55230*
55173	55204	55218	55231*
55176	55206	55219	55232*
55178	55207	55220	55233*
55182	55208	55221	55234*
55185	55209	55222	55235*
55189	55210	55223	55236*
55195	55211	55224	

Total 51

0-4-4T   2P

Introduced 1922. Pickersgill Caledonian " 431 " class (developed from " 439 " class) with cast-iron front buffer beam for banking.
Weight: 57 tons 17 cwt.
Pressure: 180 lb.
Cyls.: 18½″×26″.
Dr. Wheels: 5′ 9″.   T.E.: 19,200 lb.

55237	55238	55239	55240

Total 4

0-4-4T   2P

Introduced 1925. Post-Grouping development of Caledonian " 439 " class.
Weight: 59 tons 12 cwt.
Pressure: 180 lb.
Cyls.: 18½″×26″.
Dr. Wheels: 5′ 9″   T.E.: 19,200 lb.

55260	55263	55266	55268
55261	55264	55267	55269
55262	55265		

Total 10

0-4-0ST   0F

Introduced 1885. Drummond and McIntosh Caledonian " Pugs."
Weight: 27 tons 7 cwt.
Pressure: 160 lb.   Cyls: (O) 14″×20″.
Dr. Wheels: 3′ 8″.   T.E.: 12,115 lb.

56011	56028	56031	56038
56025S	56029	56032S	56039
56027	56030	56035	

Total 11

0-6-0T   2F

Introduced 1911. McIntosh Caledonian dock shunters, " 498 " class.
Weight: 47 tons 15 cwt.
Pressure: 160 lb.   Cyls.: (O) 17″×22″.
Dr. Wheels: 4′ 0″.   T.E.: 18,015 lb.

56151	56157	56163	56169
56152	56158	56164	56170
56153	56159	56165	56171
56154	56160	56166	56172
56155	56161	56167	56173
56156	56162	56168	

Total 23

0-6-0T   3F

Introduced 1895. McIntosh Caledonian " 29 " and " 782 " classes (56231-9 originally condensing)
Weight: 47 tons 15 cwt.
Pressure: 160 lb.   Cyls.: 18″×26″.
Dr. Wheels: 4′ 6″.   T.E.: 21,215 lb.

56230	56241	56252	56262
56232	56242	56253	56264
56233	56243	56254	56265
56234	56244	56255	56266
56235	56245	56256	56267
56236	56246	56257	56269
56238	56247	56259	56272
56239	56249	56260	56274
56240	56251	56261	56275

56277	56302	56328	56353	57273	57328	57367	57429
56278	56303	56329	56354	57274	57329	57368	57430
56279	56304	56330	56355	57275	57331	57369	57431
56280	56305	56331	56356	57276	57335	57370	57432
56281	56306	56332	56357	57278	57336	57373	57434
56282	56307	56333	56358	57279	57338	57375	57435
56283	56308	56334	56359	57284	57339	57377	57436
56284	56309	56335	56360	57285	57340	57378	57437
56285	56310	56336	56361	57287	57341	57383	57441
56286	56311	56337	56362	57288	57345	57384	57443
56287	56312	56338	56363	57291	57346	57385	57444
56288	56313	56339	56364	57292	57347	57386	57445
56289	56314	56340	56365	57295	57348	57389	57446
56290	56315	56341	56366	57296	57349	57392	57447
56291	56316	56342	56367	57299	57350	57396	57448
56292	56318	56343	56368	57300	57353	57398	57451
56293	56320	56344	56369	57302	57354	57404	57459
56294	56321	56345	56370	57303	57355	57405	57460
56295	56322	56346	56371	57307	57356	57407	57461
56296	56323	56347	56372	57309	57357	57411	57462
56297	56324	56348	56373	57311	57359	57413	57463
56298	56325	56349	56374	57314	57360	57414	57465
56299	56326	56350	56375	57317	57361	57416	57470
56300	56327	56352	56376	57319	57362	57417	57472
56301				57321	57363	57418	57473
				57324	57364	57419	
				57325	57365	57424	
				57326	57366	57426	

Total 133

0-6-0   2F

Introduced 1883. Drummond Caledonian "Standard Goods"; later additions by Lambie and McIntosh. Some rebuilt with L.M.S. boiler.*
Weight: Loco. { 41 tons 6 cwt.
{ 42 tons 4 cwt.*
Pressure: 180 lb.
Cyls.: 18" × 26".
Dr. Wheels: 5' 0".   T.E.: 21,480 lb.

57232	57242	57252	57263
57233	57243	57253	57264
57234	57244	57254	57265
57236	57245	57256	57266
57237	57246	57257	57267
57238	57247	57258	57268
57239	57249	57259	57269
57240	57250	57261	57270
57241	57251	57262	57271

Total 145

0-6-0   3F

Introducee 1899. McIntosh Caledonian "812" (Nos. 57550–57623) and "652" (remainder) classes.
Weight: Loco. 45 tons. 14 cwt.
Pressure: 180 lb.
Cyls.: 18½"×26".
Dr. Wheels: 5' 0".   T.E.: 22,690 lb.

57550	57558	57566	57575
57552	57559	57568	57576
57553	57560	57569	57577
57554	57562	57570	57579
57555	57563	57571	57580
57556	57564	57572	57581
57557	57565	57573	57562

57583	57599	57615	57632
57585	57600	57617	57633
57586	57601	57618	57634
57587	57602	57619	57635
57588	57603	57620	57637
57589	57604	57621	57638
57590	57605	57622	57640
57591	57607	57623	57642
57592	57608	57625	57643
57593	57609	57626	57644
57594	57611	57627	57645
57595	57612	57628	
57596	57613	57630	
57597	57614	57631	

Total 81

0-6-0　　　　　　　　　　3F

Introduced 1918. Pickersgill Cale-
donian "294" class (superheated)
and "670" classes.
Weight: Loco. 50 tons 13 cwt.
Pressure: 110 lb. Su.
Cyls.: 18½"×26".
Dr. Wheels: 5' 0".　　T.E.: 22,690 lb.
P.V.

57650	57661	57670	57682
57651	57663	57671	57684
57652	57665	57672	57686
57653	57666	57673	57688
57654	57667	57674	57689
57655	57668	57679	57690
57658	57669	57681	57691
57659			

Total 29

0-4-4T　　　　　　　　　　1P

*Introduced 1881. Johnson Midland
design, rebuilt with Belpaire firebox.
†Introduced 1889 with larger cylinders
and higher boiler pressure. All
rebuilt with Belpaire firebox.
‡Introduced 1895. Final Johnson
0-4-4T design, with higher-pitched
boiler and larger tanks, later rebuilt
with Belpaire firebox.
§Fitted with condensing gear.
All Push-and-Pull fitted except 58072
Weight: 53 tons 4 cwt.

Pressure: $\begin{cases} 140 \text{ lb.}^* \\ 150 \text{ lb.}†‡ \end{cases}$

Cyls.: $\begin{cases} 17"×24".^*† \\ 18"×24".† \end{cases}$　T.E.: $\begin{cases} 15,170 \text{ lb.}^* \\ 18,225 \text{ lb.}† \\ 16,255 \text{ lb.}‡ \end{cases}$

Dr. Wheels: 5' 4".

58051*	58066†	58083‡	58086‡
58065†	58072†§	58085‡	58091‡

Total 8

0-6-0　　　　　　　　　　2F

*Introduced 1875. Johnson Midland
4' 11" design with round top firebox.
†Introduced 1917. Johnson 4' 11" design
rebuilt with Belpaire firebox.
§Introduced 1917 Johnson Midland 5' 3"
design rebuilt with Belpaire firebox.
Weight: Loco. Various.
37 tons 12 cwt. to 40 tons 3 cwt.
Pressure: 160 lb.　　Cyls.: 18"×26".

Dr. Wheels: $\begin{cases} 4' 11"^* \\ 4' 11"† \\ 5' 3"§ \end{cases}$ T.E.: $\begin{cases} 19,420 \text{ lb.}^* \\ 19,420 \text{ lb.}† \\ 18,185 \text{ lb.}§ \end{cases}$

58114†	58148†	58186†	58224§
58115†	58153†	58187†	58225§
58116†	58156†	58188§	58228§
58118†	58157†	58189§	58238†
58119†	58158†	58190§	58246*
58120†	58160†	58191§	58247†
58121†	58163†	58192§	58260§
58122†	58165†	58196§	58261§
58123†	58166†	58197§	58271§
58124†	58167†	58198§	58279§
58128†	58168†	58199§	58281§
58130†	58169†	58203§	58283§
58131†	58170†	58204§	58287§
58132†	58171†	58206§	58288§
58135†	58173†	58209§	58291§
58136†	58174†	58213§	58293§
58137†	58175†	58214§	58295§
58138†	58177†	58215§	58298§
58139†	58178†	58216§	58299§
58140†	58181†	58217§	58305§
58142†	58182†	58218§	58306§
58143†	58183†	58219§	58308§
58144†	58184†	58220§	58310§
58146†	58185†	58221§	

Total 95

0-6-0T   2F

Introduced 1879 Park North London design.
Weight: 45 tons 10 cwt.
Pressure: 160 lb.
Cyls.: (O) 17" × 24".
Dr. Wheels: 4' 4".   T.E.: 18,140 lb.

| 58850 | 58856 | 58859 | 58860 |
| 58854 | 58857 | | |

Total 6

0-6-2T   2F

Introduced 1882. Webb L.N.W. "Coal Tanks."
Weight: 43 tons 15 cwt.
Pressure: 150 lb.
Cyls.: 17" × 24".
Dr. Wheels: 4' 5½".   T.E.: 16,530 lb.

58926

Total 1

SERVICE LOCOS.

0-4-0   Diesel

Introduced 1936. Fowler diesel.
Weight: 21 tons 5 cwt.

E.D.1	E.D.4	E.D.6
E.D.2	E.D.5	E.D.7
E.D.3		

0-6-0ST   2F

ntroduced 1870. Webb version of Ramsbottom "Special Tank."
Weight: 34 tons 10 cwt.
Pressure: 140 lb.
Cyls.: 17" × 24".
Dr. Wheels: 4' 5¼".   T.E.: 17,005 lb.

C.D.3 Wolverton Carriage Works
C.D.6
C.D.7   "   "   "
C.D.8 Earlestown, Wolverton C.W.

HISTORIC LOCOMOTIVES PRESERVED IN STORE

Type	Originating Company	Pre-Grouping No.	L.M.S. No.	Name	Place of Preservation
4–2–2	M.R.	118	(673)	—	Derby
2–4–0	M.R.	158A	—	—	Derby
4–4–2T	L.T. & S.	80	(2148)	Thundersley	Derby
2–2–2	L.N.W.	(49)	—	Columbine	York Museum
2–2–2	L.N.W.	3020	—	Cornwall	Crewe
2–4–0	L.N.W.	790	(5031)	Hardwicke	Crewe
0–4–0ST	L.N.W.	1439	—	—	Crewe
*0–4–0T	L.N.W.	—	—	Pet	Crewe
0–4–0	F.R.	3	—	Coppernob	Horwich
0–4–2	Liverpool & Manchester	—	—	Lion	Crewe
4–2–2	C.R.	123	(14010)	—	St. Rollox
4–6–0	H.R.	103	(17916)	—	St. Rollox

The un-bracketed numbers are the ones at present carried by the locos.
*18in. gauge works shunter.

BRITISH RAILWAYS STANDARD LOCOMOTIVES
Chief Officer (Mechanical Engineering) :
R. C. BOND

4-6-2   **7P6F**

Introduced 1951. Designed at Derby.
Weight :   Loco.   94 tons 0 cwt.
                Tender (see page 61).
Pressure : 250 lb.   Su.
Cyls. : (O) 20″ × 28″.
Driving Wheels : 6′ 2″. T.E. : 32,150 lb.
Walschaerts gear. P.V.

70000	Britannia
70001	Lord Hurcomb
70002	Geoffrey Chaucer
70003	John Bunyan
70004	William Shakespeare
70005	John Milton
70006	Robert Burns
70007	Coeur-de-Lion
70008	Black Prince
70009	Alfred the Great
70010	Owen Glendower
70011	Hotspur
70012	John of Gaunt
70013	Oliver Cromwell
70014	Iron Duke
70015	Apollo
70016	Ariel
70017	Arrow
70018	Flying Dutchman
70019	Lightning
70020	Mercury
70021	Morning Star
70022	Tornado
70023	Venus
70024	Vulcan
70025	Western Star
70026	Polar Star
70027	Rising Star
70028	Royal Star
70029	Shooting Star
70030	William Wordsworth
70031	Byron
70032	Tennyson
70033	Charles Dickens
70034	Thomas Hardy
70035	Rudyard Kipling
70036	Boadicea
70037	Hereward the Wake
70038	Robin Hood
70039	Sir Christopher Wren
70040	Clive of India
70041	Sir John Moore
70042	Lord Roberts
70043	
70044	
70045	
70046	
70047	
70048	
70049	
70050	Firth of Clyde
70051	Firth of Forth
70052	Firth of Tay
70053	Moray Firth
70054	Dornoch Firth

Total 55

4-6-2   **8P**

Introduced 1954. Designed at Derby.
Weight :   Loco.   101 tons 5 cwt.
                Tender (see page 61).
Pressure : 250 lb.   Su.
Cyls. : (3) 18″ × 28″.
Driving Wheels : 6′ 2″. T.E.: 39,080 lb.
Caprotti valve gear.

71000	Duke of Gloucester

Total 1

4-6-2   **6P5F**

Introduced 1952. Designed at Derby.
Weight :   Loco.   86 tons 19 cwt.
                Tender (see page 61).
Pressure : 225 lb.   Su.
Cyls. : (O) 19½″ × 28″.
Driving Wheels : 6′ 2″. T.E. : 27,520 lb.
Walschaerts gear. P.V.

72000	Clan Buchanan
72001	Clan Cameron
72002	Clan Campbell
72003	Clan Fraser

54

72004	Clan Macdonald	
72005	Clan Macgregor	
72006	Clan Mackenzie	
72007	Clan Mackintosh	
72008	Clan Macleod	
72009	Clan Stewart	**Total 10**

4-6-0   5

Introduced 1951. Designed at Doncaster.
*Introduced 1956. Fitted with Caprotti valve gear.
Weight : Loco.   76 tons 4 cwt.
        Tender (see page 61).
Pressure : 225 lb.   Su.
Cyls. : (O) 19″ × 28″.
Driving Wheels : 6′ 2″. T.E. : 26,120 lb.
Walschaerts gear. P.V.

73000	73031	73062	73093
73001	73032	73063	73094
73002	73033	73064	73095
73003	73034	73065	73096
73004	73035	73066	73097
73005	73036	73067	73098
73006	73037	73068	73099
73007	73038	73069	73100
73008	73039	73070	73101
73009	73040	73071	73102
73010	73041	73072	73103
73011	73042	73073	73104
73012	73043	73074	73105
73013	73044	73075	73106
73014	73045	73076	73107
73015	73046	73077	73108
73016	73047	73078	73109
73017	73048	73079	73110
73018	73049	73080	73111
73019	73050	73081	73112
73020	73051	73082	73113
73021	73052	73083	73114
73022	73053	73084	73115
73023	73054	73085	73116
73024	73055	73086	73117
73025	73056	73087	73118
73026	73057	73088	73119
73027	73058	73089	73120
73028	73059	73090	73121
73029	73060	73091	73122
73030	73061	73092	73123

73124	73136*	73148	73160
73125*	73137*	73149	73161
73126*	73138*	73150	73162
73127*	73139*	73151	73163
73128*	73140*	73152	73164
73129*	73141*	73153	73165
73130*	73142*	73154	73166
73131*	73143*	73155	73167
73132*	73144*	73156	73168
73133*	73145	73157	73169
73134*	73146	73158	73170
73135*	73147	73159	73171

Engines of this class are still being delivered.

4-6-0   4

Introduced 1951. Designed at Brighton.
Weight : Loco.   69 tons 0 cwt.
        Tender (see page 61).
Pressure : 225 lb.   Su.
Cyls. : (O) 18″ × 28″.
Driving Wheels : 5′ 8″. T.E. : 25,100 lb.
Walschaerts gear. P.V.

75000	75023	75046	75069
75001	75024	75047	75070
75002	75025	75048	75071
75003	75026	75049	75072
75004	75027	75050	75073
75005	75028	75051	75074
75006	75029	75052	75075
75007	75030	75053	75076
75008	75031	75054	75077
75009	75032	75055	75078
75010	75033	75056	75079
75011	75034	75057	75080
75012	75035	75058	75081
75013	75036	75059	75082
75014	75037	75060	75083
75015	75038	75061	75084
75016	75039	75062	75085
75017	75040	75063	75086
75018	75041	75064	75087
75019	75042	75065	75088
75020	75043	75066	75089
75021	75044	75067	
75022	75045	75068	

Engines of this class are still being delivered.

2-6-0   4

Introduced 1953. Designed at Doncaster.
Weight: Loco. 59 tons 2 cwt.
           Tender (see page 61).
Pressure: 225 lb. Su.
Cyls.: (O) 17½" × 26".
Driving Wheels: 5' 3". T.E.: 24,170 lb.
Walschaerts gear. P.V.

76000	76029	76058	76087
76001	76030	76059	76088
76002	76031	76060	76089
76003	76032	76061	76090
76004	76033	76062	76091
76005	76034	76063	76092
76006	76035	76064	76093
76007	76036	76065	76094
76008	76037	76066	76095
76009	76038	76067	76096
76010	76039	76068	76097
76011	76040	76069	76098
76012	76041	76070	76099
76013	76042	76071	76100
76014	76043	76072	76101
76015	76044	76073	76102
76016	76045	76074	76103
76017	76046	76075	76104
76018	76047	76076	76105
76019	76048	76077	76106
76020	76049	76078	76107
76021	76050	76079	76108
76022	76051	76080	76109
76023	76052	76081	76110
76024	76053	76082	76111
76025	76054	76083	76112
76026	76055	76084	76113
76027	76056	76085	76114
76028	76057	76086	

Engines of this class are still being delivered.

2-6-0   3

Introduced 1954. Designed at Swindon.
Weight: Loco. 57 tons 9 cwt.
           Tender (see page 61).
Pressure: 200 lb. Su.
Cyls.: (O) 17" × 26".
Driving Wheels: 5' 3". T.E.: 21,490 lb.
Walschaerts gear. P.V.

77000	77007	77014	77021
77001	77008	77015	77022
77002	77009	77016	77023
77003	77010	77017	77024
77004	77011	77018	
77005	77012	77019	
77006	77013	77020	

Engines of this class are still being delivered.

2-6-0   2

Introduced 1953. Designed at Derby.
Weight: Loco. 49 tons 5 cwt.
           Tender (see page 61).
Pressure: 200 lb. Su.
Cyls.: (O) 16½" × 24".
Driving Wheels: 5' 0". T.E.: 18,515 lb.
Walschaerts gear. P.V.

78000	78017	78034	78051
78001	78018	78035	78052
78002	78019	78036	78053
78003	78020	78037	78054
78004	78021	78038	78055
78005	78022	78039	78056
78006	78023	78040	78057
78007	78024	78041	78058
78008	78025	78042	78059
78009	78026	78043	78060
78010	78027	78044	78061
78011	78028	78045	78062
78012	78029	78046	78063
78013	78030	78047	78064
78014	78031	78048	
78015	78032	78049	
78016	78033	78050	

Engines of this class are still being delivered.

2-6-4T   4

Introduced 1951. Designed at Brighton.
Weight: 88 tons 10 cwt.
Pressure: 225 lb. Su.
Cyls.: (O) 18" × 28".
Driving Wheels: 5' 8" T.E. 25,100 lb.
Walschaerts gear P.V.

80000	80005	80010	80015
80001	80006	80011	80016
80002	80007	80012	80017
80003	80008	80013	80018
80004	80009	80014	80019

80020	80054	80088	80122
80021	80055	80089	80123
80022	80056	80090	80124
80023	80057	80091	80125
80024	80058	80092	80126
80025	80059	80093	80127
80026	80060	80094	80128
80027	80061	80095	80129
80028	80062	80096	80130
80029	80063	80097	80131
80030	80064	80098	80132
80031	80065	80099	80133
80032	80066	80100	80134
80033	80067	80101	80135
80034	80068	80102	80136
80035	80069	80103	80137
80036	80070	80104	80138
80037	80071	80105	80139
80038	80072	80106	80140
80039	80073	80107	80141
80040	80074	80108	80142
80041	80075	80109	80143
80042	80076	80110	80144
80043	80077	80111	80145
80044	80078	80112	80146
80045	80079	80113	80147
80046	80080	80114	80148
80047	80081	80115	80149
80048	80082	80116	80150
80049	80083	80117	80151
80050	80084	80118	80152
80051	80085	80119	80153
80052	80086	80120	80154
80053	80087	80121	

Engines of this class are still being delivered.

2-6-2T   3

Introduced 1952. Designed at Swindon.
Weight: 73 tons 10 cwt.
Pressure: 200 lb. Su.
Cyls.: (O) 17½″ × 26″.
Driving Weeels: 5′ 3″. T.E.: 21,490 lb.
Walschaerts gear, P.V.

82000	82002	82004	82006
82001	82003	82005	82007

82008	82018	82028	82038
82009	82019	82029	82039
82010	82020	82030	82040
82011	82021	82031	82041
82012	82022	82032	82042
82013	82023	82033	82043
82014	82024	82034	82044
82015	82025	82035	
82016	82026	82036	
82017	82027	82037	

Total 45

2-6-2T   2

Introduced 1953. Designed at Derby.
Weight : 63 tons 5 cwt.
Pressure : 200 lb. Su.
Cyls. : (O) 16½″ × 24″.
Driving Wheels : 5′ 0″. T.E. : 18,515 lb.
Walschaerts gear. P.V.

84000	84008	84016	84024
84001	84009	84017	84025
84002	84010	84018	84026
84003	84011	84019	84027
84004	84012	84020	84028
84005	84013	84021	84029
84006	84014	84022	
84007	84015	84023	

Engines of this class are still being delivered.

2-8-0   8F   WD

Ministry of Supply " Austerity " 2-8-0
locomotives purchased by British
Railways, 1948.
Introduced 1943. Riddles M.o.S. design.
Weight   Loco.   70 tons 4 cwt.
      Tender 55 tons 10 cwt.
Pressure : 225 lb. Su.   Cyls. : (O)19″ × 28″.
Driving Wheels : 4′ 8½″. T.E. : 34,215 lb.
Walschaerts gear. P.V.

90000	90009	90018	90027
90001	90010	90019	90028
90002	90011	90020	90029
90003	90012	90021	90030
90004	90013	90022	90031
90005	90014	90023	90032
90006	90015	90024	90033
90007	90016	90025	90034
90008	90017	90026	90035

90036	90082	90128	90174	90220	90266	90312	90358
90037	90083	90129	90175	90221	90267	90313	90359
90038	90084	90130	90176	90222	90268	90314	90360
90039	90085	90131	90177	90223	90269	90315	90361
90040	90086	90132	90178	90224	90270	90316	90362
90041	90087	90133	90179	90225	90271	90317	90363
90042	90088	90134	90180	90226	90272	90318	90364
90043	90089	90135	90181	90227	90273	90319	90365
90044	90090	90136	90182	90228	90274	90320	90366
90045	90091	90137	90183	90229	90275	90321	90367
90046	90092	90138	90184	90230	90276	90322	90368
90047	90093	90139	90185	90231	90277	90323	90369
90048	90094	90140	90186	90232	90278	90324	90370
90049	90095	90141	90187	90233	90279	90325	90371
90050	90096	90142	90188	90234	90280	90326	90372
90051	90097	90143	90189	90235	90281	90327	90373
90052	90098	90144	90190	90236	90282	90328	90374
90053	90099	90145	90191	90237	90283	90329	90375
90054	90100	90146	90192	90238	90284	90330	90376
90055	90101	90147	90193	90239	90285	90331	90377
90056	90102	90148	90194	90240	90286	90332	90378
90057	90103	90149	90195	90241	90287	90333	90379
90058	90104	90150	90196	90242	90288	90334	90380
90059	90105	90151	90197	90243	90289	90335	90381
90060	90106	90152	90198	90244	90290	90336	90382
90061	90107	90153	90199	90245	90291	90337	90383
90062	90108	90154	90200	90246	90292	90338	90384
90063	90109	90155	90201	90247	90293	90339	90385
90064	90110	90156	90202	90248	90294	90340	90386
90065	90111	90157	90203	90249	90295	90341	90387
90066	90112	90158	90204	90250	90296	90342	90388
90067	90113	90159	90205	90251	90297	90343	90389
90068	90114	90160	90206	90252	90298	90344	90390
90069	90115	90161	90207	90253	90299	90345	90391
90070	90116	90162	90208	90254	90300	90346	90392
90071	90117	90163	90209	90255	90301	90347	90393
90072	90118	90164	90210	90256	90302	90348	90394
90073	90119	90165	90211	90257	90303	90349	90395
90074	90120	90166	90212	90258	90304	90350	90396
90075	90121	90167	90213	90259	90305	90351	90397
90076	90122	90168	90214	90260	90306	90352	90398
90077	90123	90169	90215	90261	90307	90353	90399
90078	90124	90170	90216	90262	90308	90354	90400
90079	90125	90171	90217	90263	90309	90355	90401
90080	90126	90172	90218	90264	90310	90356	90402
90081	90127	90173	90219	90265	90311	90357	90403

90404	90450	90496	90542	90588	90625	90662	90699
90405	90451	90497	90543	90589	90626	90663	90700
90406	90452	90498	90544	90590	90627	90664	90701
90407	90453	90499	90545	90591	90628	90665	90702
90408	90454	90500	90546	90592	90629	90666	90703
90409	90455	90501	90547	90593	90630	90667	90704
90410	90456	90502	90548	90594	90631	90668	90705
90411	90457	90503	90549	90595	90632	90669	90706
90412	90458	90504	90550	90596	90633	90670	90707
90413	90459	90505	90551	90597	90634	90671	90708
90414	90460	90506	90552	90598	90635	90672	90709
90415	90461	90507	90553	90599	90636	90673	90710
90416	90462	90508	90554	90600	90637	90674	90711
90417	90463	90509	90555	90601	90638	90675	90712
90418	90464	90510	90556	90602	90639	90676	90713
90419	90465	90511	90557	90603	90640	90677	90714
90420	90466	90512	90558	90604	90641	90678	90715
90421	90467	90513	90559	90605	90642	90679	90716
90422	90468	90514	90560	90606	90643	90680	90717
90423	90469	90515	90561	90607	90644	90681	90718
90424	90470	90516	90562	90608	90645	90682	90719
90425	90471	90517	90563	90609	90646	90683	90720
90426	90472	90518	90564	90610	90647	90684	90721
90427	90473	90519	90565	90611	90648	90685	90722
90428	90474	90520	90566	90612	90649	90686	90723
90429	90475	90521	90567	90613	90650	90687	90724
90430	90476	90522	90568	90614	90651	90688	90725
90431	90477	90523	90569	90615	90652	90689	90726
90432	90478	90524	90570	90616	90653	90690	90727
90433	90479	90525	90571	90617	90654	90691	90728
90434	90480	90526	90572	90618	90655	90692	90729
90435	90481	90527	90573	90619	90656	90693	90730
90436	90482	90528	90574	90620	90657	90694	90731
90437	90483	90529	90575	90621	90658	90695	90732
90438	90484	90530	90576	90622	90659	90696	Vulcan
90439	90485	90531	90577	90623	90660	90697	
90440	90486	90532	90578	90624	90661	90698	
90441	90487	90533	90579				
90442	90488	90534	90580				
90443	90489	90535	90581				
90444	90490	90536	90582				
90445	90491	90537	90583				
90446	90492	90538	90584				
90447	90493	90539	90585				
90448	90494	90540	90586				
90449	90495	90541	90587				

Total 733

2-10-0   8F   **WD**

Ministry of Supply "Austerity" 2-10-0 locomotives purchased by British Railways, 1948.

Introduced 1943. Riddles M.o.S. design.

Weight: Loco. 78 tons 6 cwt.
        Tender 55 tons 10 cwt.

Pressure: 225 lbs. Su. Cyls.:(O)19" × 28".
Driving Wheels: 4' 8½". T.E.: 34,215 lb.
Walschaerts gear. P.V.

90750	90757	90764	90771
90751	90758	90765	90772
90752	90759	90766	90773
90753	90760	90767	90774
90754	90761	90768	
90755	90762	90769	
90756	90763	90770	

Total 25

2-10-0   9F

Introduced 1954. Designed at Brighton.
*Introduced 1955. Fitted with Crosti boiler.
Weight :   Loco. { 86 tons 14 cwt.
                    { 90 tons 4 cwt.*
            Tender (see page 61).
Pressure : 250 lb.   Su
Cyls. : (O) 20" × 28".
Driving Wheels : 5' 0". T.E. : 39,670 lb.
Walschaerts gear, P.V.

92000	92023*	92046	92069
92001	92024*	92047	92070
92002	92025*	92048	92071
92003	92026*	92049	92072
92004	92027*	92050	92073
92005	92028*	92051	92074
92006	92029*	92052	92075
92007	92030	92053	92076
92008	92031	92054	92077
92009	92032	92055	92078
92010	92033	92056	92079
92011	92034	92057	92080
92012	92035	92058	92081
92013	92036	92059	92082
92014	92037	92060	92083
92015	92038	92061	92084
92016	92039	92062	92085
92017	92040	92063	92086
92018	92041	92064	92087
92019	92042	92065	92088
92020*	92043	92066	92089
92021*	92044	92067	92090
92022*	92045	92068	92091

92092	92120	92148	92176
92093	92121	92149	92177
92094	92122	92150	92178
92095	92123	92151	92179
92096	92124	92152	92180
92097	92125	92153	92181
92098	92126	92154	92182
92099	92127	92155	92183
92100	92128	92156	92184
92101	92129	92157	92185
92102	92130	92158	92186
92103	92131	92159	92187
92104	92132	92160	92188
92105	92133	92161	92189
92106	92134	92162	92190
92107	92135	92163	92191
92108	92136	92164	92192
92109	92137	92165	92193
92110	92138	92166	92194
92111	92139	92167	92195
92112	92140	92168	92196
92113	92141	92169	92197
92114	92142	92170	92198
92115	92143	92171	92199
92116	92144	92172	92200
92117	92145	92173	92201
92118	92146	92174	92202
92119	92147	92175	

Engines of this class are still being delivered.

BRITISH RAILWAYS STANDARD TENDERS

N.B.—*These pairings are not permanent and are liable to alteration with changed operating conditions.*

Type	Capacity		Weight in Full W.O.		Locos to which Allocated
	Water galls.	Coal tons	tons	cwt.	
BRI ...	4,250	7	49	3	70000–24/30–44 72000–9 73000–49
BRIA ...	5,000	7	52	10	70025–29
BRIB ...	4,725	7	50	5	92020–29/60–6/97–9 73080–89 73100–09/20–34/45–71 75065–79 76053–69
BRIC ...	4,725	9	53	5	92015–19/45–59/77–86 92100–39/50–67 73065–79/90–9 73135–44
BRID ...	4,725	9	54	10	70045–54
BRIE ...	4,725	10	55	10	71000
BRIF ...	5,625	7	55	5	92010–14,30–44/67–76 92087–96 92140–49/68–92202 73110–19
BRIG ...	5,000	7	52	10	92000–9 73050–52
BRIH ...	4,250	7	49	3	73053–64
BR2 ...	3,500	6	42	3	75000–49 76000–44
BR2A ...	3,500	6	42	3	75050–64 80–9 76045–52/70–76114 77000–24
BR3 ...	3,000	4	36	17	78000–64

DIESEL MULTIPLE UNIT TRAINS

The following abbreviations are used, and although based on the British Railways standard rolling stock code, are not necessarily those carried on the vehicles, all of which are of the open, centre or off centre corridor type :—

BOGIE VEHICLES

Fitted with a driving compartment at one end and gangway connections at the other end.

Motor BS—Motor Brake Second.
Motor S—Motor Second.
Motor C—Motor Composite.
Motor CL—Motor Composite (lavatory fitted).
Driving SL—Driving Trailer Second (lavatory fitted).
Driving CL—Driving Trailer Composite (lavatory fitted).
Non driving, non motor vehicles, gangway fitted at both ends.
BSL—Trailer Brake Second (lavatory fitted).
SL—Trailer Second (lavatory fitted).

4-WHEEL VEHICLES.

Motor coaches fitted with a driving compartment at each end. None are gangway fitted.

Motor S—Motor Second. **Motor BS**—Motor Brake Second. **S**—Trailer Second.

FORMATION. Nearly all are formed into two-coach sets as under :—

Motor BS–Motor CL (Bradford area).
Motor BS–Driving CL (Majority).
Motor BS–Driving SL (East Anglian area).
Newcastle–Middlesbrough units are formed into four-coach sets :—
Motor C–BSL–SL–Motor S.
The 4-wheel vehicles are made up to three-coach sets and are used on the Watford–St. Albans Branch :—
Motor BS–S–Motor S.

BOGIE VEHICLES

Motor BS.

E79000	M79019	E79038	E79057*	M79076*	M79130	M79149
E79001	M79020	E79039	E79058*	M79077*	M79131	M79169
E79002	E79021	E79040	E79059*	M79078*	M79132	M79170
E79003	E79022	E79041	E79060*	M79079*	M79133	M79171
E79004	E79023	E79042	E79061*	M79080*	M79134	M79172
E79005	E79024	E79043	E79062*	M79081*	M79135	M79173
E79006	E79025	E79044	E79063*	M79082*	M79136	M79174
E79007	E79026	E79045	E79064*	M79118	E79137	M79175
M79008	E79027	E79046	E79065*	M79119	E79138	M79176
M79009	E79028	E79047*	E79066*	M79120	E79139	M79177
M79010	E79029	E79048*	E79067*	M79121	M79140	M79178
M79011	E79030	E79049*	E79068*	M79122	M79141	M79179
M79012	E79031	E79050*	E79069*	M79123	M79142	M79180
M79013	E79032	E79051*	E79070*	M79124	M79143	M79181
M79014	E79033	E79052*	E79071*	M79125	M79144	M79184
M79015	E79034	E79053*	E79072*	M79126	M79145	M79195
M79016	E79035	E79054*	E79073*	M79127	M79146	M79186
M79017	E79036	E79055*	E79074*	M79128	M79147	‡M79900
M79018	E79037	E79056*	E79075*	M79129	M79148	

Motor S :—

E79150, E79151, E79152, E79153, E79154.

Driving SL :—

E79250	E79254	E79258	E79262	E79266*	E79270*	E79274*
E79251	E79255	E79259	E79263*	E79267*	E79271*	E79275*
E79252	E79256	E79260	E79264*	E79268*	E79272*	E79276*
E79253	E79257	E79261	E79265*	E79269*	E79273*	E79277*

| E79278* | E79280* | E79282* | E79284* | E79286* | E79288* | E79290* |
| E79279* | E79281* | E79283* | E79285* | E79287* | E79289* | E79291* |

BSL :—
E79325, E79326, E79327, E79328, E79329.

SL:—
E79400, E79401, E79402, E79403, E79404.

Motor CL :—
M79189, M79190, M79191, E79500, E79501 ,E79502 ,E79503 ,E79504, E79505, E79506, E79507.

Motor C :—
E79508, E79509, E79510, E79511, E79512.

Driving CL :—

M79600	M79612	E79624	M79641	M79652	M79663	M79674
M79601	E79613	E79625	M79642	M79653	M79664	M79675
M79602	E79614	M79626*	M79643	M79654	M79665	M79676
M79603	E79615	M79627*	M79644	M79655	M79666	M79677
M79604	E79616	M79628*	M79645	M79656	M79667	M79678
M79605	E79617	M79629*	M79646	M79657	M79668	M79679
M79606	E79618	M79630*	M79647	E79658	M79669	M79680
M79607	E79619	M79631*	M79648	E79659	M79670	M79681
M79608	E79620	M79632*	M79649	E79660	M79671	M79682
M79609	E79621	M79639	M79650	E79661	M79672	M79683
M79610	E79622	M79640	M79651	M79662	M79673	M79684
M79611	E79623					

4-WHEEL VEHICLES.

Motor S	Motor BS	S
M79740†	M79742†	M79741†
M79745†	M79743†	M79746†
	M79744†	M79747†

* Built by Metro-Cammell C. & W. Co.

† Built by British United Traction Co.

Remainder built by British Railways at Derby.

‡ Non-gangwayed, driving compartment at both ends.

L.M. ELECTRIC MOTOR COACH NUMBERS
LONDON DISTRICT

OPEN STOCK

				28264	28274	28283	28292
M28000	28233	28248	28257	28265	28275	28284	28293
28223	28235	28249	28258	28266	28277	28285	28294
28224	28237	28252	28259	28267	28278	28286	28295
28225	28242	28253	28260	28269	28279	28287	28296
28226	28243	28254	28261	28270	28280	28288	28297
28228	28244	28255	28262	28272	28281	28289	28298
28229	28246	28256	28263	28273	28282	28290	28299
28230	28247						

COMPARTMENT STOCK

				28013	28017	28021	28025
M28001	28004	28007	28010	28014	28018	28022	
28002	28005	28008	28011	28015	28019	28023	
28003	28006	28009	28012	28016	28020	28024	

LIVERPOOL—SOUTHPORT

COMPARTMENT STOCK

M28301	28304	28307	28310
28302	28305	28308	
28303	28306	28309	

OPEN STOCK

M28311	28316	28322	28327	
28312	28317	28323	28328	
28313	28318	28324	28329	
28314	28319	28325	28330	
28315	28321	28326	28331	

28332	28342	28353	28363
28333	28343	28354	28364
28334	28344	28355	28365
28335	28345	28356	28366
28336	28347	28357	28367
28337	28348	28358	28368
28338	28349	28359	28369
28339	28350	28360	
28340	28351	28361	
28341	28352	28362	

BAGGAGE CARS

M28496	28497

MERSEY

1st CLASS					2nd CLASS			
M28405	28409	28413	28417	28418	M28419	28423	28427	28431
28406	28410	28414			28420	28424	28428	28432
28407	28411	28415			28421	28425	28429	
28408	28412	28416			28422	28426	28430	

MANCHESTER—BURY

M28500	28505	28510	28515	28521	28526	28531	28537
28501	28506	28511	28516	28522	28527	28532	
28502	28507	28512	28517	28523	28528	28533	
28503	28508	28513	28518	28524	28529	28534	
28504	28509	28514	28519	28525	28530	28535	

LANCASTER—MORECAMBE —HEYSHAM

M28219	28221
28220	28222

WIRRAL

M28371	28377	28676	28682	28688
28372	28378	28677	28683	28689
28373	28672	28678	28684	28690
28374	28673	28679	28685	
28375	28674	28680	28686	
28376	28675	28681	28687	

MANCHESTER, SOUTH JUNCTION & ALTRINCHAM

M28571	28575	28579	28583	28587	28591
28572	28576	28580	28584	28588	28592
28573	28577	28581	28585	28589	28593
28574	28578	28582	28586	28590	28594

THE a b c OF
BRITISH RAILWAYS
LOCOMOTIVES

PART 4 - Nos. 60000-99999
EASTERN, NORTH EASTERN, SCOTTISH
REGION, EX-W.D. & B.R. STANDARD
STEAM LOCOMOTIVES
also E. & N.E.R. Electric and Diesel Units
and Pullman Cars.

WINTER
1956/7
EDITION

LONDON :

Ian Allan Ltd

FOREWORD

THIS booklet lists all British Railways locomotives numbered between 60000 and 99999 and E. & N.E. electric and diesel *train* units, and Pullman Cars allocated to the East Coast Route. This series of numbers includes all Eastern, North Eastern and Scottish (ex-L.N.E.R.) Region steam locomotives, i.e. steam locomotives of the former L.N.E.R., new British Railways standard steam locomotives and ex-Ministry of Supply locos. Under the general British Railways renumbering scheme, the numbers of L.N.E.R. steam locomotives were increased by 60000, with the exception of Classes W1 and L1. A later scheme involved the renumbering of all ex-M.O.S. locomotives in the 90000 series, and there have also been minor amendments to Class B16 to make way for new locomotives.

Details of former L.N.E.R. electric, diesel electric and petrol *locomotives* will be found in ABC of British Railways Locomotives, Part 2 (Nos. 10000-39999).

NOTES ON THE USE OF THIS BOOK

In the list of locomotives which follows :

1. Many of the classes listed are sub-divided, the sub-divisions being denoted in some cases by " Parts " shown thus : D16/3. At the head of each class will be found a list of such sub-divisions, if any, usually arranged in order of introduction. Each part is given there a reference mark by which its relevant dimensions, if differing from those of other parts, and the locos included in this part, may be identified. Any other differences between locomotives are also indicated, with reference marks, below the details of the class's introduction.

2. The lists of dimensions at the head of each class show locomotives fitted with two inside cylinders, Stephenson gear and slide valves, unless otherwise stated, e.g. (O) = two outside cylinders, P.V. = piston valves.

3. The following method is used to denote superheated locomotives, the letters being inserted, where applicable, after the boiler pressure details : Su = All engines superheated.

SS = Some engines superheated.

4. The date on which the first locomotive of a class was built or modified is denoted by " Introduced ".

5. The numbers of locomotives in service have been checked to September 8th, 1956.

6. S. denotes Service (Departmental) locomotive still carrying B.R. number (see page 45). This reference letter is introduced only for the reader's guidance and is not borne by the locomotive concerned.

2

BRITISH RAILWAYS
EASTERN & NORTH EASTERN REGIONS

Chief Mechanical Engineer
A. H. Peppercorn - - 1948-1949
(post abolished)

LOCOMOTIVE SUPERINTENDENTS AND CHIEF MECHANICAL ENGINEERS OF THE L.N.E.R.

Sir Nigel Gresley 1923—1941 | E. Thompson ... 1941—1946
A. H. Peppercorn 1946—1947

Great Northern Railway

A. Sturrock	...	1850—1866
P. Stirling	...	1866—1895
H. A. Ivatt	...	1896—1911
H. N. Gresley	...	1911—1922

North Eastern Railway

E. Fletcher		1854—1883
A. McDonnell*	...	1883—1884
T. W. Worsdell	...	1885—1890
W. Worsdell		1890—1910
Sir Vincent Raven		1910—1922

Great Eastern Railway

R. Sinclair	...	1862—1866
S. W. Johnson	...	1866—1873
W. Adams	...	1873—1878
M. Bromley	...	1878—1881
T. W. Worsdell	...	1881—1885
J. Holden	...	1885—1907
S. D. Holden	...	1908—1912
A. J. Hill	...	1912—1922

Lancashire, Derbyshire and East Coast Railway

R. A. Thom	...	1902—1907

Manchester, Sheffield and Lincolnshire Railway

Richard Peacock		—1854
W. G. Craig	...	1854—1859

Charles Sacré	...	1859—1886
T. Parker		1886—1893
H. Pollitt		1893—1897

Great Central Railway

H. Pollitt		1897—1900
J. G. Robinson	...	1900—1922

Hull and Barnsley Railway

M. Stirling	...	1885—1922

Midland and Great Northern Joint Railway

W. Marriott		1884—1924

North British Railway

T. Wheatley†	...	1867—1874
D. Drummond	...	1875—1882
M. Holmes		1882—1903
W. P. Reid		1903—1919
W. Chalmers	...	1919—1922

Great North of Scotland Railway

D. K. Clark	...	1853—1855
J. F. Ruthven	...	1855—1857
W. Cowan	...	1857—1883
J. Manson	...	1883—1890
J. Johnson		1890—1894
W. Pickersgill	...	1894—1914
T. E. Heywood	...	1914—1922

* Between McDonnell and T. W. Worsdell there was an interval during which the office was covered by a Locomotive Committee.

† Previous to whom the records are indeterminate.

BRITISH RAILWAYS LOCOMOTIVE
SHEDS AND SHED CODES

EASTERN REGION

30A Stratford	**32A Norwich**	**36A Doncaster**
Brentwood	Cromer Beach	**36B Mexborough**
Chelmsford	Swaffham	Wath
Enfield Town	Wymondham	**36C Frodingham**
Epping	**32B Ipswich**	**36D Barnsley**
Ilford	Aldeburgh	**36E Retford**
Wood Street	Felixstowe Beach	Newark
(Walthamstow)	Stowmarket	
30B Hertford East	**32C Lowestoft**	
Buntingford	**32D Yarmouth (South**	**38A Colwick**
Ware	**Town)**	**38B Annesley**
30C Bishops Stortford	**32E Yarmouth (Vauxhall)**	**38C Leicester (ex-G.C.)**
30D Southend (Victoria)	**32F Yarmouth Beach**	**38D Staveley**
Southminster	**32G Melton Constable**	**38E Woodford Halse**
30E Colchester	Norwich City	
Braintree	**33A Plaistow**	**39A Gorton**
Clacton	Upminster	Dinting
Maldon	**33B Tilbury**	Hayfield
Walton-on-Naze	**33C Shoeburyness**	
30F Parkeston	**34A Kings Cross**	**40A Lincoln**
31A Cambridge	**34B Hornsey**	Lincoln (St. Mark's)
Ely	**34C Hatfield**	**40B Immingham**
Huntingdon East	**34D Hitchin**	Grimsby
Saffron Walden	**34E Neasden**	New Holland
31B March	Aylesbury	**40C Louth**
Wisbech	Chesham	**40D Tuxford**
31C Kings Lynn	**35A New England**	**40E Langwith Junction**
Hunstanton	Spalding	**40F Boston**
31D South Lynn	Stamford	
31E Bury St. Edmunds	**35B Grantham**	
Sudbury (Suffolk)	35C Peterborough (Spital)	**41A Sheffield (Darnall)**

NORTH EASTERN REGION

50A York	**52A Gateshead**	**54B Tyne Dock**
50B Leeds (Neville Hill)	Bowes Bridge	**54C Borough Gardens**
50C Selby	**52B Heaton**	**54D Consett**
50D Starbeck	**52C Blaydon**	
50E Scarborough	Alston	*55A Leeds (Holbeck)
50F Malton	Hexham	(20A)
Pickering	**52D Tweedmouth**	*Keighley*
50G Whitby	Alnmouth	*55B Stourton (20B)
	52E Percy Main	*55C Farnley Junction (25G)
	52F North Blyth	*55D Royston (20C)
51A Darlington	South Blyth	*55E Normanton (20D)
Middleton-in-		*55F Manningham (20E)
Teesdale	**53A Hull (Dairycoates)**	*Ilkley*
51B Newport (Yorks.)	**53B Hull (Botanic**	*55G Huddersfield (25B)
51C West Hartlepool	**Gardens)**	
51D Middlesbrough	**53C Hull (Springhead)**	*56A Wakefield (25A)
51E Stockton	**Alexandra Dock**	**56B Ardsley (37A)**
51F West Auckland	**53D Bridlington**	**56C Copley Hill (37B)**
51G Haverton Hill	*53E Goole (25C)	*56D Mirfield (25D)
51H Kirkby Stephen		*56E Sowerby Bridge (25E)
51J Northallerton	**54A Sunderland**	*56F Low Moor (25F)
51K Saltburn	Durham	56G Bradford (37C)

Altered Shed Codes in course of adoption, former Code in brackets.

60A Inverness
Dingwall
Kyle of Lochalsh
60B Aviemore
Boat of Garten
60C Helmsdale
Dornoch
Tain
60D Wick
Thurso
60E Forres

61A Kittybrewster
Ballater
Fraserburgh
Inverurie
Peterhead
61B Aberdeen (Ferryhill)
61C Keith
Banff
Elgin

62A Thornton
Anstruther
Burntisland
Ladybank
Methil
62B Dundee (Tay Bridge)
Arbroath
Dundee West
Montrose
St. Andrews

62C Dunfermline
Alloa

63A Perth South
Aberfeldy
Crieff
63B Stirling South
Killin
Stirling (Shore Road)
63C Forfar
63D Oban
Ballachulish

64A St. Margarets (Edinburgh)
Dunbar
Galashiels
Longniddry
North Berwick
64B Haymarket
64C Dalry Road
64D Carstairs
64E Polmont
64F Bathgate
64G Hawick
Riccarton
St. Boswells

65A Eastfield (Glasgow)
Arrochar
65B St. Rollox

65C Parkhead
65D Dawsholm
Dumbarton
65E Kipps
65F Grangemouth
65G Yoker
65H Helensburgh
65I Balloch
65J Fort William
Mallaig

66A Polmadie (Glasgow)
66B Motherwell
66C Hamilton
66D Greenock (Ladyburn)
Greenock (Princes Pier)

67A Corkerhill (Glasgow)
67B Hurlford
Beith
Muirkirk
67C Ayr
67D Ardrossan

68A Carlisle (Kingmoor)
68B Dumfries
68C Stranraer
Newton Stewart
68D Beattock
68E Carlisle Canal

ROUTE AVAILABILITY OF LOCOMOTIVES

Restrictions on the working of locomotives over the routes of the former L.N.E.R. are denoted by Route availability numbers. In general a locomotive is not permitted to work over a line of lower R.A. number than it bears. The scheme is as follows :

R.A. I : J15, J63, J65, J71, Y1, Y3, Y8, Y10, Z4, DM1, Standard 2 2-6-2T.

R.A. 2 : E4, J67/1, J72, J77, Y9, Z5.

R.A. 3 : F5, J10, J21, J25, J36, J66, J67/2, J68, J69, J88, N10, Standard 2 2-6-0.

R.A. 4 : B12/3, D40, F6, G5, J17, J26, J55, J83, N5/2, N8, N13, N14, V4, Standard 4 4-6-0, Standard 4 2-6-0, Standard 3 2-6-2T.

R.A. 5 : A5, A8, B1, B2, B17, C12, C13, C14, D16, J6, J11, J19, J20, J27, J52, J73, J94, K2, N1, N7, Standard 4 2-6-4T.

R.A. 6 : C15, C16, D11, D20, D30, D34, J35, J39, J50, K1, K4, N2, N15, O1, O2, O4, WD 2-8-0, Q6, V1, Y4.

R.A. 7 : A7, B16/1, L1, Q7, V3, Standard 6P5F 4-6-2, Standard 5 4-6-0.

R.A. 8 : B16/2, B16/3, D49, J37, J38, K3, K5, Q1, S1, T1, Standard 7P6F 4-6-2.

R.A. 9 : A1, A2, A3, A4, V2, W1.

NUMERICAL LIST OF ENGINES

The Code given in smaller bold type at the head of each class, e.g. "4MT" denotes its British Railways power classification.

4-6-2   8P6F   **Class A4**

Introduced 1935. Gresley streamlined design with corridor tender (except those marked †).
*Inside cylinder reduced to 17".
‡Kylchap blast pipe and double chimney.
Weight: Loco.   102 tons 19 cwt.
        Tender $\begin{cases} 64 \text{ tons } 19 \text{ cwt.} \\ 60 \text{ tons } 7 \text{ cwt.†} \end{cases}$
Pressure: 250 lb. Su.
Cyls.: $\begin{cases} (3) \ 18\frac{1}{2}'' \times 26''. \\ (2) \ 18\frac{1}{2}'' \times 26'', \ (1) \ 17'' \times 26''*. \end{cases}$
Driving Wheels: 6' 8".
T.E.: $\begin{cases} 35,455 \text{ lb.} \\ 33,616 \text{ lb.*} \end{cases}$
Walschaerts gear and derived motion.
P.V.

60001†	Sir Ronald Matthews
60002†	Sir Murrough Wilson
60003	Andrew K. McCosh
60004	William Whitelaw
60005*‡	Sir Charles Newton
60006†	Sir Ralph Wedgwood
60007	Sir Nigel Gresley
60008	Dwight D. Eisenhower
60009	Union of South Africa
60010	Dominion of Canada
60011	Empire of India
60012*	Commonwealth of Australia
60013	Dominion of New Zealand
60014	Silver Link
60015	Quicksilver
60016†	Silver King
60017	Silver Fox
60018†	Sparrow Hawk
60019†	Bittern
60020*†	Guillemot
60021†	Wild Swan
60022‡	Mallard
60023†	Golden Eagle
60024	Kingfisher
60025	Falcon

60026†	Miles Beevor
60027	Merlin
60028	Walter K. Whigham
60029	Woodcock
60030	Golden Fleece
60031*	Golden Plover
60032	Gannet
60033‡	Seagull
60034‡	Lord Faringdon

Total 34

4-6-2   7P6F   **Class A3**

Introduced 1927. Development of Gresley G.N. 180 lb. Pacific (introduced 1922, L.N.E.R. A1, later A10) with 220 lb. pressure (prototype and others rebuilt from A10). Some have G.N.-type tender† with coal rails, remainder L.N.E.R. pattern.
*Kylchap blast pipe and double chimney.
Weight: Loco.   96 tons 5 cwt.
        Tender $\begin{cases} 56 \text{ tons } 6 \text{ cwt.†} \\ 57 \text{ tons } 18 \text{ cwt.} \end{cases}$
Pressure: 220 lb. Su. Cyls.: (3) $19'' \times 26''$.
Driving Wheels: 6' 8". T.E.: 32,910 lb.
Walschaerts gear and derived motion.
P.V.

60035	Windsor Lad
60036	Colombo
60037	Hyperion
60038	Firdaussi
60039	Sandwich
60040	Cameronian
60041	Salmon Trout
60042	Singapore
60043	Brown Jack
60044	Melton
60045	Lemberg
60046	Diamond Jubilee
60047	Donovan
60048	Doncaster
60049	Galtee More
60050	Persimmon
60051	Blink Bonny
60052	Prince Palatine
60053	Sansovino
60054	Prince of Wales
60055	Woolwinder

60056	Centenary
60057	Ormonde
60058	Blair Athol
60059	Tracery
60060	The Tetrarch
60061	Pretty Polly
60062	Minoru
60063	Isinglass
60064	Tagalie
60065	Knight of Thistle
60066	Merry Hampton
60067	Ladas
60068	Sir Visto
60069	Sceptre
60070	Gladiateur
60071	Tranquil
60072	Sunstar
60073	St. Gatien
60074	Harvester
60075	St. Frusquin
60076	Galopin
60077	The White Knight
60078	Night Hawk
60079	Bayardo
60080	Dick Turpin
60081	Shotover
60082	Neil Gow
60083	Sir Hugo
60084	Trigo
60085	Manna
60086	Gainsborough
60087	Blenheim
60088	Book Law
60089	Felstead
60090	Grand Parade
60091	Captain Cuttle
60092	Fairway
60093	Coronach
60094	Colorado
60095	Flamingo
60096	Papyrus
60097*	Humorist
60098	Spion Kop
60099	Call Boy
60100	Spearmint
60101	Cicero
60102	Sir Frederick Banbury
60103	Flying Scotsman

60104	Solario
60105	Victor Wild
60106	Flying Fox
60107	Royal Lancer
60108	Gay Crusader
60109	Hermit
60110	Robert the Devil
60111	Enterprise
60112	St. Simon

Total 78

4-6-2   8P6F   Class A1

A1/1* Introduced 1945. Thompson rebuild of A10.
A1 Peppercorn development of A1/1 for new construction.
A1† Fitted with roller bearings.
Weight: Loco. $\begin{cases} 101 \text{ tons.*} \\ 104 \text{ tons 2 cwt.} \end{cases}$
Tender 60 tons 7 cwt.
Pressure: 250 lb. Su.
Cyls.: (3) 19" × 26".
Driving Wheels: 6' 8". T.E.: 37,400 lb.
Walschaerts gear. P.V.

60113*	Great Northern
60114	W. P. Allen
60115	Meg Merrilies
60116	Hal o' the Wynd
60117	Bois Roussel
60118	Archibald Sturrock
60119	Patrick Stirling
60120	Kittiwake
60121	Silurian
60122	Curlew
60123	H. A. Ivatt
60124	Kenilworth
60125	Scottish Union
60126	Sir Vincent Raven
60127	Wilson Worsdell
60128	Bongrace
60129	Guy Mannering
60130	Kestrel
60131	Osprey
60132	Marmion
60133	Pommern
60134	Foxhunter
60135	Madge Wildfire
60136	Alcazar
60137	Redgauntlet

60138	Boswell
60139	Sea Eagle
60140	Balmoral
60141	Abbotsford
60142	Edward Fletcher
60143	Sir Walter Scott
60144	King's Courier
60145	Saint Mungo
60146	Peregrine
60147	North Eastern
60148	Aboyeur
60149	Amadis
60150	Willbrook
60151	Midlothian
60152	Holyrood
60153†	Flamboyant
60154†	Bon Accord
60155†	Borderer
60156†	Great Central
60157†	Great Eastern
60158	Aberdonian
60159	Bonnie Dundee
60160	Auld Reekie
60161	North British
60162	Saint Johnstoun

Total 50

4-6-2 $\frac{8P7F}{(A2/1:\ 7P6F)}$ Class A2

A2/2* Introduced 1943. Original Thompson Pacific, rebuilt from Gresley Class P2 2-8-2 (introduced 1934).
Weight: Loco. 101 tons 10 cwt.
Pressure: 225 lb. Su.
Cyls.: (3) 20″ × 26″.
Driving Wheels: 6′ 2″. T.E.: 40,320 lb.

A2/1† Introduced 1944. Development of Class A2/2, incorporating Class V2 2-6-2 boiler.
Weight: Loco. 98 tons.
Pressure: 225 lb. Su.
Cyls.: (3) 19″ × 26″.
Driving Wheels: 6′ 2″. T.E. 36,385 lb.

A2/3‡ Introduced 1946. Development of Class A2/2 for new construction.
Weight: Loco. 101 tons 10 cwt.
Pressure: 250 lb. Su.
Cyls.: (3) 19″ × 26″.
Driving Wheels: 6′ 2″. T.E. 40,430 lb.

A2§ Introduced 1947. Peppercorn development of Class A2/2 with shorter wheelbase. (No. 60539 built with double blast pipe.)

A2** Rebuilt with double blast pipe and multiple valve regulator.
Weight: Loco. 101 tons.
Pressure: 250 lb. Su.
Cyls.: (3) 19″ × 26″.
Driving Wheels: 6′ 2″. T.E.: 40,430 lb.
Tender weight (all parts): 60 tons 7 cwt.
Walschaerts gear. P.V.

60500‡	Edward Thompson
60501*	Cock o' the North
60502*	Earl Marischal
60503*	Lord President
60504*	Mons Meg
60505*	Thane of Fife
60506*	Wolf of Badenoch
60507†	Highland Chieftain
60508†	Duke of Rothesay
60509†	Waverley
60510†	Robert the Bruce
60511‡	Airborne
60512‡	Steady Aim
60513‡	Dante
60514‡	Chamossaire
60515‡	Sun Stream
60516‡	Hycilla
60517‡	Ocean Swell
60518‡	Tehran
60519‡	Honeyway
60520‡	Owen Tudor
60521‡	Watling Street
60522‡	Straight Deal
60523‡	Sun Castle
60524‡	Herringbone
60525§	A. H. Peppercorn
60526**	Sugar Palm
60527§	Sun Chariot
60528§	Tudor Minstrel
60529**	Pearl Diver
60530§	Sayajirao
60531§	Bahram
60532**	Blue Peter
60533**	Happy Knight
60534§	Irish Elegance
60535§	Hornet's Beauty
60536§	Trimbush

60537§ Bachelor's Button
60538** Velocity
60539§ Bronzino

Total : Class A2 15
Class A2/1 4
Class A2/2 6
Class A2/3 15

4-6-4 8P7F Class W1

Introduced 1937. Rebuilt from Gresley experimental high-pressure 4-cyl. compound with water-tube boiler, introduced 1929.
Weight: Loco. 107 tons 17 cwt.
Tender 60 tons 7 cwt.
Pressure: 250 lb. Su.
Cyls.: (3) 19″ × 26″.
Driving Wheels: 6′ 8″. T.E.: 37,400 lb.
Walschaerts gear and derived motion. P.V.

60700   Total 1

2-6-2 7P6F Class V2

Introduced 1936. Gresley design.
Weigh:: Loco. 93 tons 2 cwt.
Tender 52 tons.
Pressure: 220 lb. Su.
Cyls.: (3) 18½″ × 26″.
Driving Wheels: 6′ 2″. T.E. 33,730 lb.
Walschaerts gear and derived motion. P.V.

60800 Green Arrow
60801
60802
60803
60804
60805
60806
60807
60808
60809 The Snapper, The East Yorkshire Regiment, The Duke of York's Own
60810
60811

60812
60813
60814
60815
60816
60817
60818
60819
60820
60821
60822
60823
60824
60825
60826
60827
60828
60829
60830
60831
60832
60833
60834
60835 The Green Howard, Alexandra, Princess of Wales's Own Yorkshire Regiment
60836
60837
60838
60839
60840
60841
60842
60843
60844
60845
60846
60847 St. Peter's School, York, A.D. 627
60848
60849
60850
60851
60852
60853
60854
60855

9

4-6-0 5MT Class B1

Introduced 1942. Thompson design.
Weight: Loco. 71 tons 3 cwt.
          Tender 52 tons.
Pressure: 225 lb. Su.
Cyls.: (O) 20″ × 26″.
Driving Wheels: 6′ 2″. T.E. 26,880 lb.
Walschaerts gear. P.V.

60856					
60857				61000	Springbok
60858				61001	Eland
60859				61002	Impala
60860	Durham School			61003	Gazelle
60861				61004	Oryx
60862				61005	Bongo
60863				61006	Blackbuck
60864				61007	Klipspringer
60865				61008	Kudu
60866				61009	Hartebeeste
60867				61010	Wildebeeste
60868				61011	Waterbuck
60869				61012	Puku
60870				61013	Topi
60871				61014	Oribi
60872	King's Own Yorkshire Light Infantry			61015	Duiker
60873	Coldstreamer			61016	Inyala
60874	60902	60930	60958	61017	Bushbuck
60875	60903	60931	60959	61018	Gnu
60876	60904	60932	60960	61019	Nilghai
60877	60905	60933	60961	61020	Gemsbok
60878	60906	60934	60962	61021	Reitbok
60879	60907	60935	60963	61022	Sassaby
60880	60908	60936	60964	61023	Hirola
60881	60909	60937	60965	61024	Addax
60882	60910	60938	60966	61025	Pallah
60883	60911	60939	60967	61026	Ourebi
60884	60912	60940	60968	61027	Madoqua
60885	60913	60941	60969	61028	Umseke
60886	60914	60942	60970	61029	Chamois
60887	60915	60943	60971	61030	Nyala
60888	60916	60944	60972	61031	Reedbuck
60889	60917	60945	60973	61032	Stembok
60890	60918	60946	60974	61033	Dibatag
60891	60919	60947	60975	61034	Chiru
60892	60920	60948	60976	61035	Pronghorn
60893	60921	60949	60977	61036	Ralph Assheton
60894	60922	60950	60978	61037	Jairou
60895	60923	60951	60979	61038	Blacktail
60896	60924	60952	60980	61039	Steinbok
60897	60925	60953	60981	61040	Roedeer
60898	60926	60954	60982		
60899	60927	60955	60983		
60900	60928	60956			
60901	60929	60957			

Total 184

61041	61079	61116	61153	61200	
61042	61080	61117	61154	61201	
61043	61081	61118	61155	61202	
61044	61082	61119	61156	61203	
61045	61083	61120	61157	61204	
61046	61084	61121	61158	61205	
61047	61085	61122	61159	61206	
61048	61086	61123	61160	61207	
61049	61087	61124	61161	61208	
61050	61088	61125	61162	61209	
61051	61089	61126	61163	61210	
61052	61090	61127	61164	61211	
61053	61091	61128	61165	61212	
61054	61092	61129	61166	61213	
61055	61093	61130	61167	61214	
61056	61094	61131	61168	61215	William Henton Carver
61058	61095	61132	61169	61216	
61059	61096	61133	61170	61217	
61060	61097	61134	61171	61218	
61061	61098	61135	61172	61219	
61062	61099	61136	61173	61220	
61063	61100	61137	61174	61221	Sir Alexander Erskine-Hill
61064	61101	61138	61175		
61065	61102	61139	61176	61222	
61066	61103	61140	61177	61223	
61067	61104	61141	61178	61224	
61068	61105	61142	61179	61225	
61069	61106	61143	61180	61226	
61070	61107	61144	61181	61227	
61071	61108	61145	61182	61228	
61072	61109	61146	61183	61229	
61073	61110	61147	61184	61230	
61074	61111	61148	61185	61231	
61075	61112	61149	61186	61232	
61076	61113	61150	61187	61233	
61077	61114	61151	61188	61234	
61078	61115	61152		61235	
61189	Sir William Gray			61236	
61190				61237	Geoffrey H. Kitson
61191				61238	Leslie Runciman
61192				61239	
61193				61240	Harry Hinchcliffe
61194				61241	Viscount Ridley
61195				61242	Alexander Reith Gray
61196				61243	Sir Harold Mitchell
61197				61244	Strang Steel
61198				61245	Murray of Elibank
61199				61246	Lord Balfour of Burleigh

61247	Lord Burghley		
61248	Geoffrey Gibbs		
61249	FitzHerbert Wright		
61250	A. Harold Bibby		
61251	Oliver Bury		

61252	61284	61316	61348
61253	61285	61317	61349
61254	61286	61318	61350
61255	61287	61319	61351
61256	61288	61320	61352
61257	61289	61321	61353
61258	61290	61322	61354
61259	61291	61323	61355
61260	61292	61324	61356
61261	61293	61325	61357
61262	61294	61326	61358
61263	61295	61327	61359
61264	61296	61328	61360
61265	61297	61329	61361
61266	61298	61330	61362
61267	61299	61331	61363
61268	61300	61332	61364
61269	61301	61333	61365
61270	61302	61334	61366
61271	61303	61335	61367
61272	61304	61336	61368
61273	61305	61337	61369
61274	61306	61338	61370
61275	61307	61339	61371
61276	61308	61340	61372
61277	61309	61341	61373
61278	61310	61342	61374
61279	61311	61343	61375
61280	61312	61344	61376
61281	61313	61345	61377
61282	61314	61346	61378
61283	61315	61347	

61379	Mayflower		

61380	61388	61396	61404
61381	61389	61397	61405
61382	61390	61398	61406
61383	61391	61399	61407
61384	61392	61400	61408
61385	61393	61401	61409
61386	61394	61402	
61387	61395	61403	

Total 409

4-6-0   5MT Class B16

B16/1 Introduced 1920. Raven N.E. design with inside Stephenson gear.

B16/2* Introduced 1937. Gresley rebuild of B16/1 with double Walschaerts gear and derived motion for inside cylinder.

B16/3† Introduced 1944. Thompson rebuild of B16/1 with three Walschaerts gears.

Weight: Loco. $\begin{cases} 77 \text{ tons } 14 \text{ cwt.} \\ 79 \text{ tons } 4 \text{ cwt.*} \\ 78 \text{ tons } 19 \text{ cwt.†} \end{cases}$
       Tender 46 tons 12 cwt.

Pressure: 180 lb. Su.

Cyls.: (3) $18\frac{1}{2}'' \times 26''$.

Driving Wheels: 5′ 8″   T.E.: 30,030 lb. P.V.

61410	61428	61446	61464†
61411	61429	61447	61465
61412	61430	61448†	61466
61413	61431	61449†	61467†
61414	61432	61450	61468†
61415	61433	61451	61470
61416	61434†	61452	61471
61417†	61435*	61453†	61472†
61418†	61436	61454†	61473
61419	61437*	61455*	61474
61420†	61438*	61456	61475*
61421*	61439†	61457*	61476†
61422	61440	61458	61477
61423	61441	61459	61478
61424	61442	61460	
61425	61443	61461†	
61426	61444†	61462	
61427	61445	61463†	

Total : Class B16/1 45
            Class B16/2   7
            Class B16/3 17

IMPORTANT NOTE

A careful reading of the notes on page 2 is essential to understand the use of reference marks in this book.

61512-61637

4-6-0 4P3F Class B12

B12/3 Introduced 1932. Gresley rebuild of Holden G.E. design of 1911 with large boiler, round-topped firebox and long-travel valves.
(B12/2 was a development of B12/1 with Lentz valves, since rebuilt to B12/3.)

Weight: Loco. 69 tons 10 cwt.
Tender 39 tons 6 cwt.

Pressure: 180 lb. Su. Cyls.: 20" × 28"

Driving Wheels: 6' 6". T.E.: 21,970 lb. P.V.

61512	61541	61557	61572
61514	61542	61558	61573
61516	61545	61561	61574
61519	61546	61564	61575
61520	61547	61565	61576
61530	61549	61566	61577
61533	61550	61567	61578
61535	61553	61568	61579
61537	61554	61569	61580
61538	61555	61570	
61540	61556	61571	

Total 42

4-6-0 4MT (B2 and B17/6: 5P4F) Classes B2 & B17

B17/1¹ Introduced 1928. Gresley design for G.E. section with G.E.-type tender.

B17/6² Introduced 1947. B17/1 fitted with 100A (B1 type) boiler.

B17/4³ Introduced 1936. Locos with L.N.E.R. 4,200-gallon tender.

B17/6⁴ Introduced 1943. B17/4 fitted with 100A (B1 type) boiler.

B17/6⁵ Rebuild of streamlined B17/5 introduced in 1937. Rebuilt with 100A boiler and de-streamlined in 1951.

Weight: Loco. 77 tons 5 cwt.
Tender { 39 tons 6 cwt.¹² / 52 tons.³⁴⁵

Pressure: { 180 lb.¹³ / 225 lb.²⁴⁵ } Su.

Cyls.: (3) 17½" × 26".

Driving Wheels: 6' 8".

T.E.: { 22,485 lb.¹³ / 28,555 lb.²⁴⁵

Walschaerts gear and derived motion. P.V.

B2⁶ Introduced 1945. Thompson 2-cyl. rebuild of B17, with 100A boiler and N.E. tender.

B2⁷ Introduced 1945, with L.N.E.R. tender.

Weight: Loco. 73 tons 10 cwt.
Tender { 46 tons 12 cwt.⁶ / 52 tons.⁷

Pressure: 225 lb. Su.

Cyls.: (O) 20" × 26".

Driving Wheels: 6' 8". T.E.: 24,865 lb.

Walschaerts gear. P.V.

61600²	Sandringham
61601²	Holkham
61602²	Walsingham
61603⁶	Framlingham
61605²	Lincolnshire Regiment
61606²	Audley End
61607⁶	Blickling
61608²	Gunton
61609²	Quidenham
61610²	Honingham Hall
61611²	Raynham Hall
61612²	Houghton Hall
61613²	Woodbastwick Hall
61614⁶	Castle Hedingham
61615⁷	Culford Hall
61616²	Fallodon
61617⁶	Ford Castle
61618¹	Wynyard Park
61619²	Welbeck Abbey
61620²	Clumber
61621¹	Hatfield House
61622²	Alnwick Castle
61623²	Lambton Castle
61625¹	Raby Castle
61626²	Brancepeth Castle
61627²	Aske Hall
61629¹	Naworth Castle
61630²	Tottenham Hotspur
61631¹	Serlby Hall
61632²	Belvoir Castle
61633²	Kimbolton Castle
61634¹	Hinchingbrooke
61635²	Milton
61636²	Harlaxton Manor
61637¹	Thorpe Hall

61638²	Melton Hall
61639⁶	Norwich City
61640²	Somerleyton Hall
61641²	Gayton Hall
61642²	Kilverstone Hall
61643²	Champion Lodge
61644⁶	Earlham Hall
61645²	The Suffolk Regiment
61646²	Gilwell Park
61647¹	Helmingham Hall
61648³	Arsenal
61649⁴	Sheffield United
61650⁴	Grimsby Town
61651⁴	Derby County
61652³	Darlington
61653⁴	Huddersfield Town
61654⁴	Sunderland
61655⁴	Middlesbrough
61656⁴	Leeds United
61657⁴	Doncaster Rovers
61658⁴	The Essex Regiment
61659⁵	East Anglian
61660³	Hull City
61661⁴	Sheffield Wednesday
61662⁴	Manchester United
61663⁴	Everton
61664⁴	Liverpool
61665⁴	Leicester City
61666⁴	Nottingham Forest
61667³	Bradford
61668⁴	Bradford City
61669⁴	Barnsley
61670⁵	City of London
61671⁷	Royal Sovereign
61672⁴	West Ham United

Total :	Class B2	10
	Class B17/1	8
	Class B17/4	4
	Class B17/6	48

2-6-2   4MT   Class V4

Introduced 1941. Gresley design.
Weight: Loco.   70 tons 8 cwt.
        Tender 42 tons 15 cwt.
Pressure: 250 lb. Su.
Cyls.: (3) 15" × 26".
Driving Wheels: 5' 8".   T.E.: 27,420 lb.
Walschaerts gear and derived motion.
P.V.

61700	Bantam Cock	
61701		**Total 2**

2-6-0   4MT   Class K2

K2/2 Introduced 1914 Gresley G.N.
design.
K2/1* Introduced 1931. Rebuilt from
small-boilered K1 (introduced 1912).
† K2/2 fitted with side-window cab.
‡ K2/1 with side-window cab.
Weight: Loco.   64 tons 8 cwt.
        Tender 43 tons 2 cwt.
Pressure: 180 lb. Su.
Cyls.: (O) 20" × 26".
Driving Wheels: 5' 8".   T.E.: 23,400 lb.
Walschaerts gear.   P.V.

61721‡	61733†	61744	61754
61723*	61735†	61745	61755†
61724*	61736	61746	61756
61725*	61737	61747	61757
61726*	61738	61748	61758†
61728*	61739	61749	61759
61729‡	61740	61750	61760
61730	61741†	61751	61761
61731	61742	61752	61762
61732	61743	61753	61763

61764†	Loch Arkaig
61765	
61766	
61767	
61768	
61769†	
61770†	
61771	
61772†	Loch Lochy
61773	
61774†	Loch Garry
61775†	Loch Treig
61776†	
61777	
61778	
61779†	
61780	
61781†	Loch Morar
61782†	Loch Eil
61783†	Loch Shiel
61784†	
61785†	

61786†
61787† Loch Quoich
61788† Loch Rannoch
61789† Loch Laidon
61790† Loch Lomond
61791† Loch Laggan
61792†
61793†
61794† Loch Oich

Total : Class K2/1 7
          Class K2/2 64

Classes
2-6-0 5P6F K3 & K5

K3/2 Introduced 1924. Development of Gresley G.N. design, built to L.N.E.R. loading gauge.
K3/3* Introduced 1929. Differ in details only, such as springs, from K3/2.
‡ K3/2 fitted with G.N. tender.
(K3/1 were G.N. locos (introduced 1920), with G.N. cabs, and K3/4, K3/5 and K3/6 were variations of K3/2 differing in weight and details. These locos. have now been modified to K3/2.)

Weight: Loco.   72 tons 12 cwt.
Tender $\begin{cases} 52 \text{ tons.} \\ 43 \text{ tons 2 cwt.‡} \end{cases}$

Pressure: 180 lb. Su.
Cyls.: (3) 18½" × 26".
Driving Wheels: 5' 8". T.E. 30,030 lb.
Walschaerts gear and derived motion. P.V.

K5† Introduced 1945. Thompson 2-cyl. rebuild of K3.
Weight: Loco. 71 tons 5 cwt.
Tender 52 tons.
Pressure: 225 lb. Su.
Cyls.: (O) 20" × 26".
Driving Wheels: 5' 8". T.E.: 29,250 lb.
Walschaerts gear. P.V.

61800	61804	61808	61812‡
61801	61805	61809	61813
61802	61806	61810	61814
61803	61807	61811	61815

61816	61861	61906	61951
61817	61862	61907	61952
61818	61863†	61908	61953
61819	61864	61909	61954
61820	61865	61910	61955
61821	61866	61911	61956
61822	61867	61912	61957
61823	61868	61913	61958
61824	61869	61914	61959
61825	61870*	61915	61960
61826	61871*	61916	61961
61827	61872*	61917	61962
61828	61873*	61918	61963
61829	61874*	61919	61964
61830	61875*	61920	61965
61831	61876*	61921	61966
61832	61877*	61922	61967
61833	61878*	61923	61968
61834	61879*	61924	61969
61835	61880*	61925	61970
61836	61881*	61926	61971
61837	61882*	61927	61972
61838	61883*	61928	61973
61839	61884*	61929	61974
61840	61885*	61930	61975
61841‡	61886*	61931	61976
61842	61887*	61932	61977
61843	61888*	61933	61978
61844	61889*	61934	61979
61845	61890	61935	61980
61846	61891	61936	61981
61847	61892	61937	61982
61848	61893	61938	61983
61849	61894	61939	61984
61850	61895	61940	61985
61851	61896	61941	61986
61852	61897	61942	61987
61853	61898	61943	61988
61854‡	61899	61944	61989
61855‡	61900	61945	61990
61856‡	61901	61946	61991
61857‡	61902	61947	61992
61858‡	61903	61948	
61859‡	61904	61949	
61860	61905	61950	

Total : Class K3/2 172
          Class K3/3 20
          Class K5   1

Classes
K1 & K4

2-6-0   5P6F

K4* Introduced 1937. Gresley locos. for West Highland line.

Weight: Loco.   68 tons 8 cwt.
        Tender 44 tons 4 cwt.

Pressure: 200 lb. Su.

Cyls.: (3) 18½" × 26".

Driving Wheels: 5' 2". T.E.: 36,600 lb.

Walschaerts gear and derived motion P.V.

K1/1† Introduced 1945. Thompson 2-cyl. loco. Rebuilt from K4.

K1 Introduced 1949. Peppercorn development of Thompson K1/1 (No. 61997) for new construction, with increased length.

Weight: Loco.   66 tons 17 cwt.
        Tender 44 tons 4 cwt.

Pressure: 225 lb. Su.

Cyls.: (O) 20" × 26".

Driving Wheels: 5' 2". T.E.: 32,080 lb.

Walschaerts gear. P.V.

61993* Loch Long
61994* The Great Marquess
61995* Cameron of Lochiel
61996* Lord of the Isles
61997† MacCailin Mor
61998* Macleod of Macleod

62001	62019	62037	62055
62002	62020	62038	62056
62003	62021	62039	62057
62004	62022	62040	62058
62005	62023	62041	62059
62006	62024	62042	62060
62007	62025	62043	62061
62008	62026	62044	62062
62009	62027	62045	62063
62010	62028	62046	62064
62011	62029	62047	62065
62012	62030	62048	62066
62013	62031	62049	62067
62014	62032	62050	62068
62015	62033	62051	62069
62016	62034	62052	62070
62017	62035	62053	
62018	62036	62054	

Total : Class K1   70
        Class K1/1   1
        Class K4   5

4-4-0   1P   **Class D40**

Introduced 1899. Pickersgill G.N. of S. design.
*Introduced 1920.   Heywood superheated loco.

Weight: Loco. { 46 tons 7 cwt.
               { 48 tons 13 cwt.*
        Tender 37 tons 8 cwt.

Pressure: 165 lb. SS. Cyls.: 18" × 26".

Driving Wheels: 6' 1". T.E.: 16,185 lb.

62264   62265   62267   62271

62277* Gordon Highlander

Total 5

4-4-0   2P   **Class D20**

D20/1 Introduced 1899. W. Worsdell N.E. design. Since superheated.
D20/2* Introduced 1936. D20/1 rebuilt with long-travel valves.
† Locos. with tender rebuilt with J39-type tank.

Weight: Loco. { 54 tons 2 cwt.
               { 55 tons 9 cwt.*
        Tender { 41 tons 4 cwt.
               { 43 tons.†

Pressure: 175 lb. Su. Cyls.: 19" × 26".

Driving Wheels: 6' 10" T.E.: 17,025 lb. P.V.

62343	62375*	62383†	62395
62345	62378	62386†	62396
62360*	62381	62387†	62397†
62372			

Total : Class D20/1 11
        Class D20/2   2

4-4-0   3P   **Class D30**

D30/2 Introduced 1914. Development of D30/1, introduced 1912 (Reid N.B. "Scott" class) with detail differences.

Weight: Loco.   57 tons 16 cwt.
        Tender 46 tons 13 cwt.

Pressure: 165 lb. Su. Cyls.: 20" × 26".

Driving Wheels: 6' 6". T.E.: 18,700 lb. P.V.

62418   The Pirate
62419   Meg Dods
62420   Dominie Sampson
62421   Laird o' Monkbarns
62422   Caleb Balderstone
62423   Dugald Dalgetty

Class A1 4-6-2 No. 60153 *Flamboyant*   [Eric Treacy

Class A4 4-6-2 No. 60009 *Union of South Africa*   [J. Robertson

Class W1 4-6-4 No. 60700   [C. J. B. Sanderson

Class A3 4-6-2 No. 60084 *Trigo*   [Eric Treacy

Class A2/3 4-6-2 No. 60517 *Ocean Swell*   [T. K. Widd

Class V2 2-6-2 No. 60847 *St. Peter's School, York, A.D. 627*   [J. Robertson

Class B17/6 4-6-0 No. 61633 *Kimbolton Castle*   [D. Penney]

Class B16/1 4-6-0 No. 61415   [J. R. Paterson]

Class B16/2 4-6-0 No. 61421   [M. Brown]

Class B12/3 4-6-0 No. 61570   [T. K. Widd

Class K3/2 2-6-0 No. 61911   [L. Marshall

Class K5 2-6-0 No. 61863   [A. R. Carpenter

Class K2/2 2-6-0 No. 61785

[*J. Robertson*

Class K1 2-6-0 No. 62029

[*T. K. Widd*

Class K4 2-6-0 No. 61995 *Cameron of Lochiel*

[*M. A. Arnold*

Class D40 4-4-0 No. 62277 *Gordon Highlander*   [*J. C. W. Halliday*

Class D34 4-4-0 No. 62470 *Glen Roy*   [*L. Marshall*

Class D30/2 4-4-0 No. 62424 *Claverhouse*   [*L. Marshall*

Class D49/1 4-4-0 No. 62702 *Oxfordshire*   [*D. Penney*

Class D49/2 4-4-0 No. 62764 *The Garth* (with Reidinger R.R. rotary valve gear)
[*K. R. Pirt*

Class D16/3 4-4-0 No. 62534   [*G. Wheeler*

Class D20/1 4-4-0 No. 62396   [P. J. Lynch

Class D11/2 4-4-0 No. 62677 *Edie Ochiltree*   [J. Robertson

Class O2/4 2-8-0 No. 63924   [K. L. Cook

62424	Claverhouse
62425	Ellangowan
62426	Cuddie Headrigg
62427	Dumbiedykes
62428	The Talisman
62429	The Abbot
62430	Jingling Geordie
62431	Kenilworth
62432	Quentin Durward
62434	Kettledrummle
62435	Norna
62436	Lord Glenvarloch
62437	Adam Woodcock
62438	Peter Poundtext
62439	Father Ambrose
62440	Wandering Willie
62441	Black Duncan
62442	Simon Glover

Total 24

4-4-0   3P   Class D34

Introduced 1913. Reid N.B. " Glen " class.

Weight: Loco.   57 tons 4 cwt.
            Tender 46 tons 13 cwt.
Pressure: 165 lb. Su. Cyls.: 20" × 26".
Driving Wheels: 6' 0". T.E.: 20,260 lb. P.V.

62467	Glenfinnan
62468	Glen Orchy
62469	Glen Douglas
62470	Glen Roy
62471	Glen Falloch
62472	Glen Nevis
62474	Glen Croe
62475	Glen Beasdale
62477	Glen Dochart
62478	Glen Quoich
62479	Glen Sheil
62480	Glen Fruin
62482	Glen Mamie
62483	Glen Garry
62484	Glen Lyon
62485	Glen Murran
62487	Glen Arklet
62488	Glen Aladale
62489	Glen Dessary
62490	Glen Fintaig

62492	Glen Garvin
62493	Glen Gloy
62494	Glen Gour
62495	Glen Luss
62496	Glen Loy
62497	Glen Mallie
62498	Glen Moidart

Total 27

4-4-0   3P1F   Class D16

D16/3[1] Introduced 1933. Gresley rebuild of D15 with larger boiler, round-topped firebox and modified footplating. D15 was Belpaire firebox development of original J. Holden (G.E.) " Claud Hamilton " Class.

D16/3[2] Introduced 1933. Rebuild of D15 with larger boiler, round-topped firebox, modified footplate and 8" piston valves.

D16/3[5] Introduced 1936. Rebuild of D15 with larger boiler, round-topped firebox, modified footplating and 9½" piston valves.

D16/3[4] Introduced 1938. Rebuild of D16/2 with round-topped firebox, but retaining original footplating and slide valves.

D16/3[6] Introduced 1939. Rebuild of D16/2 with round-topped firebox and modified footplating, retaining slide valves.

Weight: Loco.   55 tons 18 cwt.
            Tender 39 tons 5 cwt.
Pressure: 180 lb. Su. Cyls.: 19" × 26".
Driving Wheels: 7' 0". T.E.: 17,095 lb.

62510[1]	62532[3]	62558[4]	62578[4]
62511[1]	62533[1]	62561[1]	62580[4]
62513[1]	62534[1]	62562[4]	62582[1]
62514[1]	62535[3]	62564[4]	62584[4]
62515[1]	62539[1]	62565[1]	62586[1]
62516[1]	62540[1]	62566[1]	62587[2]
62517[1]	62542[4]	62567[1]	62588[2]
62518[1]	62543[4]	62568[2]	62589[4]
62519[1]	62544[4]	62569[4]	62592[4]
62521[1]	62545[1]	62570[4]	62593[1]
62522[1]	62546[2*]	62571[1]	62596[4]
62524[1]	62548[1]	62572[1]	62597[1]
62526[1]	62553[4]	62575[4]	62599[3]
62529[1]	62555[1]	62576[3]	62601[4]
62530[1]	62556[1]	62577[4]	

* Named *Claud Hamilton.*

62604¹	62609²	62613⁴	62618⁴
62605⁴	62610¹	62614⁵	62619⁴
62606⁴	62611⁴	62615⁴	
62608¹	62612⁴	62617⁴	

Total 73

4-4-0   3P2F   Class D11

D11/1* Introduced 1920. Robinson G.C. "Large Director" development of D10 (introduced 1913).

D11/2 Introduced 1924. Post-grouping locos built to Scottish loading gauge. From 1938 the class has been rebuilt with long-travel valves.

Weight: Loco.   61 tons 3 cwt.
Tender 48 tons 6 cwt.

Pressure: 180 lb. Su. Cyls.: 20″ × 26″.

Driving Wheels: 6′ 9″. T.E.: 19,645 lb. P.V.

62660* Butler-Henderson
62661* Gerard Powys Dewhurst
62662* Prince of Wales
62663* Prince Albert
62664* Princess Mary
62665* Mons
62666* Zeebrugge
62667* Somme
62668* Jutland
62669* Ypres
62670* Marne
62671 Bailie MacWheeble
62672 Baron of Bradwardine
62673 Evan Dhu
62674 Flora MacIvor
62675 Colonel Gardiner
62676 Jonathan Oldbuck
62677 Edie Ochiltree
62678 Luckie Mucklebackit
62679 Lord Glenallan
62680 Lucy Ashton
62681 Captain Craigengelt
62682 Haystoun of Bucklaw
62683 Hobbie Elliott

62684 Wizard of the Moor
62685 Malcolm Graeme
62686 The Fiery Cross
62687 Lord James of Douglas
62688 Ellen Douglas
62689 Maid of Lorn
62690 The Lady of the Lake
62691 Laird of Balmawhapple
62692 Allan-Bane
62693 Roderick Dhu
62694 James Fitzjames

Total : Class D11/1   11
Class D11/2   24

4-4-0   4P   Class D49

D49/1* Introduced 1927. Gresley design with piston valves. Walschaerts gear and derived motion.
D49/2† Introduced 1928. Development of D49/1 with Lentz Rotary Cam poppet valves.
D49/2‡ Introduced 1949. Fitted with Reidinger R.R. Rotary valve gear. (D49/3 comprised locos. 62720-4 as built with Lentz Oscillating Cam poppet valves. From 1938 these locos were converted to D49/1. 62751-75 have larger valves than the earlier D49/2, and were at first classified D49/4).
¹Fitted with G.C. tender.
²Fitted with N.E. tender.
⁵The remainder have L.N.E.R. tenders.

Weight: Loco. ⎰ 66 tons.*†
⎱ 64 tons 10 cwt.‡
Tender ⎰ 48 tons 6 cwt.¹
⎰ 44 tons 2 cwt.²
⎱ 52 tons.⁵

Pressure: 180 lb. Su.
Cyls.: (3) 17″ × 26″.
Driving Wheels: 6′ 8″. T.E.: 21,555 lb.

62700*¹ Yorkshire
62701*¹ Derbyshire
62702*¹ Oxfordshire
62703*² Hertfordshire
62704*¹ Stirlingshire
62705*¹ Lanarkshire
62706*¹ Forfarshire

62707*¹	Lancashire
62708*¹	Argyllshire
62709*¹	Berwickshire
62710*¹	Lincolnshire
62711*¹	Dumbartonshire
62712*¹	Morayshire
62713*¹	Aberdeenshire
62714*¹	Perthshire
62715*¹	Roxburghshire
62716*¹	Kincardineshire
62717*¹	Banffshire
62718*¹	Kinross-shire
62719*¹	Peebles-shire
62720*¹	Cambridgeshire
62721*¹	Warwickshire
62722*¹	Huntingdonshire
62723*²	Nottinghamshire
62724*¹	Bedfordshire
62725*¹	Inverness-shire
62726†³	The Meynell
62727†²	The Quorn
62728*¹	Cheshire
62729*¹	Rutlandshire
62730*¹	Berkshire
62731*¹	Selkirkshire
62732*¹	Dumfries-shire
62733*¹	Northumberland
62734*²	Cumberland
62735*²	Westmorland
62736†³	The Bramham Moor
62737†³	The York and Ainsty
62738†³	The Ze land
62739†³	The Badsworth
62740†³	The Bedale
62741†³	The Blankney
62742†³	The Braes of Derwent
62743†³	The Cleveland
62744†³	The Holderness
62745†³	The Hurworth
62746†³	The Middleton
62747†³	The Percy
62748†³	The Southwold
62749†³	The Cottesmore
62750†³	The Pytchley
62751†³	The Albrighton
62752†²	The Atherstone
62753†³	The Belvoir
62754†⁸	The Berkeley

62755†³	The Bilsdale
62756†²	The Brocklesby
62757†³	The Burton
62758†³	The Cattistock
62759†³	The Craven
62760†³	The Cotswold
62761†³	The Derwent
62762†³	The Fernie
62763‡³	The Fitzwilliam
62764‡³	The Garth
62765†³	The Goathland
62766†³	The Grafton
62767†³	The Grove
62769†³	The Oakley
62770†³	The Puckeridge
62771†³	The Rufford
62772†³	The Sinnington
62773†³	The South Durham
62774†³	The Staintondale
62775†³	The Tynedale

Total : Class D49/1 34
Class D49/2 41

2-4-0   IMT   Class E4

Introduced 1891. J. Holden G.E. design.
*Fitted with side-window cab.
Weight: Loco.   40 tons 6 cwt.
Tender 30 tons 13 cwt.
Pressure: 160 lb. Cyls.: 17½″ × 24″.
Driving Wheels: 5′ 8″. T.E.: 14,700 lb.

62785	62788*	62796	62797*
62787	62789		

Total 6

0-8-0   6F   Class Q6

Introduced 1913. Raven N.E. design.
* Some locos. are fitted with tender from withdrawn B15 locos.
Weight: Loco.   65 tons 18 cwt.
Tender { 44 tons 2 cwt.
{ 44 tons.*
Pressure: 180 lb. Su.
Cyls.: (O) 20″ × 26″.
Driving Wheels: 4′ 7½″. T.E. 28.800 lb.
P.V.

63340	63341	63342	63343

63344	63373	63402	63431
63345	63374	63403	63432
63346	63375	63404	63433
63347	63376	63405	63434
63348	63377	63406	63435
63349	63378	63407	63436
63350	63379	63408	63437
63351	63380	63409	63438
63352	63381	63410	63439
63353	63382	63411	63440
63354	63383	63412	63441
63355	63384	63413	63442
63356	63385	63414	63443
63357	63386	63415	63444
63358	63387	63416	63445
63359	63388	63417	63446
63360	63389	63418	63447
63361	63390	63419	63448
63362	63391	63420	63449
63363	63392	63421	63450
63364	63393	63422	63451
63365	63394	63423	63452
63366	63395	63424	63453
63367	63396	63425	63454
63368	63397	63426	63455
63369	63398	63427	63456
63370	63399	63428	63457
63371	63400	63429	63458
63372	63401	63430	63459

Total 120

0-8-0   8F   Class Q7

Introduced 1919. Raven N.E. design.

Weight: Loco.   71 tons 12 cwt.
Tender 44 tons 2 cwt.

Pressure: 180 lb. Su.

Cyls.: (3) $18\frac{1}{2}'' \times 26''$.

Driving Wheels: 4' 7$\frac{1}{4}$''. T.E.: 36,965 lb. P.V.

63460	63464	63468	63472
63461	63465	63469	63473
63462	63466	63470	63474
63463	63467	63471	

Total 15

Classes

2-8-0   8F (O1)   O1 & O4
7F (O4)

O4/1[1] Introduced 1911. Robinson G.C. design with small boiler, Belpaire firebox, steam and vacuum brakes and water scoop.

O4/3[2] Introduced 1917. R.O.D. locos. with steam brake only and no scoop.

O4/2[3] Introduced 1925.   O4/3 with cab and boiler mountings reduced.

O4/5[4] Introduced 1932. Rebuilt with shortened O2-type boiler and separate smokebox saddle.

O4/6[5] Introduced 1924. Rebuilt from O5 retaining higher cab (63913-20 with side-windows)

O4/7[6] Introduced 1939. Rebuilt with shortened O2-type boiler, retaining G.C. smokebox.

O4/8[7] Introduced 1944. Rebuilt with 100A (B1) boiler, retaining original cylinders.
(O4/4 were rebuilds with O2 boilers, since rebuilt again ; O5 was a G.C. development of O4 with larger boiler and Belpaire firebox.)

Weight: Loco. {
73 tons 4 cwt.[1]
73 tons 4 cwt.[2]
73 tons 4 cwt.[3]
74 tons 13 cwt.[4]
73 tons 4 cwt.[5]
73 tons 17 cwt.[6]
72 tons 10 cwt.[7]

Tender { 48 tons 6 cwt. (with scoop)
47 tons 6 cwt. (without scoop)

Pressure: 180 lb. Su.

Cyls.: (O) $21'' \times 26''$.

Driving Wheels: 4' 8''. T.E.: 31,325 lb. P.V.

O1[8] Introduced 1944. Thompson rebuild with 100A boiler, Walschaerts valve gear and new cylinders.

Weight: Loco.   73 tons 6 cwt.
Tender as O4.

Pressure: 225 lb. Su.

Cyls.: (O) $20'' \times 26''$.

Driving Wheels: 4' 8''. T.E.: 35,520 lb. Walschaerts gear.   P.V.

63570[6]	63579[8]	63589[8]	63598[1]
63571[8]	63581[8]	63590[8]	63599[1]
63572[1]	63582[6]	63591[8]	63600[6]
63573[7]	63583[8]	63592[8]	63601[1]
63574[8]	63584[1]	63593[1]	63602[1]
63575[7]	63585[1]	63594[8]	63603[6]
63576[1]	63586[8]	63595[6]	63604[6]
63577[1]	63587[8]	63596[8]	63605[1]
63578[8]	63588[6]	63597[1]	63606[6]

63607[7]	63656[2]	63704[7]	63752[8]	63801[7]	63836[7]	63862[2]	63889[2]
63608[1]	63657[2]	63705[6]	63753[2]	63802[7]	63837[7]	63863[8]	63890[8]
63609[1]	63658[1]	63706[6]	63754[2]	63803[8]	63838[7]	63864[2]	63891[6]
63610[8]	63659[2]	63707[1]	63755[8]	63804[2]	63839[7]	63865[8]	63893[7]
63611[1]	63660[1]	63708[6]	63756[2]	63805[7]	63840[2]	63867[8]	63894[8]
63612[7]	63661[6]	63709[2]	63757[1]	63806[8]	63841[7]	63868[8]	63895[7]
63613[7]	63662[7]	63710[1]	63758[8]	63807[7]	63842[2]	63869[8]	63897[7]
63614[1]	63663[8]	63711[8]	63759[2]	63808[8]	63843[6]	63870[2]	63898[2]
63615[6]	63664[1]	63712[8]	63760[8]	63812[2]	63845[2]	63872[8]	63899[7]
63616[6]	63665[2]	63713[2]	63761[6]	63813[2]	63846[2]	63873[7]	63900[2]
63617[1]	63666[7]	63714[2]	63762[1]	63816[7]	63847[3]	63874[8]	63901[8]
63618[1]	63667[2]	63715[2]	63763[7]	63817[8]	63848[6]	63876[8]	63902[5]
63619[8]	63668[2]	63716[2]	63764[2]	63818[7]	63850[7]	63877[2]	63904[5]
63620[1]	63669[6]	63717[2]	63765[2]	63819[7]	63851[4]	63878[8]	63905[5]
63621[1]	63670[8]	63718[7]	63766[2]	63821[2]	63852[7]	63879[8]	63906[5]
63622[1]	63671[1]	63719[1]	63767[2]	63822[2]	63853[7]	63880[6]	63907[5]
63623[1]	63672[2]	63720[2]	63768[2]	63823[2]	63854[8]	63881[2]	63908[5]
63624[7]	63673[6]	63721[7]	63769[2]	63824[6]	63855[2]	63882[7]	63911[5]
63625[1]	63674[3]	63722[1]	63770[6]	63827[7]	63856[7]	63883[2]	63912[5]
63626[1]	63675[6]	63723[1]	63771[2]	63828[7]	63857[6]	63884[6]	63913[5]
63627[8]	63676[8]	63724[2]	63772[6]	63829[2]	63858[7]	63885[2]	63914[7]
63628[7]	63677[1]	63725[2]	63773[8]	63832[2]	63859[2]	63886[8]	63915[7]
63629[2]	63678[8]	63726[4]	63774[2]	63833[2]	63860[6]	63887[8]	63917[5]
63630[8]	63679[2]	63727[1]	63775[2]	63835[2]	63861[2]	63888[2]	63920[5]
63631[1]	63680[3]	63728[7]	63776[7]				
63632[1]	63681[2]	63729[2]	63777[8]				
63633[7]	63682[3]	63730[3]	63779[2]				
63634[6]	63683[7]	63731[7]	63780[8]				
63635[1]	63684[1]	63732[7]	63781[2]				
63636[2]	63685[2]	63733[2]	63782[2]				
63637[2]	63686[2]	63734[7]	63783[2]				
63638[2]	63687[8]	63735[2]	63784[8]				
63639[7]	63688[2]	63736[1]	63785[7]				
63640[1]	63689[8]	63737[2]	63786[6]				
63641[2]	63690[3]	63738[7]	63787[2]				
63642[2]	63691[7]	63739[2]	63788[4]				
63643[6]	63692[1]	63740[8]	63789[8]				
63644[7]	63693[1]	63741[2]	63790[2]				
63645[7]	63694[2]	63742[2]	63791[2]				
63646[8]	63695[2]	63743[1]	63792[8]				
63647[3]	63696[2]	63744[2]	63793[2]				
63648[3]	63697[2]	63745[4]	63794[6]				
63649[2]	63698[1]	63746[8]	63795[8]				
63650[8]	63699[6]	63747[6]	63796[8]				
63651[7]	63700[1]	63748[6]	63797[1]				
63652[8]	63701[2]	63749[6]	63798[2]				
63653[7]	63702[2]	63750[7]	63799[1]				
63654[1]	63703[7]	63751[2]	63800[7]				
63655[6]							

Total :

Class O1	58	Class O4/5	4
Class O4/1	56	Class O4/6	11
Class O4/2	9	Class O4/7	40
Class O4/3	92	Class O4/8	54

2-8-0   8F   Class O2

O2/1* Introduced 1921. Development of experimental Gresley G.N. 3-cyl. loco. (L.N.E.R. 3921). Subsequently rebuilt with side-window cab, and reduced boiler mountings.

O2/2† Introduced 1924. Development of O2/1 with detail differences.

O2/3 Introduced 1932. Development of O2/2 with side-window cab and reduced boiler mountings.

O2/4‡ Introduced 1943. Rebuilt with 100A (B1 type) boiler and smokebox extended backwards (63924 retaining G.N. tender).

Weight: Loco. { 75 tons 16 cwt.*† / 78 tons 13 cwt.‡ / 74 tons 2 cwt.‡ }

Tender { 43 tons 2 cwt. (63922-46) / 52 tons. (63947-87) }

Pressure: 180 lb. Su.

63922-64373

Cyls.: (3) 18¼" × 26".
Driving Wheels: 4' 8". T.E.: 36,740 lb.
Walschaerts gear and derived motion.
P.V.

63922*	63939†	63956	63973
63923*	63940†	63957	63974
63924‡	63941†	63958	63975
63925*	63942†	63959	63976
63926*	63943†	63960	63977
63927*	63944†	63961	63978
63928*	63945†	63962‡	63979
63929*	63946†	63963	63980
63930*	63947	63964	63981
63931*	63948	63965	63982
63932‡	63949‡	63966	63983
63933†	63950‡	63967	63984
63934†	63951	63968	63985
63935†	63952	63969	63986
63936†	63953	63970	63987
63937†	63954	63971	
63938†	63955	63972	

Total : Class O2/1   9
Class O2/2   14
Class O2/3   38
Class O2/4   5

0-6-0   2P3F   Class J6

Introduced 1911. Gresley G.N. design.
Weight: Loco.   50 tons 10 cwt.
Tender   43 tons 2 cwt.
Pressure: 170 lb. Su. Cyls.: 19" × 26".
Driving Wheels: 5' 2". T.E. 21,875 lb.
P.V.

64170	64185	64201	64217
64171	64186	64202	64218
64172	64187	64203	64219
64173	64188	64204	64220
64174	64189	64205	64221
64175	64190	64206	64222
64176	64191	64207	64223
64177	64192	64208	64224
64178	64193	64209	64225
64179	64195	64210	64226
64180	64196	64211	64227
64181	64197	64213	64228
64182	64198	64214	64229
64183	64199	64215	64230
64184	64200	64216	64231

64232	64245	64257	64269
64233	64246	64258	64270
64234	64247	64259	64271
64235	64248	64260	64272
64236	64249	64261	64273
64237	64250	64262	64274
64238	64251	64263	64275
64239	64252	64264	64276
64240	64253	64265	64277
64241	64254	64266	64278
64243	64255	64267	64279
64244	64256	64268	

Total 107

0-6-0   2P3F   Class J11

Introduced 1901. Robinson G.C. design.
Parts 1 and 4 have 3,250 gallon
tenders; Parts 2 and 5, 4,000 gallon.
Parts 1 and 5 have higher boiler
mountings; Parts 4 and 5 low. All
Parts 4 and 5 are superheated, and
some of Parts 1 and 2. There are
frequent changes between parts.
J11/3* Introduced 1942. Rebuilt with
long-travel piston valves and boiler
higher pitched.

Weight: Loco. { 51 tons 19 cwt. (Sat.)
52 tons 2 cwt. (Su.)
53 tons 6 cwt.*

Tender { 44 tons 3 cwt. (3,250 gall.)
48 tons 6 cwt. (4,000 gall.)
Pressure: 180 lb. SS. Cyls.: 18½" × 26".
Driving Wheels: 5' 2". T.E.: 21,960 lb.

64280	64304*	64325	64349
64281	64305	64327	64351
64283*	64306	64328	64352*
64284*	64308	64329	64353
64285	64310	64330	64354*
64287	64311	64331	64355
64288	64312	64332*	64357
64290	64313	64333*	64359*
64292	64314*	64336	64361
64293	64315	64337	64362*
64294	64316*	64338	64363
64295	64317*	64340	64364*
64296	64318*	64341	64365
64297	64319	64343	64366
64298	64320	64344	64368
64300	64321	64345	64371
64302	64322	64346*	64372
64303	64324*	64348	64373*

64375*	64396	64417*	64437
64376	64397	64418*	64438
64377	64398	64419	64439*
64378	64399	64420*	64440
64379*	64401	64421	64441*
64381	64402*	64422	64442*
64382	64403	64423	64443
64383	64404	64424	64444
64384	64405	64425	64445
64385	64406*	64427*	64446
64386*	64407	64428	64447
64387	64408	64429	64448
64388	64409	64430	64449
64389	64410	64431	64450*
64392	64411	64432	64451
64393*	64412	64433	64452
64394*	64414	64434	64453
64395*	64416	64435	

Total : **Class J11/3 33**
Class J11 (other parts) **110**

0-6-0   3F   Class J35

J35/5* Introduced 1906.   Reid N.B.
    design with piston valves.
J35/4 Introduced 1908. Slide valves.
    (Parts 1, 2 and 3 were variations of
    Parts 4 and 5 before superheating.)
Weight: Loco. $\begin{cases} 51 \text{ tons.*} \\ 50 \text{ tons 15 cwt.} \end{cases}$
    Tender $\begin{cases} 38 \text{ tons 1 cwt.*} \\ 37 \text{ tons 15 cwt.} \end{cases}$
Pressure: 180 lb. Su. Cyls.: $18\frac{1}{4}'' \times 26''$.
Driving Wheels: 5' 0". T.E. 22,080 lb.

64460*	64478	64494	64511
64461*	64479	64495	64512
64462*	64480	64496	64513
64463*	64482	64497	64514
64464*	64483	64498	64515
64466*	64484	64499	64516
64468*	64485	64500	64517
64470*	64486	64501	64518
64471*	64487	64502	64519
64472*	64488	64504	64520
64473*	64489	64505	64521
64474*	64490	64506	64522
64475*	64491	64507	64523
64476*	64492	64509	64524
64477*	64493	64510	64525

64526	64529	64532	64535
64527	64530	64533	
64528	64531	64534	

Total : **Class J35/4   55**
Class J35/5   15

0-6-0   5F   Class J37

Introduced 1914.   Reid N.B. design.
    Superheated development of J35.
Weight: Loco.   54 tons 14 cwt.
    Tender 40 tons 19 cwt.
Pressure: 180 lb. Su. Cyls.: $19\frac{1}{2}'' \times 26''$.
Driving Wheels: 5' 0". T.E.: 25,210 lb.
    P.V.

64536	64562	64588	64614
64537	64563	64589	64615
64538	64564	64590	64616
64539	64565	64591	64617
64540	64566	64592	64618
64541	64567	64593	64619
64542	64568	64594	64620
64543	64569	64595	64621
64544	64570	64596	64622
64545	64571	64597	64623
64546	64572	64598	64624
64547	64573	64599	64625
64548	64574	64600	64626
64549	64575	64601	64627
64550	64576	64602	64628
64551	64577	64603	64629
64552	64578	64604	64630
64553	64579	64605	64631
64554	64580	64606	64632
64555	64581	64607	64633
64556	64582	64608	64634
64557	64583	64609	64635
64558	64584	64610	64636
64559	64585	64611	64637
64560	64586	64612	64638
64561	64587	64613	64639

Total **104**

0-6-0   3P5F   Class J19

Introduced 1912.   S. Holden G.E.
    design rebuilt with round-topped
    firebox from 1934.
* Rebuilt with 19" cyls. and 180 lb.
    pressure.
† Rebuilt with 19" cyls. and 160 lb.
    pressure.

Weight: Loco.   50 tons 7 cwt.
           Tender 38 tons 5 cwt.
Pressure $\begin{cases} 170 \text{ lb. Su.} \\ 180 \text{ lb. Su.}^* \\ 160 \text{ lb. Su.}^\dagger \end{cases}$

Cyls. $\begin{cases} 20'' \times 26''. \\ 19'' \times 26''.^{*\dagger} \end{cases}$

Driving Wheels: 4' 11".

T.E. $\begin{cases} 27,430 \text{ lb.} \\ 26,215 \text{ lb.}^* \\ 23,300 \text{ lb.}^\dagger \end{cases}$

64640	64649	64658	64667
64641	64650	64659	64668
64642	64651	64660	64669
64643	64652	64661	64670
64644	64653	64662	64671*
64645	64654	64663	64672†
64646	64655	64664*	64673
64647	64656	64665	64674
64648	64657	64666	

Total 35

0-6-0   5F   Class J20

J20/1 Introduced 1943. Hill G.E.
design with Belpaire firebox (intro-
duced 1920) rebuilt with B12/1 type
boiler with round-topped firebox.
Weight: Loco.   54 tons 15 cwt.
           Tender 38 tons 5 cwt.
Pressure: 180 lb. Su. Cyls.: 20" × 28".
Driving Wheels: 4' 11". T.E.: 29,045 lb.
P.V.

64675	64682	64688	64694
64676	64683	64689	64695
64677	64684	64690	64696
64678	64685	64691	64697
64679	64686	64692	64698
64680	64687	64693	64699
64681			

Total 25

0-6-0   4P5F   Class J39

Introduced 1926. Gresley design.
J39/1 Standard 3,500 gallon tender.
J39/2* Standard 4,200 gallon tender.
J39/3† Various N.E. tenders (3,940
gallon on 64843-5, 4,125 gallon on
64855-9).

Weight: Loco.   57 tons 17 cwt.
Tender $\begin{cases} 44 \text{ tons }\ 4 \text{ cwt.} \\ 52 \text{ tons } 13 \text{ cwt.}^* \end{cases}$ and others
Pressure: 180 lb. Su. Cyls.: 20" × 26".
Driving Wheels: 5' 2". T.E.: 25,665 lb.
P.V.

64700†	64743	64786*	64829
64701	64744	64787*	64830
64702	64745	64788*	64831
64703	64746	64789*	64832
64704	64747	64790*	64833
64705	64748	64791*	64834
64706	64749	64792*	64835
64707	64750	64793*	64836
64708	64751	64794*	64837
64709	64752	64795*	64838*
64710	64753	64796	64839*
64711	64754	64797	64840*
64712	64755	64798	64841*
64713	64756	64799	64842*
64714	64757	64800	64843†
64715	64758	64801	64844†
64716	64759	64802	64845†
64717	64760	64803	64846
64718	64761	64804	64847
64719	64762	64805	64848
64720	64763	64806	64849
64721	64764	64807	64850
64722	64765	64808	64851
64723	64766	64809	64852
64724	64767	64810	64853
64725	64768	64811	64854
64726	64769	64812	64855†
64727	64770	64813	64856†
64728	64771	64814	64857†
64729	64772	64815	64858†
64730	64773	64816	64859†
64731	64774	64817	64860
64732	64775	64818	64861
64733	64776	64819	64862
64734	64777	64820*	64863
64735	64778	64821*	64864
64736	64779	64822*	64865
64737	64780	64823	64866
64738	64781	64824	64867
64739	64782	64825	64868
64740	64783	64826	64869
64741	64784*	64827	64870
64742	64785*	64828	64871

Class J17 0-6-0 No. 65500

[R. E. Vincent

Class J19 0-6-0 No. 64666

[Brian E. Morrison

Class J20/1 0-6-0 No. 64683

[G. D. Parkes

Class J6 0-6-0 No. 64266   *[Brian E. Morrison*

Class J10/6 0-6-0 No. 65202   *[D. Penney*

Class J11 0-6-0 No. 64327   *[T. K. Widd*

64872*	64902*	64932*	64962*
64873*	64903*	64933	64963*
64874*	64904*	64934	64964*
64875*	64905*	64935	64965*
64876*	64906*	64936	64966*
64877*	64907*	64937	64967*
64878*	64908*	64938	64968*
64879*	64909*	64939	64969*
64880*	64910*	64940	64970*
64881*	64911*	64941	64971†
64832*	64912*	64942	64972*
64883*	64913*	64943	64973†
64884*	64914*	64944	64974†
64885*	64915*	64945*	64975*
64886*	64916*	64946*	64976†
64887*	64917*	64947*	64977*
64888*	64918*	64948*	64978†
64889*	64919*	64949*	64979†
64890*	64920*	64950*	64980†
64891*	64921*	64951*	64981†
64892*	64922*	64952*	64982†
64893*	64923*	64953*	64983†
64894*	64924*	64954*	64984*
64895*	64925*	64955*	64985†
64896*	64926†	64956*	64986†
64897*	64927*	64957*	64987†
64898*	64928*	64958*	64988†
64899*	64929*	64959*	
64900*	64930*	64960*	
64901*	64931*	64961*	

Total : Class J39/1 156

Class J39/2 106

Class J39/3 27

0-6-0   2F   Class J21

Introduced 1886. T. W. Worsdell N.E. design. Majority built as 2-cyl. compounds and later rebuilt as simple locos.

* Rebuilt with superheater, Stephenson gear and piston valves.

† Rebuilt with piston valves, superheater removed.

Weight: Loco. $\begin{cases} 43 \text{ tons } 15 \text{ cwt.*} \\ 42 \text{ tons } 9 \text{ cwt.†} \end{cases}$
Tender 36 tons 19 cwt.
Pressure: 160 lb. SS.
Cyls.: 19″ × 24″.
T.E. : 19,240 lb.
Driving Wheels: 5′ 1¼″.

65033*	65064*	65091*	65110*
65039†	65070†	65099†	65117†
65061*	65078*	65103*	

Total 11

0-6-0   2F   Class J10

J10/4* Introduced 1896. Pollitt development of J10/2 with larger bearings and larger tender.

J10/6 Introduced 1901. Robinson locos with larger bearings and small tender.

Weight: Loco. 41 tons 6 cwt.
Tender $\begin{cases} 37 \text{ tons } 6 \text{ cwt.} \\ 43 \text{ tons.*} \end{cases}$
Pressure: 160 lb. Cyls.: 18″ × 26″.
Driving Wheels: 5′ 1″. T.E. 18,780 lb.

65131	65147*	65171*	65191
65132*	65148*	65173	65192
65133*	65153*	65175	65194
65134*	65156*	65176	65196
65135*	65157*	65177	65198
65138*	65158*	65178*	65199
65139	65159*	65180	65200
65140*	65160*	65181	65202
65142*	65162	65182	65203
65143*	65166*	65184	65208
65144*	65167*	65185	65209
65145*	65169*	65186	
65146*	65170*	65187	

Total : Class J10/4 25

Class J10/6 25

0-6-0   2F   Class J36

Introduced 1888. Holmes N.B. design.
Weight : Loco. 41 tons 19 cwt.
Tender 33 tons 9 cwt.
Pressure : 165 lb. Cyls. : 18¼″ × 26″.
Driving Wheels : 5′ 0″. T.E. : 19,690 lb.

65210	65211	65213	65214

Class J36 0-6-0 No. 65210

[J. Robertson

Class J21 0-6-0 No. 65033

Class J27 0-6-0 No. 65874

[J. Robertson

65216	Byng		
65217	French		
65218			
65221			
65222	Somme		
65224	Mons		
65225			
65227			
65228			
65229			
65230			
65232			
65233	Plumer		
65234			
65235	Gough		
65237			
65239			
65241			
65242			
65243	Maude		
65244			
65246			
65247			
65249			
65250			
65251			
65252			
65253	Joffre		
65257			
65258			
65259			
65260			
65261			
65265			
65266			
65267			
65268	Allenby		
65270	65281	65293	65304
65273	65282	65295	65305
65275	65285	65296	65306
65276	65287	65297	65307
65277	65288	65300	65309
65280	65290	65303	65310
65311	Haig		
65312	65317	65321	65327
65313	65318	65323	65329
65315	65319	65324	65330
65316	65320	65325	65331

65333	65338	65342	65345
65334	65339	65343	65346
65335	65341	65344	

Total 93

0-6-0   1P2F   Class J15

Introduced 1883. Worsdell G.E. design, modified by J. Holden.
* Fitted with side-window cab for Colne Valley line.
Weight: Loco.   37 tons 2 cwt.
　　　　Tender 30 tons 13 cwt.
Pressure: 160 lb. Cyls.: $17\frac{1}{2}'' \times 24''$.
Driving Wheels: 4' 11". T.E.: 16,940 lb.

65356	65435	65452	65466
65361	65438*	65453	65467
65388	65440	65454	65468
65389	65441	65455	65469
65390	65442	65456	65470
65391*	65443	65457	65471
65404	65444	65458	65472
65405*	65445	65459	65473
65420	65446	65460	65474
65424*	65447	65461	65475
65425	65448	65462	65476
65432*	65449	65463	65477
65433	65450	65464	65478
65434	65451	65465	65479

Total 56

0-6-0   2P4F   Class J17

Introduced 1901. J. Holden G.E. design. Many rebuilt from round-top firebox J16, introduced 1900.
* Fitted with small tender.
Weight: Loco.　　45 tons 8 cwt.
　　　　Tender $\begin{cases} 38 \text{ tons } 5 \text{ cwt.} \\ 30 \text{ tons } 12 \text{ cwt.*} \end{cases}$
Pressure: 180 lb. Su. Cyls.: $19'' \times 26''$.
Driving Wheels: 4' 11". T.E.: 24,340 lb.

37

65500	65523	65545	65568
65501*	65525	65546	65570
65502*	65526	65548	65571
65503*	65527	65549	65572
65504*	65528*	65551	65573
65505	65529	65553	65575
65506*	65530	65554	65576
65507*	65531	65555	65577
65508*	65532	65556	65578
65509	65533	65557	65580
65511*	65534	65558	65581
65512*	65535	65559	65582
65513*	65536	65560	65583
65514*	65537	65561	65584
65515*	65538	65562	65586
65518*	65539	65563	65587
65519*	65540	65565	65588
65520	65541	65566	65589
65521	65542	65567	
65522	65544		

Total 78

0-6-0   3F   Class J25

Introduced 1898. W. Worsdell N.E. design.

* Original design, saturated, with slide valves.

† Rebuilt with superheater and piston valves.

‡ Rebuilt with piston valves, superheater removed.

Weight: Loco.
{ 39 tons 11 cwt.*
{ 41 tons 14 cwt.†
{ 40 tons 17 cwt.‡
Tender 36 tons 19 cwt.

Pressure: 160 lb. SS. Cyls.: 18½" × 26".
Driving Wheels: 4' 7¼". T.E.: 21,905 lb.

65645†	65656*	65670*	65683‡
65648*	65657*	65673‡	65685*
65650*	65662†	65675*	65687*
65654‡	65663*	65677‡	65691*
65655*	65666*	65680*	65693*
65695*	65699*	65712*	65720*
65696*	65700*	65713*	65726*
65697*	65702‡	65714*	65727*
65698*	65706†	65717†	65728*

Total 36

0-6-0   5F   Class J26

Introduced 1904. W. Worsdell N.E. design.

Weight: Loco.   46 tons 16 cwt.
Tender   36 tons 19 cwt.
Pressure: 180 lb. Cyls.: 18½" × 26".
Driving Wheels: 4' 7¼". T.E.: 24,640 lb.

65730	65743	65756	65769
65731	65744	65757	65770
65732	65745	65758	65771
65733	65746	65759	65772
65734	65747	65760	65773
65735	65748	65761	65774
65736	65749	65762	65775
65737	65750	65763	65776
65738	65751	65764	65777
65739	65752	65765	65778
65740	65753	65766	65779
65741	65754	65767	
65742	65755	65768	

Total 50

0-6-0   5F   Class J27

Introduced 1906. W. Worsdell N.E. design developed from J26.

* Introduced 1921. Raven ocos. Superheated, with piston valves.

† Introduced 1943. Piston valves, superheater removed.

Weight: Loco. { 47 tons Sat.
{ 49 tons 10 cwt. Su.
Tender   36 tons 19 cwt.
Pressure: 180 lb. SS. Cyls.: 18½" × 26".
Driving Wheels: 4' 7¼". T.E. 24,640 lb.

65780	65782	65784	65786
65781	65783	65785	65787

Class Q6 0-8-0 No. 63450   [T. K. Widd

Class Q7 0-8-0 No. 63462   [T. K. Widd

Class Y8 0-4-0T No. 55 (Departmental)   [Brian E. Morrison

Class G5 0-4-4T No. 67340 (with enlarged tanks)

Class F5 2-4-2T No. 67192

[R. K. Evans

Class F5 2-4-2T No. 67219 (with side-window cab)

[G. Wheeler

65788	65815	65842	65869*
65789	65816	65843	65870†
65790	65817	65844	65871*
65791	65818	65845	65872*
65792	65819	65846	65873†
65793	65820	65847	65874*
65794	65821	65848	65875†
65795	65822	65849	65876†
65796	65823	65850	65877†
65797	65824	65851	65878*
65798	65825	65852	65879†
65799	65826	65853	65880*
65800	65827	65854	65881*
65801	65828	65855	65882†
65802	65829	65856	65883*
65803	65830	65857	65884*
65804	65831	65858	65885*
65805	65832	65859	65886*
65806	65833	65860†	65887*
65807	65834	65861†	65888†
65808	65835	65862†	65889*
65809	65836	65863*	65890*
65810	65837	65864†	65891†
65811	65838	65865†	65892*
65812	65839	65866*	65893*
65813	65840	65867†	65894*
65814	65841	65868†	

Total 115

0-6-0   6F   Class J38

Introduced 1926. Gresley design. Predecessor of J39, with 4' 8" wheels, boiler 6" longer than J39 and smokebox 6" shorter.
* Rebuilt with J39 boiler.
Weight: Loco.   58 tons 19 cwt.
                        Tender 44 tons 4 cwt.
Pressure: 180 lb. Su. Cyls.: 20" × 26".
Driving Wheels: 4' 8". T.E.: 28,415 lb. P.V.

65900	65909	65918*	65927*
65901	65910	65919	65928
65902	65911	65920	65929
65903*	65912	65921	65930
65904	65913	65922	65931
65905	65914	65923	65932
65906*	65915	65924	65933
65907	65916	65925	65934
65908*	65917*	65926*	

Total 35

2-4-2T   IMT   Class F5

Introduced 1911. S. D. Holden G. E. design. (Rebuilt from Worsdell G. E. F4.)
* Introduced 1949, Push-and-pull fitted.
Weight: 53 tons 19 cwt.
Pressure: 180 lb. Cyls.: 17½" × 24".
Driving Wheels: 5' 4". T.E.: 17,570 lb.

67189	67199*	67208	67216
67192	67200*	67209	67218*
67193*	67201	67211	67219
67194	67202*	67212	
67195	67203*	67214	

Total 18

2-4-2T   IMT   Class F6

Introduced 1911. S.D. Holden G. E. design, development of Worsdell G. E. F4 with higher pressure and larger tanks.
Weight: 56 tons 9 cwt.
Pressure: 180 lb. Cyls.: 17½" × 24".
Driving Wheels: 5' 4". T.E.: 17,570 lb.

67221	67227	67229	67231
67224	67228	67230	

Total 7

For full details of
ELECTRIC AND DIESEL LOCOS
on the E., N.E.& Scottish Regions
see the
ABC OF B.R. LOCOMOTIVES
Part II, Nos. 10000-39999

For full details of
CLASS "4" AND "2" 2-6-0s
Nos. 43000-43161 & 46400-46725
on the E., N.E.& Scottish Regions
see the
ABC OF B.R. LOCOMOTIVES
Part III, Nos. 40000-59999

67246-67474

0-4-4T IMT Class G5

Introduced 1894. W. Worsdell N.E. design.
* Push-and-pull fitted.
† Push-and-pull fitted and rebuilt with larger tanks.
Weight: 54 tons 4 cwt.
Pressure: 160 lb. Cyls.: 18″ × 24″.
Driving Wheels: 5′ 1¼″. T.E. 17,265 lb.

67246	67270	67297*	67326
67248	67273*	67298	67329
67250*	67274	67305*	67333
67253*	67277*	67311*	67337*
67254	67278	67315	67338
67256	67279*	67318	67339*
67258	67280*	67319	67340†
67259	67281*	67320	67341
67261*	67282*	67321	67342
67262	67284	67322*	67343
67263	67286*	67323*	67346
67265	67289	67324	
67269*	67294	67325	

Total 50

4-4-2T IMT Class C12

Introduced 1898. Ivatt G.N. design.
*†Boiler pressure reduced to 170 lb.
††Push-and-pull fitted.
Weight: 62 tons 6 cwt.
Pressure: $\begin{cases} 175 \text{ lb.} \\ 170 \text{ lb.*†} \end{cases}$
Cyls.: 18″ × 26″.
Driving Wheels: 5′ 8″.
T.E. $\begin{cases} 18,425 \text{ lb.} \\ 17,900 \text{ lb.*†} \end{cases}$

67352	67366	67380	67394
67357	67367	67386‡	67395
67362	67374†	67391	67397
67363†	67376	67392	67398*
67365	67379		

Total 18

4-4-2T 2P1F Class C13

Introduced 1903. Robinson G.C. design, later rebuilt with superheater.
* Push-and-pull fitted.
Weight: 66 tons 13 cwt.
Pressure: 160 lb. Su. Cyls.: 18″ × 26″.
Driving Wheels: 5′ 7″. T.E.: 17,100 lb.

67400	67417*	67423	67433*
67407	67418*	67424	67434
67409	67419	67427	67437
67413	67420*	67428	67438*
67416*	67421*	67431	67439

Total 20

4-4-2T 2P1F Class C14

Introduced 1907. Robinson G.C. design, later superheated, development of C13, with detail differences.
Weight: 71 tons.
Pressure: 160 lb. Su. Cyls.: 18″ × 26″.
Driving Wheels: 5′ 7″. T.E.: 17,100 lb.

67440	67443	67446	67449
67441	67444	67447	67450
67442	67445	67448	67451

Total 12

4-4-2T 2P Class C15

Introduced 1911. Reid N.B. design.
Push-and-pull fitted.
Weight: 68 tons 15 cwt.
Pressure: 175 lb. Cyls.: 18″ × 26″.
Driving Wheels: 5′ 9″. T.E.: 18,160 lb.

67460   67474

Total 2

4-4-2T 2P Class C16

Introduced 1915. Reid N.B. design, superheated development of C15.
Weight: 72 tons 10 cwt.
Pressure: 165 lb. Su. Cyls.: 19″ × 26″.
Driving Wheels: 5′ 9″ T.E.: 19,080 lb.
P.V.

67482	67487	67491	67497
67484	67488	67492	67500
67485	67489	67494	67501
67486	67490	67496	67502

Total 16

Classes
2-6-2T V1 (3MT) V1 & V3
V3 (4MT)

V1 Introduced 1930. Gresley design.
V3* Introduced 1939. Development of V1 with higher pressure (locos. numbered below 67682 rebuilt from V1).

Weight: { 84 tons.
{ 86 tons 16 cwt.*

Pressure: { 180 lb. Su.
{ 200 lb. Su.*

Cyls.: (3) 16″ × 26″.
Driving Wheels: 5′ 8″.
T.E.: { 22,465 lb.
{ 24,960 lb.*

Walschaerts gear, derived motion. P.V.

67600*	67623	67646*	67669*
67601*	67624*	67647	67670*
67602	67625*	67648	67671
67603	67626*	67649	67672*
67604*	67627*	67650	67673
67605*	67628	67651*	67674
67606*	67629	67652*	67675*
67607	67630	67653*	67676
67608	67631	67654*	67677
67609*	67632	67655	67678
67610	67633	67656*	67679*
67611*	67634*	67657*	67680
67612*	67635	67658	67681
67613	67636*	67659	67682*
67614	67637	67660*	67683*
67615*	67638*	67661	67684*
67616	67639	67662*	67685*
67617	67640	67663*	67686*
67618	67641	67664	67687*
67619	67642	67665	67688*
67620*	67643*	67666	67689*
67621	67644	67667	67690*
67622	67645	67668*	67691*

Total : Class V1 50
Class V3 42

2-6-4T 4MT Class L1

Introduced 1945. Thompson design.
* Introduced 1954. Boiler pressure reduced to 200 lb.
† Introduced 1954. Cylinder diameter reduced.

Weight: 89 tons 9 cwt.
Pressure: { 225 lb.
{ 200 lb.*
Cyls.: { (O) 20″ × 26″.
{ (O) 18½″ × 26″.†
Driving Wheels: 5′ 2″.
T.E.: { 32,080 lb.
{ 28,515 lb.*
{ 28,180 lb.†
Walschaerts gear. P.V.

67701	67726	67751	67776†
67702	67727	67752	67777
67703	67728	67753	67778
67704	67729	67754	67779†
67705	67730	67755	67780
67706	67731	67756	67781
67707	67732	67757	67782
67708	67733	67758	67783
67709	67734	67759	67784
67710	67735	67760	67785
67711	67736	67761*	67786
67712	67737	67762	67787
67713	67738	67763	67788
67714	67739	67764	67789
67715	67740	67765	67790
67716	67741	67766	67791
67717	67742	67767	67792
67718	67743	67768	67793
67719	67744	67769	67794
67720	67745	67770†	67795
67721	67746	67771†	67796
67722	67747*	67772†	67797
67723	67748	67773	67798*
67724	67749	67774	67799
67725	67750	67775	67800

Total 100

0-6-0ST 4F Class J94

Introduced 1943. Riddles M.o.S. design. (Bought from M.o.S. 1946.)
Weight: 48 tons 5 cwt.
Pressure: 170 lb. Cyls.: 18″ × 26″.
Driving Wheels: 4′ 3″. T.E.: 23,870 lb.

68006	68025	68044	68063
68007	68026	68045	68064
68008	68027	68046	68065
68009	68028	68047	68066
68010	68029	68048	68067
68011	68030	68049	68068
68012	68031	68050	68069
68013	68032	68051	68070
68014	68033	68052	68071
68015	68034	68053	68072
68016	68035	68054	68073
68017	68036	68055	68074
68018	68037	68056	68075
68019	68038	68057	68076
68020	68039	68058	68077
68021	68040	68059	68078
68022	68041	68060	68079
68023	68042	68061	68080
68024	68043	68062	

Total 75

0-4-0ST   OF   Class Y9

Introduced 1882. Holmes N.B. design.
* Locos. running permanently attached
to wooden tender.
Weight: Loco.   27 tons 16 cwt.
        Tender   6 tons.*
Pressure: 130 lb. Cyls.: (O) 14" × 20".
Driving Wheels: 3' 8" T.E.: 9,845 lb.

68095	68102*	68113	68118*
68097*	68104	68114*	68119*
68099*	68106*	68115	68123
68100*	68108*	68116*	68124
68101	68110	68117*	

Total 19

0-4-0T   Dock Tank   Class Y4

Introduced 1913.   Hill G.E. design.
Weight: 38 tons 1 cwt.
Pressure: 180 lb. Cyls.: (O) 17" × 20".
Driving Wheels: 3' 10". T.E : 19,225 lb.
Walschaerts gear.
(See also page 45)

68126   68128

Total 3

0-4-0T   Unclass.   Class Y1

Sentinel Wagon Works design. Single-
speed Geared Sentinel locomotives.
The parts of this class differ in details,
including size of boiler and fuel
capacity.
Y1/1* Introduced 1925.
Y1/2† Introduced 1927.
Y1/4‡ Introduced 1927.
§ Sprocket gear ratio 9:25 (remainder
11:25).
Weight: { 20 tons 17 cwt.*
          19 tons 16 cwt.†
          19 tons 7 cwt.‡
Pressure: 275 lb. Su. Cyls.: 6¾" × 9".
Driving Wheels: 2' 6".
T.E.: { 7,260 lb.*†‡
        8,870 lb. §
Poppet valves.
(See also page 45)

68138†	68145†§	68150†§
68142†	68149†§	

Total : Class Y1/1 5
          Class Y1/2 6
          Class Y1/4 1

0-4-0T   Unclass.   Class Y3

Sentinel Wagon Works design. Two-
speed Geared Sentinel locos.
Introduced 1927.
* Sprocket gear ratio 15 : 19 (re-
mainder 19 : 19).
Weight: 20 tons 16 cwt.
Pressure: 275 lb. Su. Cyls.: 6¾" × 9"
Driving Wheels: 2' 6"
T.E. { Low Gear: 12,600 lb.
        High Gear: 4,705 lb.
        Low Gear: 15,960 lb.*
        High Gear: 5,960 lb.*
Poppet valves.
(See also page 45)

68159   6816   068164   68182*

Total 13

0-4-2T   OF   Class Z4

Introduced 1915.   Manning-Wardle
design for G.N. of S.
Weight: 25 tons 14 cwt.
Pressure: 160 lb. Cyls.: (O) 13" × 20".
Driving Wheels: 3' 6". T.E.: 10,945 lb.

68190   68191

Total 2

44

DEPARTMENTAL LOCOMOTIVES

In addition to service locomotives (denoted by a bold "S" in these pages) that are still shown with numbers in the British Railways series, a number of E. & N.E. Region departmental locomotives have been renumbered between 1 and 100. These are shown below with their former B.R. number in brackets.

0-6-0ST 3F Class J52/2

(For dimensions see page 48)

1 (68845)	2 (68816)

0-4-0T Unclass. Class Y3

(15:19 gear ratio—for dimensions see page 44)

3 (68181)	38 (68168)
5 (68165)	40 (68173)
7 (68166)	41 (68177)
8 (68183)	42 (68178)
21 (68162)	

0-4-0T Unclass. Class Y1/1

(For dimensions see page 44)

4 (68132)	37 (68130)
6 (68133)	39 (68131)
	53 (68152)

0-6-0T 2F Class J66

Introduced 1886. J. Holden G.E. design.
Weight: 40 tons 6 cwt.
Pressure: 160 lb. Cyls.: 16½″ × 22″.
Driving Wheels: 4′ 0″.
T.E.: 16,970 lb.

31 (68382)	36 (68378)
32 (68370)	Total 3

0-4-0T Dock Tank Class Y4

(For dimensions see page 44)

33 (68129)

0-4-0T Unclass. Class Y1/4

(For dimensions see page 44)

51 (68136)

0-4-0 Diesel Mechanical

Introduced 1950, Hibberd & Co. for North Eastern Region.
Weight: 11 tons.
Engine: English National Gas type DA 4, 4-cyls., 52 h.p. at 1,250 r.p.m. Transmission spur type gear box with roller chains: three forward and three reverse gears.

52 (11104)	Total 1

0-4-0T Unclass. Class Y1/2

(For dimensions see page 44)

54 (68153)

0-4-0T Dock Tank Class Y8

Introduced 1890. T. W. Worsdell N.E. design.
Weight: 15 tons 10 cwt.
Pressure: 140 lb. Cyls.: 11″ × 15″.
Driving Wheels: 3′ 0″.
T.E.: 6,000 lb.

55 (68091)	Total 1

0-4-0 Diesel Mechanical

Introduced 1956. Ruston Hornsby 88 h.p. Shunting locomotive.

56

68192-68364

0-4-2T 0F Class Z5

Introduced 1915. Manning-Wardle design for G.N. of S.
Weight: 30 tons 18 cwt.
Pressure: 160 lb. Cyls.: (O) 14″ × 20″.
Driving Wheels: 4′ 0″. T.E.: 11,105 lb.

68192   **Total 1**

0-6-0T Dock Tank Class J63

Introduced 1906. Robinson G.C. design.
Weight: 37 tons 9 cwt.
Pressure: 150 lb. Cyls.: (O) 13″ × 20″.
Driving Wheels: 3′ 6″. T.E.: 10,260 lb.

68210   **Total 1**

0-6-0T Unclass. Class J65

Introduced 1889. J. Holden G.E. design.
Weight: 36 tons 11 cwt.
Pressure: 160 lb. Cyls.: 14″ × 20″.
Driving Wheels: 4′ 0″. T.E.: 11,105 lb.

68214   **Total 1**

0-6-0T Unclass. Class J71

Introduced 1886. T. W. Worsdell N.E. design.
*†Altered cylinder dimensions.
Weight: 37 tons 12 cwt.
Pressure: 140 lb. Dr. Wheels: 4′ 7½″.

Cyls.: $\begin{cases} 16″ × 22″. \\ 16\frac{3}{4}″ × 22″.* \\ 18″ × 22″.† \end{cases}$ T.E.: $\begin{cases} 12,130 \text{ lb.} \\ 13,300 \text{ lb.}* \\ 15,355 \text{ lb.}† \end{cases}$

68230*	68252*	68273	68296
68232	68253*	68275	68298
68233	68254	68276	68301
68235	68260	68278	68305*
68239	68262	68280*	68306*
68240	68263	68283	68308*
68242	68264	68287*	68309*
68244	68265	68290	68312†
68245	68266	68293*	68314
68246*	68267	68294	68316*
68250*	68269	68295	
68251	68272		

Total 46

0-6-0T 0F Class J88

Introduced 1904. Reid N.B. design with short wheelbase.
Weight: 38 tons 14 cwt.
Pressure: 130 lb. Cyls.: (O) 15″ × 22″.
Driving Wheels: 3′ 9″. T.E.: 12,155 lb.

68320	68329	68339	68349
68321	68330	68340	68350
68322	68331	68342	68351
68323	68332	68343	68352
68324	68333	68344	68353
68325	68334	68345	68354
68326	68335	68346	
68327	68336	68347	
68328	68338	68348	

Total 33

0-6-0T 3F Class J73

Introduced 1891. W. Worsdell N.E. design.
Weight: 46 tons 15 cwt.
Pressure: 160 lb. Cyls.: 19″ × 24″.
Driving Wheels: 4′ 7¼″. T.E.: 21,320 lb.

68355	68359	68361	68363
68356	68360	68362	68364
68357			

Total 9

0-6-0T 2F Class J77

Introduced 1899. W. Worsdell N.E. rebuild of Fletcher 0-4-4T originally built 1874-84.

Some engines of this class have square-cornered and some round-cornered cab-roofs.

Weight: 43 tons.

Pressure: 160 lb. Cyls.: 17″ × 22″.

Driving Wheels: 4′ 1¼″. T.E.: 17,560 lb.

68391	68406	68417	68431
68392	68408	68423	68434
68397	68409	68424	68435
68399	68410	68425	68438
68402	68412	68426	
68405	68414	68427	

Total 22

0-6-0T 2F Class J83

Introduced 1900. Holmes N.B. design.

Weight: 45 tons 5 cwt.

Pressure: 150 lb. Cyls.: 17″ × 26″.

Driving Wheels: 4′ 6″. T.E.: 17,745 lb.

68442	68452	68463	68472
68443	68453	68464	68474
68444	68454	68465	68475
68445	68456	68466	68477
68447	68457	68467	68478
68448	68458	68468	68479
68449	68459	68469	68480
68450	68460	68470	68481
68451	68461	68471	

Total 35

Classes
0-6-0T 2F J67 & J69

J67/1* Introduced 1890. J. Holden G.E. design with 160 lb. pressure.

J69/1† Introduced 1902. Development of J67 with 180 lb. pressure, larger tanks and larger firebox (some rebuilt from J67).

J67/2‡ Introduced 1937. Rebuild of J69 with 160 lb. boiler and small firebox.

J69/2§ Introduced 1950. J67/1 rebuilt with 180 lb. boiler and large firebox.

Weight: { 40 tons.*‡
          40 tons 9 cwt.†§

Pressure: { 160 lb.*‡
            180 lb.†§

Cyls.: 16½″ × 22″.

Driving Wheels: 4′ 0″.

T.E.: { 16,970 lb.*‡
        19,090 lb.†§

68490§	68529†	68566†	68603†
68491†	68530†	68567†	68605†
68494†	68532†	68568†	68607†
68495†	68535†	68569†	68608*
68497†	68536‡	68570†	68609†
68498§	68537†	68571†	68610‡
68499†	68538†	68573†	68612†
68500†	68541†	68574†	68613†
68501†	68542†	68575†	68616*
68502†	68543†	68576†	68617†
68503†	68545†	68577†	68618†
68507†	68546†	68578†	68619†
68508†	68549†	68579†	68621†
68510§	68550†	68581†	68623†
68511*	68551†	68583*	68625†
68512§	68552†	68585†	68626†
68513§	68553†	68587†	68628‡
68515*	68554†	68588†	68629†
68516*	68555†	68591†	68630†
68518*	68556†	68593†	68631†
68519§	68557†	68595*	68632†
68520§	68558†	68596†	68633†
68522§	68560†	68598†	68635†
68524†	68561†	68599†	68636†
68526†	68562†	68600†	
68527†	68563†	68601†	
68528†	68565†	68602†	

Total : Class J67/1 9

Class J67/2 3

Class J69/1 85

Class J69/2 8

68638-68888

0-6-0T 2F Class J68

Introduced 1912. Hill G.E. development of J69 with side-window cab.
Weight: 42 tons 9 cwt.
Pressure: 180 lb. Cyls.: 16¼" × 22".
Driving Wheels: 4' 0". T.E.: 19,090 lb.

68638	68646	68654	68662
68639	68647	68655	68663
68640	68648	68656	68664
68641	68649	68657	68665
68642	68650	68658	68666
68643	68651	68659	
68644	68652	68660	
68645	68653	68661	

Total 29

0-6-0T 2F Class J72

Introduced 1898. W. Worsdell N.E. design.
* Altered cylinder dimensions.
Weight: 38 tons 12 cwt.
Pressure: 140 lb. Cyls.: $\begin{cases} 17" \times 24" \\ 18" \times 24".* \end{cases}$
Driving Wheels: 4' 1¼".
T.E.: $\begin{cases} 16,760 \text{ lb.} \\ 18,790 \text{ lb.*} \end{cases}$

68670	68692	68714	68736
68671	68693	68715	68737
68672	68694	68716	68738
68673	68695	68717	68739
68674	68696	68718	68740
68675	68697	68719	68741
68676	68698	68720	68742
68677	68699	68721	68743
68678	68700	68722	68744
68679	68701	68723	68745
68680	68702	68724	68746
68681	68703	68725	68747
68682	68704	68726	68748
68683	68705	68727	68749
68684	68706	68728	68750
68685*	68707	68729	68751
68686	68708	68730	68752
68687	68709	68731	68753
68688	68710	68732	68754
68689	68711	68733	
68690	68712	68734	
68691	68713	68735	

(Class continued with No. 69001)

0-6-0ST 3F Class J52

J52/2 Introduced 1897. Ivatt standard G.N. saddletank with domed boiler.
J52/1* Introduced 1922. Rebuild of Stirling domeless saddletank (introduced 1892)—non-condensing.
J52/1† Introduced 1922. Condensing rebuild of Stirling locos.
‡ J52/2 with boiler pressure raised to 175 lb.
Weight: 51 tons 14 cwt.
Pressure: $\begin{cases} 170 \text{ lb.} \\ 175 \text{ lb.‡} \end{cases}$ Cyls.: 18" × 26".
Driving Wheels: 4' 8".
T.E.: $\begin{cases} 21,735 \text{ lb.} \\ 22,370 \text{ lb.‡} \end{cases}$
(See also page 45)

68761†	68823	68841	68866
68768*	68824	68842	68867
68778†	68826	68843	68869
68784†	68828	68846	68870
68785†	68829	68847	68871
68800*	68831	68848	68874
68808	68832	68849	68875
68809	68834	68851	68877
68811	68835	68855	68882
68813	68836	68857	68885
68815	68837	68860‡	68886
68817	68839	68862	68887
68822	68840‡	68863	68888

Total : Class J52/1   6
Class J52/2   48

0-6-0T 4F Class J50

J50/2* Introduced 1922. Gresley G.N. design (68900-19 rebuilt from smaller J51, built 1915-22).
J50/3† Introduced 1926. Post-grouping development with detail differences.
J50/1‡ Introduced 1929. Rebuilt from smaller J51, built 1913-14.
J50/4§ Introduced 1937. Development of J50/3 with larger bunker.
Weight: $\begin{cases} 57 \text{ tons.*} \\ 56 \text{ tons 6 cwt.‡} \\ 58 \text{ tons 3 cwt.†§} \end{cases}$
Pressure: 175 lb. Cyls.: 18½" × 26".
Driving Wheels: 4' 8". T.E.: 23,635 lb.

Right: Class C12
4-4-2T No. 67363
[*Brian E. Morrison*

Below: Class C15
4-4-2T No. 67474
[*W. S. Sellar*

Right: Class C16
4-4-2T No. 67489
[*W. S. Sellar*

Class V1 2-6-2T No. 67664   [K. R. Pirt

Class L1 2-6-4T No. 67730   [Brian E. Morrison

Class A8 4-6-2T No. 69893   [L. Marshall

Class N2/2 0-6-2T No. 69513   [P. H. Groom

Class N2/2 0-6-2T No. 69513   [P. H. Groom

Class N2/4 0-6-2T No. 69579   [G. Wheeler

Class Y9 0-4-0ST No. 68119 (coupled to wooden tender)   [D. Cartmel

Class Z5 0-4-2T No. 68192   [J. Robertson

Class Y4 0-4-0T No. 68128   Brian E. Morrison

Class J77 0-6-0T No. 68392   [P. J. Robinson

Class N10 0-6-2T No. 69104   [Brian E. Morrison

Class N13 0-6-2T No. 69114   [R. K. Evans

Class N7/4 0-6-2T No. 69601   [*G. Wheeler*

Class J83 0-6-0T No. 68463   [*J. Robertson*

Class N15/1 0-6-2T No. 69182   [*L. Marshall*

Above: Class J72
0-6-0T No. 69008
[*Brian E. Morrison*

Right: Class J88
0-6-0T No. 68347

Below: Class J52/2
0-6-0ST No. 68832
[*G. Clarke*

Class J66 0-6-0T No. 36 (Departmental)   [Brian E. Morrison

Class J69/I 0-6-0T No. 68529   Brian E. Morrison

Class J68 0-6-0T No. 68660   [A. R. Carpenter

68890‡	68916*	68942†	68968†
68891‡	68917†	68943†	68969†
68892‡	68918*	68944†	68970†
68893‡	68919*	68945†	68971†
68894‡	68920*	68946†	68972†
68895‡	68921*	68947†	68973†
68896‡	68922*	68948†	68974†
68897‡	68923*	68949†	68975†
68898‡	68924*	68950†	68976†
68899‡	68925*	68951*	68977†
68900*	68926*	68952†	68978§
68901*	68927*	68953†	68979§
68902*	68928*	68954†	68980§
68903*	68929*	68955†	68981§
68904*	68930*	68956†	68982§
68905*	68931*	68957†	68983§
68906*	68932*	68958†	68984§
68907*	68933*	68959†	68985§
68908*	68934*	68960†	68986§
68909*	68935*	68961†	68987§
68910*	68936*	68962†	68988§
68911*	68937*	68963†	68989§
68912*	68938*	68964†	68990§
68913*	68939*	68965†	68991§
68914*	68940†	68966†	
68915*	68941†	68967†	

Total : Class J50/1   10
Class J50/2   40
Class J50/3   38
Class J50/4   14

0-6-0T   2F   Class J72

(Continued from 68754)

69001	69008	69015	69022
69002	69009	69016	69023
69003	69010	69017	69024
69004	69011	69018	69025
69005	69012	69019	69026
69006	69013	69020	69027
69007	69014	69021	69028

Total 113

0-6-2T   3F   Class N10

Introduced 1902.   W. Worsdell N.E. design.
Weight: 57 tons 14 cwt.
Pressure: 160 lb.   Cyls.: $18\frac{1}{4}'' \times 26''$.
Driving Wheels: 4' 7¼". T.E.: 21,905 lb.

69090	69096	69101	69107
69091	69097	69102	69108
69092	69098	69104	69109
69093	69099	69105	
69094	69100	69106	

Total 18

0-6-2T   3F   Class N13

Introduced 1913. Stirling H. & B. design.
Weight: 61 tons 9 cwt.
Pressure: 175 lb.   Cyls.: $18'' \times 26''$.
Driving Wheels: 4' 6". T.E.: 23,197 lb.

69114   Total 1

0-6-2T   3MT   Class N15

N15/2* Introduced 1910. Reid N.B. design developed from N14. Cowlairs Incline banking locos.
N15/1 Introduced 1910. Development of N15/2 with smaller bunker for normal duties.

Weight $\begin{cases} 62 \text{ tons } 1 \text{ cwt.*} \\ 60 \text{ tons } 18 \text{ cwt.} \end{cases}$
Pressure : 175 lb.
Cyls.: $18'' \times 26''$.
Driving Wheels: 4' 6".
T.E.: 23,205 lb.

69126*	69128*	69130*	69132
69127*	69129*	69131*	69133

57

69134	69157	69180	69203
69135	69158	69181	69204
69136	69159	69182	69205
69137	69160	69183	69206
69138	69161	69184	69207
69139	69162	69185	69208
69140	69163	69186	69209
69141	69164	69187	69210
69142	69165	69188	69211
69143	69166	69189	69212
69144	69167	69190	69213
69145	69168	69191	69214
69146	69169	69192	69215
69147	69170	69193	69216
69143	69171	69194	69217
69149	69172	69195	69218
69150	69173	69196	69219
69151	69174	69197	69220
69152	69175	69198	69221
69153	69176	69199	69222
69154	69177	69200	69223
69155	69178	69201	69224
69156	69179	69202	

Total : Class N15/1 93
Class N15/2 6

69323	69335	69348	69360
69325	69341	69349	69361
69326	69342	69350	69362
69327	69343	69351	69365
69328	69344	69354	69369
69329	69345	69355	69370
69331	69346	69356	
69332	69347	69358	

Total 74

0-6-2T 2MT Class N8

Introduced 1886. T. W. Worsdell N.E. design rebuilt with superheater, Stephenson valve gear and piston valves.

Weight: 58 tons 14 cwt.
Pressure: 160 lb.
Cyls.: 19" × 24".
Driving Wheels: 5' 1¼".
T.E.: 19,235 lb.

69390   Total 1

0-6-2T 2MT Class N5

N5/2 Introduced 1891. Parker M.S. & L. design developed from N4
* Push-and-pull fitted.
Weight: 62 tons 7 cwt.
Pressure: 160 lb. Cyls.: 18" × 25".
Driving Wheels: 5' 1". T.E.: 18,780 lb.

69257*	69270	69293	69308
69258	69271	69294	69309
69259	69274	69295	69312
69261	69276	69296	69314
69262	69277	69297	69315
69263	69281	69298	69316
69265	69283	69299	69318
69266	69284	69300	69319
69267	69286	69302	69320
69268	69290	69305	69321
69269	69292	69307	69322

0-6-2T 2MT Class N1

* Introduced 1907. Ivatt G.N. design, prototype of class.

†‡§ Introduced 1907. Standard design with shorter tanks and detail differences.

§ Rebuilt with superheater and reduced pressure.

‡ Fitted with condensing apparatus.

Weight: $\begin{cases} 64 \text{ tons } 14 \text{ cwt.*} \\ 65 \text{ tons } 17 \text{ cwt.} \end{cases}$

Pressure: $\begin{cases} 175 \text{ lb.*†‡} \\ 170 \text{ lb. Su.§} \end{cases}$

Cyls.: 18" × 26".

Driving Wheels: 5' 8".

T.E.: $\begin{cases} 18,430 \text{ lb.*†‡} \\ 17,900 \text{ lb.§} \end{cases}$

69430*	69447†	69462‡	69478§
69434‡	69450†	69469‡	69484‡
69440†	69452§	69472§	
69443†	69453‡	69474†	
69444†	69457‡	69477‡	

Total 17

0-6-2T 3P2F Class N2

N2/2* Introduced 1925. Post-grouping development of Gresley G.N. N2/1, introduced 1920, which class is now included in N2/2. Built with condensing gear and small chimney.

N2/2† Condensing gear removed.

N2/3‡ Introduced 1925. Locos. built non-condensing, originally fitted with large chimney. Some now with small chimney.

N2/4§ Introduced 1928. Development of N2/2, slightly heavier. Built with condensing gear and small chimney.

(The small chimneys are to suit the Metropolitan loading gauge, for working to Moorgate. Condensing gear has been removed from or added to certain locos. transferred from or to the London area.)

Weight: $\begin{cases} 70 \text{ tons } 5 \text{ cwt.*†} \\ 70 \text{ tons } 8 \text{ cwt.‡} \\ 71 \text{ tons } 9 \text{ cwt.§} \end{cases}$

Pressure: 170 lb. Su. Cyls.: 19″ × 26″.
Driving Wheels: 5′ 8″. T.E.: 19,945 lb. P.V.

69490*	69512*	69535*	69557†
69491*	69513*	69536*	69558†
69492*	69515†	69537*	69559†
69493*	69516†	69538*	69560†
69494*	69517*	69539*	69561†
69495*	69518†	69540*	69563‡
69496*	69519†	69541*	69564‡
69497*	69520*	69542*	69565‡
69498*	69521*	69543*	69566‡
69499*	69522*	69544*	69567‡
69500†	69523*	69545*	69568§
69501†	69524*	69546*	69569§
69502†	69525*	69547*	69570§
69503†	69526*	69548*	69571§
69504*	69527*	69549*	69572§
69505†	69528*	69550†	69573§
69506*	69529*	69551†	69574§
69507†	69530*	69552†	69575§
69508†	69531*	69553†	69576§
69509†	69532*	69554†	69577§
69510†	69533*	69555†	69578§
69511†	69534*	69556§	69579§

69580§	69585§	69590§	69595‡
69581§	69586§	69591§	69596‡
69582§	69587§	69592§	
69583§	69588§	69593§	
69584§	69589§	69594‡	

Total : Class N2/2   70
    Class N2/3   8
    Class N2/4   27

0-6-2T 3MT Class N7

N7/1¹ Introduced 1925. Post-grouping development of Hill G.E. design with detail differences.

N7/2² Introduced 1926. Development of N7/1 with long-travel valves.

N7/3³ Introduced 1927. Doncaster-built version of N7/2 with round-topped firebox.

N7/4⁴ Introduced 1940. Pre-grouping N7 (G.E.) rebuilt with round-topped firebox, retaining short-travel valves.

N7/5⁵ Introduced 1943. N7/1 rebuilt with round-topped firebox, retaining short-travel valves.

N7/3⁶ Introduced 1943. N7/2 rebuilt with round-topped firebox.

Weight: $\begin{cases} 63 \text{ tons } 13 \text{ cwt.}^1 \\ 64 \text{ tons } 17 \text{ cwt.}^2 \\ 64 \text{ tons.}^3 \\ 61 \text{ tons } 16 \text{ cwt.}^4 \\ 64 \text{ tons.}^5 \\ 64 \text{ tons.}^6 \end{cases}$

Pressure: 180 lb. Su. Cyls.: 18″ × 24″.
Driving Wheels: 4′ 10″. T.E.: 20,515 lb.
Walschaerts gear. P.V.

69600⁴	69610⁴	69620⁴	69630⁵
69601⁴	69611⁴	69621⁴	69631⁵
69602⁴	69612⁴	69622⁵	69632⁵
69603⁴	69613⁴	69623⁵	69633⁵
69604⁴	69614⁴	69624⁵	69634⁵
69605⁴	69615⁴	69625⁵	69635⁵
69606⁴	69616⁴	69626⁵	69636⁵
69607⁴	69617⁴	69627¹	69637⁵
69608⁴	69618⁴	69628⁵	69638⁵
69609⁴	69619⁴	69629⁵	69639⁵

69640-69894

69640[5]	69664[5]	69688[6]	69711[3]
69641[5]	69665[5]	69689[2]	69712[3]
69642[5]	69666[5]	69690[2]	69713[3]
69643[5]	69667[5]	69691[6]	69714[3]
69644[5]	69668[5]	69692[6]	69715[3]
69645[5]	69669[5]	69693[6]	69716[3]
69646[5]	69670[5]	69694[6]	69717[3]
69647[5]	69671[5]	69695[2]	69718[3]
69648[5]	69672[6]	69696[6]	69719[3]
69649[5]	69673[6]	69697[6]	69720[3]
69650[5]	69674[6]	69698[6]	69721[3]
69651[5]	69675[6]	69699[6]	69722[3]
69652[5]	69676[6]	69700[6]	69723[3]
69653[5]	69677[6]	69701[6]	69724[3]
69654[5]	69678[6]	69702[3]	69725[3]
69655[5]	69679[6]	69703[3]	69726[3]
69656[5]	69680[6]	69704[3]	69727[3]
69657[5]	69681[6]	69705[3]	69728[3]
69658[5]	69682[6]	69706[3]	69729[3]
69659[5]	69683[6]	69707[3]	69730[3]
69660[5]	69684[6]	69708[3]	69731[3]
69661[5]	69685[6]	69709[3]	69732[3]
69662[5]	69686[6]	69710[3]	69733[3]
69663[5]	69687[6]		

Total : Class N7/1   1
Class N7/2   3
Class N7/3   59
Class N7/4   22
Class N7/5   49

4-6-2T   3F   Class A7

Introduced 1910. Raven N.E. design, later rebuilt with superheater and reduced pressure.

Weight: 87 tons 10 cwt.

Pressure: 160 lb. Su.

Cyls.: (3) 16½" × 26".

Driving Wheels: 4' 7¼".

T.E.: 26,140 lb.

P.V.

69772	69782	69783	69786
69781			

Total 5

4-6-2T   3MT   Class A5

A5/1 Introduced 1911. Robinson G.C. design.

A5/2* Introduced 1925. Post-grouping development of A5/1 with reduced boiler mountings and detail differences.

Weight: { 85 tons 18 cwt.
90 tons 11 cwt.*

Pressure: 180 lb. Su. Cyls.: 20" × 26'

Driving Wheels: 5' 7"   T.E.: 23,750 lb

P.V

69800	69811	69822	69833*
69801	69812	69823	69834*
69802	69813	69824	69835*
69803	69814	69825	69836*
69804	69815	69826	69837*
69805	69816	69827	69838*
69806	69817	69828	69839*
69807	69818	69829	69840*
69808	69819	69830*	69841*
69809	69820	69831*	69842*
69810	69821	69832*	

Total :   Class A5/1 30
Class A5/2 13

4-6-2T   3MT   Class A8

Introduced 1931. Gresley rebuild of Raven N.E. Class " D " 4-4-4T (introduced 1913).

Weight: 86 tons 18 cwt.

Pressure: 175 lb. Su.

Cyls.: (3) 16½" × 26".

Driving Wheels: 5' 9".   T.E.: 22,940 lb.

P.V.

69850	69862	69874	69886
69851	69863	69875	69887
69852	69864	69876	69888
69853	69865	69877	69889
69854	69866	69878	69890
69855	69867	69879	69891
69856	69868	69880	69892
69857	69869	69881	69893
69858	69870	69882	69894
69859	69871	69883	
69860	69872	69884	
69861	69873	69885	

Total 45

0-8-4T 6F Class S1

S1/2* Introduced 1932. S1/1 (Robinson G.C. design, 1907) rebuilt with booster and superheater, booster later removed.

S1/3† Introduced 1932. New design with booster, booster later removed.

Weight: { 99 tons 2 cwt.*
{ 99 tons 1 cwt.†

Pressure: 180 lb. Su.

Cyls.: (3) 18″ × 26″.

Driving Wheels: 4′ 8″. T.E. 34,525 lb.

69901*   69905†

Total : Class S1/2 1
Class S1/3 1

4-8-0T 5F Class T1

Introduced 1909. W. Worsdell N.E. design.

Weight: 85 tons 8 cwt.

Pressure: 175 lb.

Cyls.: (3) 18″ × 26″.

Driving Wheels: 4′ 7¼″. T.E. 34,080 lb. P.V.

69910	69913	69917	69921
69911	69915	69918	69922
69912	69916	69920	

Total 11

0-8-0T 5F Class Q1

Thompson rebuild of Robinson G.C. Q4 0-8-0, introduced 1902.

Q1/1* Introduced 1942. 1,500 gallon tanks.

Q1/2 Introduced 1943. 2,000 gallon tanks.

Weight: { 69 tons 18 cwt.*
{ 73 tons 13 cwt.

Pressure: 180 lb. Cyls.: (O) 19″ × 26″.

Driving Wheels: 4′ 8″. T.E. 25,645 lb.

69926*	69930	69933	69936
69928*	69931	69934	69937
69929	69932	69935	

Total 11

PULLMAN CARS ALLOCATED TO THE E. & N.E. REGIONS

B—Brake Car.

K—Kitchen Car.

First Class.

ADRIAN	(K)
AGATHA	
BELINDA	(K)
CYNTHIA	(K)
EUNICE	
EVADNE	(K)
IOLANTHE	(K)
IONE	(K)
JOAN	(K)
JUANA	
LORAINE	(K)
LUCILLE	
LYDIA	(K)
NILAR	(K)
PHYLLIS	(K)
SHEILA	
THELMA	(K)
URSULA	

Second Class.

CAR No.		
,, ,,	32	(K)
,, ,,	33	(K)
,, ,,	58	(K)
,, ,,	59	(HADRIAN BAR)
,, ,,	62	(B)
,, ,,	63	(B)
,, ,,	64	
,, ,,	65	(B)
,, ,,	66	(K)
,, ,,	67	(K)
,, ,,	68	(K)
,, ,,	69	(K)
,, ,,	70	(K)
,, ,,	71	(K)
,, ,,	72	(K)
,, ,,	73	
,, ,,	74	
,, ,,	75	
,, ,,	76	
,, ,,	77	(B)
,, ,,	78	(B)
,, ,,	79	(B)
,, ,,	80	(B)
,, ,,	81	(K)
,, ,,	82	(K)
,, ,,	83	
,, ,,	84	
,, ,,	105	(K)
,, ,,	106	(K)
,, ,,	107	(K)
,, ,,	161	(B)
,, ,,	162	(B)
,, ,,	209	(B)
,, ,,	248	(B)

BRITISH RAILWAYS STANDARD LOCOMOTIVES

Chief Officer (Mechanical Engineering) :
R. C. BOND

4-6-2   Class 7P6F

Introduced 1951
  Designed at Derby.
Weight : Loco.   94 tons 0 cwt.
          Tender (see page 69)
Pressure : 250 lb. Su.
Cyls. : (O) 20″ × 28″.
Driving Wheels: 6′ 2″. T.E.: 32,150 lb.
Walschaerts gear. P.V.

70000	Britannia
70001	Lord Hurcomb
70002	Geoffrey Chaucer
70003	John Bunyan
70004	William Shakespeare
70005	John Milton
70006	Robert Burns
70007	Coeur-de-Lion
70008	Black Prince
70009	Alfred the Great
70010	Owen Glendower
70011	Hotspur
70012	John of Gaunt
70013	Oliver Cromwell
70014	Iron Duke
70015	Apollo
70016	Ariel
70017	Arrow
70018	Flying Dutchman
70019	Lightning
70020	Mercury
70021	Morning Star
70022	Tornado
70023	Venus
70024	Vulcan
70025	Western Star
70026	Polar Star
70027	Rising Star
70028	Royal Star
70029	Shooting Star
70030	William Wordsworth
70031	Byron
70032	Tennyson
70033	Charles Dickens
70034	Thomas Hardy
70035	Rudyard Kipling
70036	Boadicea
70037	Hereward the Wake
70038	Robin Hood
70039	Sir Christopher Wren
70040	Clive of India
70041	Sir John Moore
70042	Lord Roberts
70043	Earl Kitchener
70044	Earl Haig
70045	
70046	
70047	
70048	
70049	
70050	Firth of Clyde
70051	Firth of Forth
70052	Firth of Tay
70053	Moray Firth
70054	Dornoch Firth

The names of Nos. 70043/4 are
temporarily not affixed.

               Total 55

4-6-2   Class 8P

Introduced 1954.   Designed at Derby.
Weight: Loco.   101 tons 5 cwt.
          Tender (see page 69)
Pressure: 250 lb. Su.
Cyls.: (3) 18″ × 28″.
Driving Wheels: 6′ 2″.   T.E.: 39,080 lb.
Caprotti valve gear.

71000   Duke of Gloucester
               Total 1

4-6-2   Class 6P5F

Introduced 1952.   Designed at Derby.
Weight: Loco.   86 tons 19 cwt.
          Tender (see page 69).
Pressure: 225 lb. Su.
Cyls.: (O) 19¼″ × 28″.
Driving Wheels: 6′ 2″.   T.E.: 27,520 lb.
Walschaerts gear.   P.V.

72000	Clan Buchanan
72001	Clan Cameron
72002	Clan Campbell
72003	Clan Fraser
72004	Clan Macdonald
72005	Clan Macgregor
72006	Clan Mackenzie
72007	Clan Mackintosh
72008	Clan Macleod
72009	Clan Stewart

Total 10

4-6-0 Class 5

Introduced 1951. Designed at Doncaster.
*Introduced 1956. Fitted with Caprotti valve gear.
Weight: Loco. 76 tons 4 cwt.
Tender (see page 69).
Pressure: 225 lb. Su.
Cyls.: (O) 19" × 28".
Driving Wheels: 6' 2". T.E.: 26,120 lb.
Walschaerts gear. P.V.

73000	73024	73048	73072
73001	73025	73049	73073
73002	73026	73050	73074
73003	73027	73051	73075
73004	73028	73052	73076
73005	73029	73053	73077
73006	73030	73054	73078
73007	73031	73055	73079
73008	73032	73056	73080
73009	73033	73057	73081
73010	73034	73058	73082
73011	73035	73059	73083
73012	73036	73060	73084
73013	73037	73061	73085
73014	73038	73062	73086
73015	73039	73063	73087
73016	73040	73064	73088
73017	73041	73065	73089
73018	73042	73066	73090
73019	73043	73067	73091
73020	73044	73068	73092
73021	73045	73069	73093
73022	73046	73070	73094
73023	73047	73071	73095

73096	73115	73134*	73153
73097	73116	73135*	73154
73098	73117	73136*	73155
73099	73118	73137*	73156
73100	73119	73138*	73157
73101	73120	73139*	73158
73102	73121	73140*	73159
73103	73122	73141*	73160
73104	73123	73142*	73161
73105	73124	73143*	73162
73106	73125*	73144*	73163
73107	73126*	73145	73164
73108	73127*	73146	73165
73109	73128*	73147	73166
73110	73129*	73148	73167
73111	73130*	73149	73168
73112	73131*	73150	73169
73113	73132*	73151	73170
73114	73133*	73152	73171

Engines of this class are still being delivered.

4-6-0 Class 4

Introduced 1951. Designed at Brighton.
Weight: Loco. 69 tons 0 cwt.
Tender (see page 69).
Pressure: 225 lb. Su.
Cyls.: (O) 18" × 28".
Driving Wheels: 5' 8". T.E.: 25,100 lb.
Walschaerts gear. P.V.

75000	75017	75034	75051
75001	75018	75035	75052
75002	75019	75036	75053
75003	75020	75037	75054
75004	75021	75038	75055
75005	75022	75039	75056
75006	75023	75040	75057
75007	75024	75041	75058
75008	75025	75042	75059
75009	75026	75043	75060
75010	75027	75044	75061
75011	75028	75045	75062
75012	75029	75046	75063
75013	75030	75047	75064
75014	75031	75048	75065
75015	75032	75049	75066
75016	75033	75050	75067

75068	75074	75080	75086
75069	75075	75081	75087
75070	75076	75082	75088
75071	75077	75083	75089
75072	75078	75084	
75073	75079	75085	

Engines of this class are still being delivered.

2-6-0 Class 4

Introduced 1953. Designed at Doncaster.
Weight: Loco. 59 tons 2 cwt.
  Tender (see page 69).
Pressure: 225 lb. Su.
Cyls.: (O) 17½" × 26".
Driving Wheels: 5' 3". T.E.: 24,170 lb.
Walschaerts gear. P.V.

76000	76029	76058	76087
76001	76030	76059	76088
76002	76031	76060	76089
76003	76032	76061	76090
76004	76033	76062	76091
76005	76034	76063	76092
76006	76035	76064	76093
76007	76036	76065	76094
76008	76037	76066	76095
76009	76038	76067	76096
76010	76039	76068	76097
76011	76040	76069	76098
76012	76041	76070	76099
76013	76042	76071	76100
76014	76043	76072	76101
76015	76044	76073	76102
76016	76045	76074	76103
76017	76046	76075	76104
76018	76047	76076	76105
76019	76048	76077	76106
76020	76049	76078	76107
76021	76050	76079	76108
76022	76051	76080	76109
76023	76052	76081	76110
76024	76053	76082	76111
76025	76054	76083	76112
76026	76055	76084	76113
76027	76056	76085	76114
76028	76057	76086	

Engines of this class are still being delivered.

2-6-0 Class 3

Introduced 1954. Designed at Swindon.
Weight: Loco. 57 tons 10 cwt.
  Tender (see page 69).
Pressure: 200 lb. Su.
Cyls.: (O) 17½" × 26".
Driving Wheels: 5' 3". T.E.: 21,490 lb.
Walschaerts gear. P.V.

77000	77007	77014	77021
77001	77008	77015	77022
77002	77009	77016	77023
77003	77010	77017	77024
77004	77011	77018	
77005	77012	77019	
77006	77013	77020	

Engines of this class are still being delivered.

2-6-0 Class 2

Introduced 1953. Designed at Derby.
Weight: Loco. 49 tons 5 cwt.
  Tender (see page 69).
Pressure: 200 lb. Su.
Cyls.: (O) 16½" × 24".
Driving Wheels: 5' 0". T.E.: 18,515 lb.
Walschaerts gear. P.V.

78000	78017	78034	78051
78001	78018	78035	78052
78002	78019	78036	78053
78003	78020	78037	78054
78004	78021	78038	78055
78005	78022	78039	78056
78006	78023	78040	78057
78007	78024	78041	78058
78008	78025	78042	78059
78009	78026	78043	78060
78010	78027	78044	78061
78011	78028	78045	78062
78012	78029	78046	78063
78013	78030	78047	78064
78014	78031	78048	
78015	78032	78049	
78016	78033	78050	

Engines of this class are still being delivered.

2-6-4T Class 4

Introduced 1951. Designed at Brighton.
Weight: 88 tons 10 cwt.
Pressure: 225 lb. Su.
Cyls.: (O) 18" × 28".
Driving Wheels: 5' 8". T.E.: 25,100 lb.
Walschaerts gear. P.V.

80000	80039	80078	80117
80001	80040	80079	80118
80002	80041	80080	80119
80003	80042	80081	80120
80004	80043	80082	80121
80005	80044	80083	80122
80006	80045	80084	80123
80007	80046	80085	80124
80008	80047	80086	80125
80009	80048	80087	80126
80010	80049	80088	80127
80011	80050	80089	80128
80012	80051	80090	80129
80013	80052	80091	80130
80014	80053	80092	80131
80015	80054	80093	80132
80016	80055	80094	80133
80017	80056	80095	80134
80018	80057	80096	80135
80019	80058	80097	80136
80020	80059	80098	80137
80021	80060	80099	80138
80022	80061	80100	80139
80023	80062	80101	80140
80024	80063	80102	80141
80025	80064	80103	80142
80026	80065	80104	80143
80027	80066	80105	80144
80028	80067	80106	80145
80029	80068	80107	80146
80030	80069	80108	80147
80031	80070	80109	80148
80032	80071	80110	80149
80033	80072	80111	80150
80034	80073	80112	80151
80035	80074	80113	80152
80036	80075	80114	80153
80037	80076	80115	80154
80038	80077	80116	

Engines of this class are still being delivered.

2-6-2T Class 3

Introduced 1952. Designed at Swindon.
Weight: 73 tons 10 cwt.
Pressure: 200 lb. Su.
Cyls.: (O) $17\frac{1}{2}$" × 26".
Driving Wheels: 5' 3". T.E.: 21,490 lb.
Walschaerts gear P.V.

82000	82012	82024	82036
82001	82013	82025	82037
82002	82014	82026	82038
82003	82015	82027	82039
82004	82016	82028	82040
82005	82017	82029	82041
82006	82018	82030	82042
82007	82019	82031	82043
82008	82020	82032	82044
82009	82021	82033	
82010	82022	82034	
82011	82023	82035	

Total 45

2-6-2T Class 2

Introduced 1953 Designed at Derby.
Weight: 63 tons 5 cwt.
Pressure: 200 lb. Su.
Cyls.: (O) $16\frac{1}{4}$" × 24".
Driving Wheels: 5' 0". T.E.: 18,515 lb.
Walschaerts gear P.V.

84000	84008	84016	84024
84001	84009	84017	84025
84002	84010	84018	84026
84003	84011	84019	84027
84004	84012	84020	84028
84005	84013	84021	84029
84006	84014	84022	
84007	84015	84023	

Engines of this class are still being delivered.

2-8-0   8F   Class WD

Ministry of Supply " Austerity " 2-8-0 locomotives purchased by British Railways, 1948.

Introduced 1943. Riddles M.o.S. design.

Weight: Loco.   70 tons 5 cwt.
        Tender 55 tons 10 cwt.

Pressure: 225 lb. Su.

Cyls.: (O) 19″ × 28″.

Driving Wheels: 4′ 8½″. T.E.: 34,215 lb.

Walschaerts gear.   P.V.

90000	90038	90076	90114	90152	90200	90248	90296
90001	90039	90077	90115	90153	90201	90249	90297
90002	90040	90078	90116	90154	90202	90250	90298
90003	90041	90079	90117	90155	90203	90251	90299
90004	90042	90080	90118	90156	90204	90252	90300
90005	90043	90081	90119	90157	90205	90253	90301
90006	90044	90082	90120	90158	90206	90254	90302
90007	90045	90083	90121	90159	90207	90255	90303
90008	90046	90084	90122	90160	90208	90256	90304
90009	90047	90085	90123	90161	90209	90257	90305
90010	90048	90086	90124	90162	90210	90258	90306
90011	90049	90087	90125	90163	90211	90259	90307
90012	90050	90088	90126	90164	90212	90260	90308
90013	90051	90089	90127	90165	90213	90261	90309
90014	90052	90090	90128	90166	90214	90262	90310
90015	90053	90091	90129	90167	90215	90263	90311
90016	90054	90092	90130	90168	90216	90264	90312
90017	90055	90093	90131	90169	90217	90265	90313
90018	90056	90094	90132	90170	90218	90266	90314
90019	90057	90095	90133	90171	90219	90267	90315
90020	90058	90096	90134	90172	90220	90268	90316
90021	90059	90097	90135	90173	90221	90269	90317
90022	90060	90098	90136	90174	90222	90270	90318
90023	90061	90099	90137	90175	90223	90271	90319
90024	90062	90100	90138	90176	90224	90272	90320
90025	90063	90101	90139	90177	90225	90273	90321
90026	90064	90102	90140	90178	90226	90274	90322
90027	90065	90103	90141	90179	90227	90275	90323
90028	90066	90104	90142	90180	90228	90276	90324
90029	90067	90105	90143	90181	90229	90277	90325
90030	90068	90106	90144	90182	90230	90278	90326
90031	90069	90107	90145	90183	90231	90279	90327
90032	90070	90108	90146	90184	90232	90280	90328
90033	90071	90109	90147	90185	90233	90281	90329
90034	90072	90110	90148	90186	90234	90282	90330
90035	90073	90111	90149	90187	90235	90283	90331
90036	90074	90112	90150	90188	90236	90284	90332
90037	90075	90113	90151	90189	90237	90285	90333
				90190	90238	90286	90334
				90191	90239	90287	90335
				90192	90240	90288	90336
				90193	90241	90289	90337
				90194	90242	90290	90338
				90195	90243	90291	90339
				90196	90244	90292	90340
				90197	90245	90293	90341
				90198	90246	90294	90342
				90199	90247	90295	90343

90344	90392	90440	90488	90536	90584	90632	90680
90345	90393	90441	90489	90537	90585	90633	90681
90346	90394	90442	90490	90538	90586	90634	90682
90347	90395	90443	90491	90539	90587	90635	90683
90348	90396	90444	90492	90540	90588	90636	90684
90349	90397	90445	90493	90541	90589	90637	90685
90350	90398	90446	90494	90542	90590	90638	90686
90351	90399	90447	90495	90543	90591	90639	90687
90352	90400	90448	90496	90544	90592	90640	90688
90353	90401	90449	90497	90545	90593	90641	90689
90354	90402	90450	90498	90546	90594	90642	90690
90355	90403	90451	90499	90547	90595	90643	90691
90356	90404	90452	90500	90548	90596	90644	90692
90357	90405	90453	90501	90549	90597	90645	90693
90358	90406	90454	90502	90550	90598	90646	90694
90359	90407	90455	90503	90551	90599	90647	90695
90360	90408	90456	90504	90552	90600	90648	90696
90361	90409	90457	90505	90553	90601	90649	90697
90362	90410	90458	90506	90554	90602	90650	90698
90363	90411	90459	90507	90555	90603	90651	90699
90364	90412	90460	90508	90556	90604	90652	90700
90365	90413	90461	90509	90557	90605	90653	90701
90366	90414	90462	90510	90558	90606	90654	90702
90367	90415	90463	90511	90559	90607	90655	90703
90368	90416	90464	90512	90560	90608	90656	90704
90369	90417	90465	90513	90561	90609	90657	90705
90370	90418	90466	90514	90562	90610	90658	90706
90371	90419	90467	90515	90563	90611	90659	90707
90372	90420	90468	90516	90564	90612	90660	90708
90373	90421	90469	90517	90565	90613	90661	90709
90374	90422	90470	90518	90566	90614	90662	90710
90375	90423	90471	90519	90567	90615	90663	90711
90376	90424	90472	90520	90568	90616	90664	90712
90377	90425	90473	90521	90569	90617	90665	90713
90378	90426	90474	90522	90570	90618	90666	90714
90379	90427	90475	90523	90571	90619	90667	90715
90380	90428	90476	90524	90572	90620	90668	90716
90381	90429	90477	90525	90573	90621	90669	90717
90382	90430	90478	90526	90574	90622	90670	90718
90383	90431	90479	90527	90575	90623	90671	90719
90384	90432	90480	90528	90576	90624	90672	90720
90385	90433	90481	90529	90577	90625	90673	90721
90386	90434	90482	90530	90578	90626	90674	90722
90387	90435	90483	90531	90579	90627	90675	90723
90388	90436	90484	90532	90580	90628	90676	90724
90389	90437	90485	90533	90581	90629	90677	90725
90390	90438	90486	90534	90582	90630	90678	90726
90391	90439	90487	90535	90583	90631	90679	90727

90728	90730	90732 Vulcan
90729	90731	

Total 733

2-10-0　8F　Class WD

Ministry of Supply " Austerity " 2-10-0 locomotives purchased by British Railways, 1948.

Introduced 1943. Riddles M.o.S. design.

Weight: Loco.　7B tons　6 cwt.
　　　　　Tender 55 tons 10 cwt.

Pressure: 225 lb. Su.

Cyls.: (O) 19″ × 28″.

Driving Wheels: 4′ 8½″.　T.E.: 34,215 lb

Walschaerts gear.　P.V.

90750	90757	90763	90769
90751	90758	90764	90770
90752	90759	90765	90771
90753	90760	90766	90772
90754	90761	90767	90773
90755	90762	90768	90774
90756			

Total 25

2-10-0　　Class 9F

Introduced 1954.　Designed at Crewe.

* Introduced 1955. Fitted with Crosti boiler.

Weight: Loco. { 86 tons 14 cwt.
　　　　　　　 { 90 tons　4 cwt.*

　　　　　Tender (see page 69).

Pressure: 250 lb. Su.

Cyls.: (O) 20″ × 28″

Driving Wheels: 5′ 0″.　T.E.: 39,670 lb.

Walschaerts gear.　P.V.

92000	92005	92010	92015
92001	92006	92011	92016
92002	92007	92012	92017
92003	92008	92013	92018
92004	92009	92014	92019

92020*	92066	92112	92158
92021*	92067	92113	92159
92022*	92068	92114	92160
92023*	92069	92115	92161
92024*	92070	92116	92162
92025*	92071	92117	92163
92026*	92072	92118	92164
92027*	92073	92119	92165
92028*	92074	92120	92166
92029*	92075	92121	92167
92030	92076	92122	92168
92031	92077	92123	92169
92032	92078	92124	92170
92033	92079	92125	92171
92034	92080	92126	92172
92035	92081	92127	92173
92036	92082	92128	92174
92037	92083	92129	92175
92038	92084	92130	92176
92039	92085	92131	92177
92040	92086	92132	92178
92041	92087	92133	92179
92042	92088	92134	92180
92043	92089	92135	92181
92044	92090	92136	92182
92045	92091	92137	92183
92046	92092	92138	92184
92047	92093	92139	92185
92048	92094	92140	92186
92049	92095	92141	92187
92050	92096	92142	92188
92051	92097	92143	92189
92052	92098	92144	92190
92053	92099	92145	92191
92054	92100	92146	92192
92055	92101	92147	92193
92056	92102	92148	92194
92057	92103	92149	92195
92058	92104	92150	92196
92059	92105	92151	92197
92060	92106	92152	92198
92061	92107	92153	92199
92062	92108	92154	92200
92063	92109	92155	92201
92064	92110	92156	92202
92065	92111	92157	

Engines of this class are still being delivered.

BRITISH RAILWAYS STANDARD TENDERS

N.B.—These pairings are not permanent and are liable to alteration with changed operating conditions.

Type	Capacity		Weight in Full W.O.		Locos. to which Allocated
	Water galls.	Coal tons	tons	cwt.	
BRI ...	4,250	7	49	3	70000–24/30–44 72000–9 73000–49
BRIA ...	5,000	7	52	10	70025–9
BRIB ...	4,725	7	50	5	73080–9 73100–9/20–34/45–71 75065–79 76053–69 92020–9/60–6/97–9
BRIC ...	4,725	9	53	5	73065–79/90–9 73135–44 92015–9/45–59/77–86 92100–39/50–67
BRID ...	4,725	9	54	10	70045–54
BRIE ...	4,725	10	55	10	71000
BRIF ...	5,625	7	55	5	73110–3 92010–4/30–44/67–76 92087–96 92140–9/68–92202
BRIG ...	5,000	7	52	10	73050–2 92000–9
BRIH ...	4,250	7	49	3	73053–64
BR2 ...	3,500	6	42	3	75000–49 76000–44
BR2A ...	3,500	6	42	3	75050–64/80–9 76045–52/70–76114 77000–24
BR3 ...	3,000	4	36	17	78000–64

ELECTRIC UNIT NUMBERS

LIVERPOOL ST.—SHENFIELD 3-CAR ELECTRIC TRAIN UNITS

01	11	21	31	41	51	61	71	81	91
02	12	22	32	42	52	62	72	82	92
03	13	23	33	43	53	63	73	83	
04	14	24	34	44	54	64	74	84	
05	15	25	35	45	55	65	75	85	
06	16	26	36	46	56	66	76	86	
07	17	27	37	47	57	67	77	87	
08	18	28	38	48	58	68	78	88	
09	19	29	39	49	59	69	79	89	
10	20	30	40	50	60	70	80	90	

GRIMSBY—IMMINGHAM ELECTRIC TRAMS

1	7	13	17	21	25	29	32
4	8	14	18	22	26	30	33
5	11	15	19	23	27	31	34
6	12	16	20	24	28		

SOUTH TYNESIDE ELECTRIC MOTOR COACHES

E.65311E	E.65314E	E.65317E	E.65320E	E.65323E
E.65312E	E.65315E	E.65318E	E.65321E	E.65324E
E.65313E	E.65316E	E.65319E	E.65322E	E.65325E

Motor Parcels Van E.29493E

NORTH TYNESIDE ELECTRIC TWIN-UNIT MOTOR COACHES

E.29101E	E.29114E	E.29125E	E.29136E	E.29148E	E.29159E
E.29102E	E.29115E	E.29126E	E.29137E	E.29149E	E.29160E
E.29103E	E.29116E	E.29127E	E.29138E	E.29150E	E.29161E
E.29104E	E.29117E	E.29128E	E.29139E	E.29151E	E.29162E
E.29105E	E.29118E	E.29129E	E.29140E	E.29152E	E.29163E
E.29106E	E.29119E	E.29130E	E.29141E	E.29153E	E.29164E
E.29107E	E.29120E	E.29131E	E.29142E	E.29154E	E.29235E
E.29108E	E.29121E	E.29132E	E.29144E	E.29155E	E.29257E
E.29109E	E.29122E	E.29133E	E.29145E	E.29156E	E.29316E
E.29110E	E.29123E	E.29134E	E.29146E	E.29157E	E.29376E
E.29111E	E.29124E	E.29135E	E.29147E	E.29158E	E.29386E
E.29113E					

Motor Parcels Vans		Motor Coaches	
E.29467E	E.29468E	E.29165E	E.29166E

MANCHESTER — SHEFFIELD ELECTRIC MOTOR COACHES

E59401	E59403	E59405	E59407
E59402	E59404	E59406	E59408

DIESEL MULTIPLE UNIT TRAINS

The following abbreviations are used, and although based on the British Railways standard rolling stock code, are not necessarily those carried on the vehicles, all of which are of the open, centre or off centre corridor type :—

BOGIE VEHICLES

Fitted with a driving compartment at one end and gangway connections at the other end.

Motor BS—Motor Brake Second.
Motor S—Motor Second.
Motor C—Motor Composite.
Motor CL—Motor Composite (lavatory fitted).
Driving SL—Driving Trailer Second (lavatory fitted).
Driving CL—Driving Trailer Composite (lavatory fitted).

Non driving, non motor vehicles, gangway fitted at both ends.

BSL—Trailer Brake Second (lavatory fitted).
SL—Trailer Second (lavatory fitted).

4-WHEEL VEHICLES

Motor coaches fitted with a driving compartment at each end. None are gangway fitted.

Motor S—Motor Second. **Motor BS**—Motor Brake Second. **S**—Trailer Second.

FORMATION. Nearly all are formed into two coach sets as under :—

Motor BS–Motor CL (Bradford area).
Motor BS–Driving CL (Majority).
Motor BS–Driving SL (East Anglian area).
Newcastle–Middlesbrough units are formed into four coach sets :—
Motor C–BSL–SL–Motor S.

The 4-wheel vehicles are made up to three coach sets and are used on the Watford–St. Albans Branch :—

Motor BS–S–Motor S.

BOGIE VEHICLES

Motor BS :—

E79000	M79019	E79038	E79057*	M79076*	M79130	M79149
E79001	M79020	E79039	E79058*	M79077*	M79131	M79169
E79002	E79021	E79040	E79059*	M79078*	M79132	M79170
E79003	E79022	E79041	E79060*	M79079*	M79133	M79171
E79004	E79023	E79042	E79061*	M79080*	M79134	M79172
E79005	E79024	E79043	E79052*	M79081*	M79135	M79173
E79006	E79025	E79044	E79063*	M79082*	M79136	M79174
E79007	E79026	E79045	E79064*	M79118	E79137	M79175
M79008	E79027	E79046	E79065*	M79119	E79138	M79176
M79009	E79028	E79047*	E79066*	M79120	E79139	M79177
M79010	E79029	E79048*	E79067*	M79121	E79140	M79178
M79011	E79030	E79049*	E79068*	M79122	M79141	M79179
M79012	E79031	E79050*	E79069*	M79123	M79142	M79180
M79013	E79032	E79051*	E79070*	M79124	M79143	M79181
M79014	E79033	E79052*	E79071*	M79125	M79144	M79184
M79015	E79034	E79053*	E79072*	M79126	M79145	M79185
M79016	E79035	E79054*	E79073*	M79127	M79146	M79186
M79017	E79036	E79055*	E79074*	M79128	M79147	‡M79900
M79018	E79037	E79056*	E79075*	M79129	M79148	

Motor S :—

E79150   E79151,   E79152,   E79153,   E79154.

Driving SL :—

E79250	E79256	E79262	E79268*	E79274*	E79280*	E79286*
E79251	E79257	E79263*	E79269*	E79275*	E79281*	E79287*
E79252	E79258	E79264*	E79270*	E79276*	E79282*	E79288*
E79253	E79259	E79265*	E79271*	E79277*	E79283*	E79289*
E79254	E79260	E79266*	E79272*	E79278*	E79284*	E79290*
E79255	E79261	E79267*	E79273*	E79279*	E79285*	E79291*

BSL :—

E79325, E79326, E79327, E79328, E79329.

SL :—

E79400, E79401, E79402, E79403, E79404.

Motor CL: —

M79189, M79190, M79191, E79500, E79501, E79502, E79503, E79504, E79505, E79506, E79507.

Motor C :—

E79508, E79509, E79510, E79511, E79512.

Driving CL :—

M79600	M79612	E79624	M79642	M79653	M79664	M79675
M79601	E79613	E79625	M79643	M79654	M79665	M79676
M79602	E79614	M79626*	M79644	M79655	M79666	M79677
M79603	E79615	M79627*	M79645	M79656	M79667	M79678
M79604	E79616	M79628*	M79646	M79657	M79668	M79679
M79605	E79617	M79629*	M79647	E79658	M79669	M79680
M79606	E79618	M79630*	M79648	E79659	M79670	M79681
M79607	E79619	M79631*	M79649	E79660	M79671	M79682
M79608	E79620	M79632*	M79650	E79661	M79672	M79683
M79609	E79621	M79639	M79651	M79662	M79673	M79684
M79610	E79622	M79640	M79652	M79663	M79674	
M79611	E79623	M79641				

4-WHEEL VEHICLES

Motor S	Motor BS	S
M79740†	M79742†	M79741†
M79745†	M79743†	M79746†
	M79744†	M79747†

* Built by Metro-Cammell C. & W. Co.

† Built by British United Traction Co.

Remainder built by British Railways at Derby.

:Non-gangwayed, Driving Compartment both ends.